PANCHO VILLA

PANCHO VILLA

BY

WILLIAM DOUGLAS LANSFORD

SHERBOURNE PRESS, INC.
LOS ANGELES, CALIFORNIA

Library of Congress Catalog Card Number 65-23704

First Edition

Manufactured in the United States of America
By The Book Press, Brattleboro, Vermont

This book is for Francisco Z. Vega
(El Palomito), who lived so much of it
and retold it to Willy.

ACKNOWLEDGMENTS

THE RECONSTRUCTION of a life from cold history isn't a simple task. If one attempts it honestly, he must base his characterization only on the established facts of that life. This means dependence on the professional historian, on the *aficionado,* and on those fortunates whose lives crossed the actual moment.

Since I am indebted to precisely those sources, I must express my gratitude to the following people without whose kindness, interest and material assistance this book could never have passed from concept to completion.

INDIVIDUALS: Mr. Cleofas Calleros, Historian; Mr. José Andow, José Andow Studio, El Paso; Sra. Luz Corral Viuda de Villa; Dr. R. H. Ellis, Medical Surgeon, *División del Norte;* Maj. Jesús Zapata, *División del Norte;* Sgt. Desedero Espinoza, Brigada Fierro; Mr. Ben Turner, Machine Gun Section, Villa's American Legion; Mr. Frank Ahlgren, El Paso *Herald-Post;* Mr. Larry Harris, Author; Editor & Staff, El Paso *Herald Post;* many citizens of El Paso and Chihuahua, Mexico.

EL PASO PUBLIC LIBRARY: Mr. Walter N. Babbitt, Head Librarian; Mr. Henry O. Vaag, Assist. Librarian; Mrs. Rosemary Ryan Corcoran, Head of General Reference; Mrs. Marcelle Lively Harmon, Head of Southwest Research Section.

LOS ANGELES PUBLIC LIBRARY: Mr. Irwin Stein, Historical Department.

I should like to pay special tribute to Mrs. Harmon upon her retirement from a profession she has graced for so many years. Also to Miss Marguarite Irby, for her early help. Most of all I should like to salute the memory of a great American photographer, Otis Aultman, and his Mexican counterpart, Gustavo Casasola.

AUTHOR'S PREFACE

MY AVOWED PURPOSE in writing this book is to stand Pancho Villa up, right there in front of you, and let him be still while you walk around him. If I succeed, you should be able to discover how tall he was, how he moved, the actual configuration of his face and body; his likes, hates, fears; his way of thinking, and his manner of speech. Then I'll set him in motion like a resurrected man, and let you see what he was, how he became that . . . and why.

WILLIAM DOUGLAS LANSFORD

DON PORFIRIO DÍAZ was for over 31 years "President" of Mexico. A great hero in the Mexican War against the French (in which Mexico won her freedom from Maximilian), don Porfirio became *presidente,* then dictator. He was finally forced out by Madero, in 1911, and went into exile in Europe.

FRANCISCO I. MADERO was a small, gentle dreamer given to great bursts of courage and idealism. Of Spanish-Jewish parentage, well educated, Madero led a provisional Mexican government in the United States where he had taken asylum from don Porfirio Díaz's dictatorship. In 1910, when Díaz decided to elect himself *"presidente"* for another term, Madero called for a revolution and picked up hundreds, then thousands of men, forming them into a formidable army. Then he took Mexico City, assumed control of the government and was assassinated: he trusted Huerta against the advice of his top generals.

GENERAL VICTORIANO HUERTA was an officer of the corrupt *científicos,* a clan of men built by the dictatorship of Díaz. To grab the government and reinstate his old *científicos* with himself as president, Huerta wormed his way into Madero's trust, then had him killed.

GENERAL FRANCISCO (PANCHO) VILLA, leader of the famed *"División de Norte,"* began life as Doroteo Arango, a bronc buster and cowboy on a big landowner's rancho. At 16, having shot the ranchero's son for abusing his sister, young Doroteo fled into the hills and eventually took the alias by which he is famous today. It had formerly been the name of an old bandit-chief. After the outbreak of revolution, Villa offered his men and himself as soldiers to Madero. He was commissioned a captain and rose to the rank of general. After Madero's murder by

General Huerta, Villa; like Zapata and Carranza, declared war on the government which Huerta had usurped.

GENERAL RODOLFO FIERRO was chief of Villa's railway systems. Later he was relieved of this duty and given command of a crack mounted brigade. He was one of Villa's intimates and he frequently acted as Villa's bodyguard.

GENERAL EMILIANO ZAPATA was to the southern provinces what Villa was to the north. Born a farmer, he rebelled at Díaz's treatment of the farmers and joined Madero's force with his own revolutionaries. He and Villa became friends, for they were both brave, idealistic, simple men. After Madero's murder, both turned on Huerta, who claimed himself President, and defeated him.

VENUSTIANO CARRANZA, unlike Villa and Zapata, had much education, much ambition and little personal honor. He, too, had followed Madero, but his bent was more for organization than for combat. When Huerta usurped the government, Carranza joined Villa and Zapata in ousting him, but where Villa and Zapata both felt themselves unworthy of becoming *presidente,* Carranza felt no such qualms and promptly declared himself *"primer jefe."* Eventually, the brilliant young general Álvaro Obregón joined Carranza, and United States President Woodrow Wilson clinched his position by recognizing Carranza officially as President of Mexico. A United States embargo was placed on arms for Villa, and Carranza's troops were permitted to outmaneuver Villa's positions by traveling over United States soil, on United States trains. When Villa met Obregón at Celaya and ran out of ammunition and supplies, he was finished, and Carranza had won. Villa was thereafter rather bitter toward the United States —not without reason.

ÁLVARO OBREGÓN studied military science, was a brilliant, fearless soldier and unfortunately chose Carranza's side. Disdaining the picturesque, head-on tactics of Villa and Zapata, he employed European tactics in the trench style of World War I, relying heavily upon mass, artillery and position. At Celaya he handed

Villa his greatest defeat, but paid for it with his right arm, which was sliced off by a shell. Later Obregón succeeded Carranza as chief of the Constitutionalists and became President. Like Villa, Zapata, Carranza and Madero, he died by assassination.

GENERAL PASCUAL OROZCO was a wagonmaster. When Madero lifted the banner of revolution against Don Porfirio Díaz, Orozco organized a band of miners as fighters and joined the revolt. Later, after Madero's murder, Orozco joined with Huerta, and his "Redflaggers" became government guerrillas. Villa, Zapata and Carranza considered him an opportunist and a turncoat.

TABLE OF CONTENTS

THE BEGINNING OF THE END

WHEN THE YOUNG MAN stepped out and raised his hat, none of those in the grey Dodge touring car paid much attention. Miguel Trillo, sitting beside the round-faced, intent driver, was a gentle fellow, disposed to good manners. The stranger raised his hat once more, crossing the street toward a juice-vendor, and it seemed to Trillo gratifying to see such courtesy in this day and age.

The others took no notice. The robust man behind the wheel loved driving. He smiled constantly as he guided the sleek, 1919 auto along the streets of Parral. Daniel Tamayo, Rosalio Rosales, and Tomás Medrano chatted in the back seat. Claro Hurtado, and big Ramón Contreras rode the runningboards, since they came as bodyguards.

It was 8 o'clock, July 23, 1923. The ascending sun already drenched the white Chihuahua desert, and Trillo's precise, secretarial mind had just calculated that at their present speed they should arrive at Canutillo Ranch in a bit over three hours.

"*Mi general*," said Trillo to the driver, "did you ever dream that some day you'd be traveling at speeds up to 45 miles an hour, in a machine?"

"Never," said the driver laughing. "Impossible!"

As the Dodge turned off *Avenida Juárez* to *Calle Gabina Barrera*, all dreams ended abruptly. From a stunted adobe building, dead ahead, a rifle barrel appeared.

From the Dodge rose a startled cry as a bullet crashed through the windshield. The bodyguards on the runningboards leaped

off, but shots from the adobe dropped them without a chance.
With a rapidity which dazzled onlookers, eight men ran yelling
into the street, firing rifles and pistols at the car. Under their
murderous attack the auto swerved. Its front tires struck a curb
and bounced. As the frantic driver started the machine again, it
leaped forward, jumped the sidewalk and smashed into a large
elm tree.

Crying out for vengeance, the ambushers closed in on the
Dodge, still firing into its occupants. All appeared dead but the
driver, whose resistance to death seemed inhuman. His eyes
glared red as the blood pouring from his chest and mouth. His
copperhued face was like an angry, cornered animal's. Seeing he
couldn't escape, he twisted free of the dead Trillo. His right
hand pulled a pistol from his left holster.

I've seen you before, he thought. *This circle, this trap, this
death. I've beaten you . . . all of you . . . before. Here's my
answer.*

The pistol roared. The circle of men closed in. One of them
fell, but the others, screaming curses, continued firing, firing,
firing into that terrible man of iron who would not die.

1. RECRUITING

HE GLANCES UP *at the circle of faces as though he's never seen them before. Each man stares down at him. Each Indian seems stunned in the presence of new death. Each head is reverently uncovered. Indian-brown fingers form the sign of the cross. The silent peons in white stand straight, like so many whitewashed posts planted around the cold body of his father.*

Shawled women kneel, arranging the corpse. Some whisper comforting words to the new widow. The sunbaked body seems more dignified in death than its soul had ever been in life. A silent crone places a candle at each corner of the grass mat on which the dead man lies. Their yellow glow causes grotesque shadows to leap, dancing out of the sunken features of the dead man's face.

Black wings of death enveloped that hut. After sundown, at the workday's end, the boy had run home. He had heard that his father was finally dead. "Gone to God," one old woman called it.

Finally, the boy thinks. After 40 years of suffering and work. All his strength and life went to make other men comfortable and rich. Finally he can rest.

What has killed his father isn't important. The 12 year old peasant boy can't even pronounce the words which mean slow starvation and the consumption of a man's lungs. What does matter is that a man humble, honest and God-fearing—a man who never tasted freedom, or genuine pleasure, has ceased to exist. Eroded like the earth, burned out like a field of rotten corn. Run to death so that the landed class might enjoy its horses, its Spanish wines and its inviolable position.

*The boy understands none of this. But he can feel it. One day
he will hate it. And this is the beginning.*

*Silently, listening to the low sobs of Martina, his favorite sister
and Hipólito, his nine year old brother beside him, the boy
watches his mother folding the cold, stiff fingers over the corpse's
breast. And suddenly she screams, and screams again.*

*"Oh, God. Dios mío! Why did you have to take him from us?
Why so soon, when he was such a good man? He is gone,
Doroteo. Your father is dead. Why couldn't God spare him?"*

*The stoic mask is shattered. The women moan and cry beside
the widow, while their silent men look down on the wasted
remains of their friend and compadre in confused compassion,
knowing it might have been any of them.*

*"Mamacita," says the boy, embracing his mother. "Mamacita,
don't cry. I'll take care of you. I'll look after all of us. Hipólito
and I can plant, and Antonio will help us when he grows up,
Martina and the girls will bring us water and food, the way they
did papá."*

*But while glancing at that still, waxen figure something breaks
deep inside the boy and unable to contain his anguish he rushes
out, covering his eyes.*

*Outside, having wept himself calm, he looks up at the stars
and thinks:* I am the man of this house now.

*He can't erase the image of his mother fixing those lifeless
hands. Nor of his anguished sisters, nor of the two awed little
babies—his brothers—not completely realizing that their father
has left them forever. Most of all, Doroteo Arango cannot forget
his father's face. The face of a man who prayed each day, who
never complained, and who never asked aloud for what crime he
was condemned to his misery and death.* . . .

"Will you do it then?" asked the older man emphatically.
"Without hope of redemption or of return, if we should fail in
our effort, will you accept this summons of your country, Captain
Villa?"

The tall, square man whirled to look at him. He had stood at the window of *don* Abraham González's house, staring into the courtyard where his men waited by the horses. He had stood staring, without seeing or hearing the present, while recalling a lifetime of the past when he had been a boy called Doroteo Arango.

"What did you say?" he asked.

"I asked you, Captain Villa, whether . . ."

"Why do you call me 'Captain?' " asked Villa, annoyed.

The greying, heavyset Mexican looked nonplussed. "Why, I supposed that you would understand. A commission, naturally, goes with your assignment."

"With due respect, *don* Abraham," Villa replied drily, "You politicians are great supposers. I am a bandit, *señor;* some say a murderer, and a vandal. For 16 years, I've lived in and out of those mountains up there, chased by the law which looks to collect on certain unpaid accounts. I can suppose nothing. I came here to listen and to make up my mind, not to jump at suppositions."

Don Abraham, Chief of the Antireelectionists in Chihuahua, looked at the man before him, dismay crowding his heart. Villa was mercurial. Perhaps he was impossible, unmanageable as some claimed: a savage. But he was also a living legend of those mountains. He was the man who'd killed more soldiers than the plague. Even the fierce *rurales,* the Mexican Rangers, couldn't hunt him down. Ambush after ambush had been set for him, and always, Villa had fought out of them with the *rurales* bearing the lopsided losses. How many years had Villa said: 16? That would make him about 33 now. The story went that he'd killed his first man—a foppish young son of an *hacendado*—when not quite 17, and his first five *rurales* within the following year. And since then, countless others. No, Francisco Villa had no reason to love the *rurales,* the government soldiers or *don* Porfirio Díaz, under whose "benevolent" rule of 31 years, spoils systems, and oppression had grown.

On first meeting Villa, *don* Abraham had instantly read the bandit's history in those narrowed, watchful eyes. If Villa had grown distrustful of men and their promises, if suspicion always seemed to lurk behind those eyes, it was not without sufficient reason. These were the very factors which would make this bloody man invaluable to Madero, and to the Revolution . . . if he could be convinced. If he could be made to understand—and care.

"The Antireelectionist movement, *señor* Villa, has its roots deep in the credo that man was born to make free determination of his own destiny; that anyone, however humble, has the God-given right to elect his own leaders. It was conceived by Mexican idealists and intellectuals, university students, professors, artists, jurists and a few decent *hacendados* or *políticos* like *don* Francisco Madero who leads us. But it cannot succeed without the support of those close to the soil, of the masses of oppressed peoples who stand most to gain by it."

"Are you telling me a peasant could choose a *presidente?*" asked Villa, "even somebody like me?"

"Why not you?" asked González, "Mexico is your country."

"Then you're crazy," said Villa. "Do you imagine they would let me? You're not a peasant, so you've never felt the whips of the *rurales*. You never had a spur laid across your face, or a lariat over your neck. What the *peón* plants, the *rurales* rip out faster. They have sweet, little games, *don* Abraham. Little *juegos* you wouldn't like, such as slicing off your tongue for cursing an *hacendado*, or shaving the bottoms of your feet, then making you walk over cactus. And they can do it, because, *amigo*, everybody knows the Federal Rural Police cannot do wrong. *No, señor*, the *peón*, his *vieja*, even his babies can do wrong. But never the rich man, never Díaz and never his stinking *federales*."

Villa swatted his boots with his *sombrero*, trying to control his anger, but he could not. *Don* Abraham González saw those terrible eyes, felt that astounding power of which he'd heard so much. A power which frightened even friends.

The outlaw was in the prime of his manhood; a suntanned, weather-hardened man perhaps 5 feet 10-inches tall, 170 pounds.

His broad shoulders and limbs bulged his *charro* pants and jacket with thickness rather than muscularity.

One strong, brown hand held the curling brim of his *sombrero*, which hung almost to his ankles. The other hand, its thumb hooked into the broad pistol belt, rested not far from the fabled six-shooter. Although he'd spent his adult life in hiding, there was a natural style about his clothes. The hat, of camel-hued felt, had a diamond design around the brim, in red and white, a richer man might have envied. A white silk scarf hid the shirt beneath his short, green jacket, which was overlaid by criss-crossed cartridge belts. His *vaquero* trousers were of buckskin and tight down to the big-rawled Mexican spurs he wore over a handsome pair of jodhpur boots. His hair was auburn and almost curly, his broad moustache reddish, and the deep-etched lines on his round, copper-colored face indicated that he laughed often. The hint of a belly under the trace of white shirt visible at his waist was surprising considering the hard life he'd led and particularly so if one had realized that Villa never drank, never smoked, and ate less than the average child.

"But don't you see?" said *don* Abraham. "That's exactly what we're trying to combat. Cossacks and dictators have no place in a civilized nation. That's why we Antireelectionists are willing to risk everything—yes, our lives if need be—to rectify such evils. But we need you. We need men like you!"

"What you mean," said Villa skeptically, "is: 'We need cannon-fodder,' isn't that right, *don Antireelectionista?*"

In desperate fear that he was losing the bandit's confidence, Abraham González resorted to florid patriotism. Harking back to the eagle and the serpent, he marched Mexico's patriots through the fields and into battle, banners flying. He raised the cry of war with Hidalgo, and executed General Morelos. He resuscitated Benito Juárez, shot Maximilian and posed a comparison between Díaz—the one-time liberator turned dictator—and *señor* Francisco Indalecio Madero, the recognized head of the Antireelectionist Party.

"Now I ask you, *señor* Villa," he finished grandly, "what was

Madero's crime? That of preaching freedom. Of publicly stating
that *don* Porfirio Díaz should hold free elections and not simply
keep succeeding himself in office. For this, did he deserve to be
thrown into jail?"

"Excuse me," said Villa motioning for *don* Abraham's silence.
"*Señor* Madero was tossed into the *calabozo* by Díaz?"

"Of course, don't you read the newspapers? The periodicals
were full of it last year."

"*Don* Abraham," said Villa. "One of the disadvantages of
being a peasant is that there's more need of you in the fields
than in the schoolroom. I've never learned how to read. But, go
on. I didn't mean to stop you. A man who's been in Díaz's jail
can't be a complete waste."

"Last year," continued *don* Abraham gingerly, "General Díaz
informed an American newspaperman that any qualified candidate might run against him. All we Antireelectionists asked was
that our man *señor* Madero might declare his candidacy for
presidente. Little enough—*menos mal*—it was a start. We took
Díaz at his word, you see. But the dictator had already changed
his mind. *Don* Francisco was warned to withdraw. When he
refused—*Bueno, señor*. It must be plain. *Señor* Madero's crime
was preaching democracy."

"And it's plain you've got me, *don* Abraham," Villa said.
"Demo—that word you just used. What does it mean—in plain
language?"

"It means *nobility,* sir!" *Don* Abraham was aroused to oratori-
cal zeal.

"You mean like kings? Like Maximilian? Like that Spanish
bastard, and those other leeches? This, for Mexico?"

"*Señor,* you misunderstand me," cried González. "I speak of
the nobility of the soul. I speak of man's nobility. I—"

"Never mind nobility," Villa said impatiently. "It's clear I don't
understand nobilities. Tell me in simple language what your man
—*señor* Madero—wants. I mean, besides wanting to be president
in place of Díaz. What does he stand for?"

"He stands for democracy," said González like a grandfather

speaking to a child. "Democracy, *señor*." Then, with the incurability of the Mexican *político* struck with a phrase, he added: "Democracy is *nobility*."

"Do you see that horse out there?" Villa said, pointing to the huge black stallion one of his men held in the yard. "He's my nobility. And do you see this gun here, on my waist? That's nobility, too. My nobility. I've just come out of those hills—at some considerable risk to my nobility, my life and the nobilities and lives of my 15 men out there. For what? To listen to you spout nobilities and other crap? If you can't even give me a straight answer . . . if you can't tell me what your party's victory would mean in terms of food and land for the people—then to hell with you and your nobilities. And with *señor* Madero, too!"

Before Abraham González could move, the bandit Villa was in the courtyard with one foot in the stirrup.

"*Señor!*" González cried, dashing out in panic. "For the love of God, wait! Wait. You must forgive me. You must give me—give the country—a chance. An opportunity to—"

"To talk like a man, instead of like a parrot?" asked Villa.

Don Abraham González, scholar, political soul of Chihuahua and of the budding revolution, nodded his capitulation.

"*Sí, señor.* Precisely as you ask. As man to man. As Mexican to Mexican."

Villa reconsidered for an instant, then tossed the reins back to a smiling young bandit in a large, black hat. "Here," he said. "Take care of my little pony, Urbina. *Don* Abraham and I are going to try again. But just one more nobility, *señor*—and this revolution has lost Pancho Villa."

2

"Well, what do you think?"

"What do I think of what?" asked Urbina.

"You know. About us and this revolution business," said Eleuterio Soto rolling his large, grey eyes as if distressed.

"*Ahhhh,*" said Urbina winking.

"*Ahhhh,*" said Soto, irked. "And what the hell is *ahhhh?*"

"Well, don't you see? We can't lose. What are we?"

"What else?" asked Soto exasperated. "We're millionaires on vacation, don't you have eyes?"

Soto was a serious young man, vaguely related to Villa, who had joined the celebrated bandit when he'd been reported as the head of a large band of men, but was actually holding the *rurales* off alone. Sometime after, Tomás Urbina, this small, dark and ferretlike man, had met up with them and enlisted himself. But Soto had never entirely trusted or completely understood Urbina. Where Villa and Eleuterio were reluctant outlaws (Soto had been conscripted by the army and promptly deserted), Urbina was a born thief and a man who laughed, cried and lied excessively. Moreover, while Soto took everything literally, Urbina was prone to present life in terms larger than life— generally with some ulterior motive. Soto, simple and mountain- bred, believed in God, Honor and Home—in that order. Urbina —bred apparently by the devil—believed in no order but Urbina, and anything less than Villa and himself were subjects for mockery. Villa no one mocked. But nobody. Not even Tomás Urbina.

"*Burro,*" said Urbina as the other men drew closer to listen. "Let me sing it to you. We are *bandidos,* with prices on our heads, *verdad?* Now, Pancho puts us in the war . . ."

"And if we win, we're pardoned!" said Soto happily.

"You are really stupid," observed Urbina sadly. "*Hombre,* if we win, we not only go home pardoned, but we go home loaded. Think of the plunder. Think of the towns we'll loot. Of the rich bastards we'll gouge for everything they've got. Think of the good *aguardiente* and *tequila* we'll guzzle, and of the hundreds of sweet little tarts we'll somersault with their skirts over their heads. *Amigo,* that's heroism."

The others were delighted and chuckled approval, but Eleuterio Soto was appalled.

"Tomás," he said, "you're an impossibility, an atrocity. A man who exists only for his pocketbook and his pecker."

"Of course," Urbina said. "Do you think I'm crazy?"

Minutes later, Villa emerged, shook hands with González and mounted. *"Bueno,"* he said. "You can tell *señor* Madero that Villa will back him. The one thing I don't like is this business of being under Cástulo Herrera."

"It's simply a military formality," González apologized. *"Señor* Herrera is a colonel."

"Well, as I've said, if he colonels me too much, I'm going to ripen his mango," Villa replied, turning his beautiful black animal and letting him dance. "Meanwhile, Villa keeps his word. I've fed half the people in this province, and given all my money to the other half. We'll see now if they remember when I need them."

With a feeling of growing pride in his own accomplishment, *don* Abraham González watched as the well-armed, splendidly mounted outlaws aligned themselves—rifles at the ready—before their *jefe,* Villa.

"Urbina, Soto, Sánchez, Domínguez. You and the others—I want you to hit all the surrounding country and tell the farmers Pancho Villa needs recruits for the revolution. Any man with a horse, a weapon and enough balls for a fight is welcomed. But no camp followers. Not yet. Tell them to leave their *viejas* home. I'll give them nights off to use their other guns . . . if they survive."

"I'll bring my cousin," Urbina joked. "He used to be a soldier, but he lost his projectile in the war. He was an artillery-man."

"Tell him to stay home and send his wife," yelled Pánfilo Solis. "I have a projectile she can practice with."

"Bring your grandmothers, but be sure they're armed," said Villa to quiet them. "We'll meet at our last camp, in the Sierra Azul. And I'll expect no less than 10 men with each of you."

Two days later, when the last of the bandits had returned, Captain Francisco Villa, former outlaw, and now a leader of Irregular Cavalry in the Madero Revolution, lined up his original 15, with their recruits behind them. That afternoon, as he rode

down to meet "Colonel" Cástulo Herrera, encamped just outside
the tiny town of San Andrés, Villa was greeted by a man whose
mouth was open.

"*Imposible!*" said Herrera staring from his new captain to
the mass of mounted men behind him.

"What's impossible?"

"How many men have you there?"

"Three hundred and sixty," Villa replied, puzzled.

"Good God!" said Herrera. "I think you've just doubled the
size of the revolutionary army."

II. THE CRY OF WAR

ON OCTOBER 4, 1910, Villa had solidified his force by adding
Eleuterio Soto, José Sánchez, Tomás Urbina, Feliciano Domín-
guez, Pánfilo Solis, Lucio Escárcega, Antonio Sotello, José
Chavarriá, Andrés Ribera, B. Carrillo, Cesáreo Solis and Cerefino
Pérez.

After his first conference with *don* Abraham González, the
other men had joined him in his hideout in the Blue Mountain.
News had come to Villa that *señor* Pascual Orozco, a young,
comfortably-off wagon master and mule-train operator for the
mining regions near Guerrero City, was talking revolution, and
threatening to raise a force to support Madero's free election
demands. Villa already knew something about Orozco. He was
30 years old; a tall, dark sonofabitch of a man, as straight and
tough as a cornstalk. He was short on words and humor, but long
on action—and one hell of a rifle shot, so they said. *Don* Abraham had word that Orozco would rally his people, mostly
miners and mule-drivers, on November 20th, the day Madero's
ultimatum to Díaz expired, unless *el presidente* resigned. And
it didn't seem Díaz would.

On the afternoon of November 19th, Colonel Cástulo Herrera walked up to Villa, who sat drawing pictures in the sand, and informed him González and the other *junta* leaders wanted them ready to support Colonel Pascual Orozco if he should carry out his threat to attack Guerrero City.

"Another Colonel," muttered Villa, who was bored.

"My thought, and theirs," Herrera added prudently, "was that we should assault San Andrés, wipe out the garrison there and capture the barracks. We can wait for tonight and do it with very few casualties."

"Let's wait till tomorrow morning and do it without *any* casualties," suggested Villa ironically.

"Assault a town by daylight?" objected the Colonel.

"Goddammit," exploded Villa, rising and staring at Herrera. "What's all this talk about 'assault?' Most of the men from San Andrés are in this camp right now. Do you think they're going to ride into their own town, shooting their own wives and kids, just to give you a show?"

"But the garrison . . ." said Herrera.

"The garrison is 15 conscripts and a doddering old captain. Most of them are related to my boys. Do you think they're going to put up a ferocious battle when they see 375 determined men riding up to their barracks?"

"It wouldn't seem so," said Herrera, crestfallen.

"Well?" demanded Villa.

"Well, anything you say, Captain Villa."

Pancho Villa's hand slowly moved away from the vicinity of his pistol, and he smiled. "Thank you, my Colonel. You just keep on doing things sensibly, and they'll make you a general before you know it. *Conforme?*"

"*Conforme,*" said the Colonel. "We are agreed in every sense."

2

"Well, boys, we're all amateurs here, one might say. We're not as pretty or as educated as our little soldier friends. And you wouldn't mistake Soto, Urbina, or your humble servant here, for any of those sweet-scented officers from the military college in Chapultepec. But I'll tell you what we're going to do. We're going to stop that federal train; we're going to attack those sons of their whoring mothers—and we're going to show them how real men wear their balls. Now, what do you say, *muchachos?*"

The reply was deafening and filled the newly taken plaza of San Andrés. "*Que viva* Villa! *Viva la revolución! Viva el señor* Madero!"

"Well, *Mi coronel,*" said Villa to Cástulo Herrera. "No rooster crows clearer than that. If you'll please keep the peace here at San Andrés, we'll head for Chihuahua City and see what we can do about turning back Navarro's reinforcements."

"General Navarro's no fool," said Herrera. "And he's no coward, either. When you hit him, you're going to have a tiger by the tail."

"Well," smiled Villa, "we'll feed him a little milk. Can you hold things down with 75 men?"

"I'll manage. Watch yourself, Pancho. Look, maybe I should come with you. I'm perfectly willing, you know."

"*Gracias, amigo,*" said Villa, patting Herrera's arm. "Like the ugly girl at the dance—I know it was well meant, and I appreciate your asking, but I'm going to turn you down."

"Pancho," said Tomás Urbina, clanking up loaded with weapons and ammunition belts and spurs. "The boys are ready."

"Mount them up," said Villa, "and let's not keep the army waiting."

"Ay-ay-ay-ayiii!" howled Urbina waving the eager men into their saddles. "Look and tell me—who's the grasshopper in this field?"

"Who's the vulture with ten beaks?" called Domínguez. "Who's the eagle and the hawk? Who makes kitties out of lions?"

Captain Pancho Villa swung to his waiting horse, brought him around and dashed to the head of his 300 men, leaving the shouting to his troops. He was proud. For the first time in his life, life was more than mere existence; more than vengeance or the narrow game of hide-and-seek. His feelings were out now.

Words like democracy and justice began to make sense, even to seem real, and not a hoax perpetrated on the poor and humble by the crafty rich. God was above, and the blue skies grew ever wider. The sun was a peach for a man to slice and nourish on. The moon was a silver *peso* for the poor to spend. Good God. Good God! With times like these, what might not the lowest *peón* among them find within his reach? With willingness, arms and the force of right behind him, Pancho Villa might just stir this sleeping giant, Mexico, awake.

He wanted to sing. He wanted to cry. Swelling deep within his peasant's heart, the cry of war came rushing to the surface, like the hot, red fires of a volcano. Angry, ready and frightened, Captain Villa dug spurs to his mount and led his men toward the rail line that connected Guerrero with Chihuahua.

True to his word, that morning, Pascual Orozco had attacked the Plaza of Guerrero but he hadn't had the brains to cut the telegraph lines. And now the *federales* were coming to get him. But only if Villa didn't get them first.

III. THE TRAIN

LIEUTENANT COLONEL PABLO M. YÉPEZ, commandant of the relief train from Chihuahua City to Guerrero, was marked that morning for a tragic distinction. Before noon he would become the highest-ranking Federal officer to die thus far in the Madero revolution of 1910.

It's doubtful whether the greying, dignified and immaculately attired soldier would have wasted much time worrying had he suspected his fate. He belonged and subscribed to a peculiar caste system which considered itself invincible in spirit and unmatchable in war; a caste whose passwords through life were Honor, Duty and Valor. To Colonel Yépez, the venerable *señor general de División, don* Porfirio Díaz, *presidente de la Republica de México,* was the living personification of *noblesse oblige;* the paragon and paladin of the nation; the rarest fruit from the womb of Liberty Victorious. Hadn't he been Benito Juárez' right hand? His bravest general? His *Beau Sabreur?* Hadn't he freed Mexico from the Austrian, then turned the Capital into the showplace of the western world? Hadn't he nurtured Culture, saved the Aristocracy and espoused the causes of Science? Indeed, the Díaz regime and its *científicos*— (these scientifically-oriented exponents of Politics, War and Religion of a whole new era)— were sun, moon and truth. They *were* Mexico. But what could peons and rabble understand about such matters? *Don* Porfirio had made himself "Papá Díaz" for them. And this was how they repaid him.

The train carried elements of the 12th Infantry Battalion to relieve *Ciudad* Guerrero, whose Plaza (the core of military defense in all Mexican communities) was under attack by a pack of rabid miners, peons and muleskinners, under Pascual Orozco, a local malcontent. It was imperative that such people be taught a lesson, and Yépez was determined to do it.

His plan was straightforward and militarily neat. He would enter Guerrero, disarm the rebels, arrest their leaders and summarily punish them. Nothing drastic, although he'd considered executing Orozco as an example.

With these considerations aligned in his orderly mind, Colonel Yépez ordered his train to start. In it rode 500 of the finest troops in Mexico. A proud, well-disciplined unit, the 12th. Each *soldado* splendid in his French Foreign Legion-styled uniform of white square-brimmed *kepi,* blue coat and trousers, horseshoe rolled pack, was armed with the latest bolt-action Mauser. Even General Navarro's favorite 20th Battalion displayed no keener gloss or spirit. To the gratified commandant, the job at hand was a matter of two days, most of it travel.

If Lieutenant Colonel Pablo Yépez thought and dreamed in Arthurian clichés it wasn't without reason. Under Díaz the ruling class labored under the happy delusion that knighthood was still in flower. And not the least of the dreamers was the Mexican Army. Witness their uniforms and armament. A man was either French or German. Colonel Yépez affected the French uniform, slim moustache, and suave approach. General Juan J. Navarro, on the other hand, was Prussian, from the tip of his snap-brimmed cap to the hem of his ankle-length greatcoat. Wishbone spurs and riding crop were indispensable, as was moustache-wax and a delicate pinky for sipping Spanish chocolate.

No one, of course, seemed to recall that President Díaz had been an Indian, before he had become a general.

Having insured the comfort of his troops, conferred with his subordinates and seen to the placement of his baggage, *coronel del federales,* Pablo Yépez, returned to his private car and made himself at home. Fifteen minutes later, while no more than 10 kilometers out of Chihuahua, one of Yépez's company commanders glanced out the window and said, *"Mi coronel,* there are men up on that ridge."

Turning an exquisite profile, Yépez looked where the captain pointed. "You are absolutely correct," he agreed, and went back to his reading.

"More men," said a second captain after a moment. "And they appear to be armed."

Yépez glanced out again, nodded, then returned to his romantic novel, crossing his polished boots on the facing seat. *"Señores,"* he said almost indolently. "It is a very pleasant morning for this time of year, and I fully intend to enjoy it. If those peasants wish to attack us—" he shrugged. "Well, they will find us quite prepared."

2

Chihuahua City lies almost directly in the center of the state for which it was named. It sprawls inside an immense desert crater formed by the rugged mountains surrounding it. Mountains rich in ore; bare and ugly to a stranger's eye, yet perfectly fashioned for the *guerrillero's* purpose.

Under the torrid Mexican sun Captain Francisco Villa was happy. The stocky ex-bandit leaned on a brown boulder, by an immense patch of cactus, just where the train tracks finished a sharp curve and stretched out for about half a mile. Opposite Villa, along the steep incline of the facing ridge, Tomás Urbina held a similar ambush position. Spreading over that hill, lay Urbina's 100 determined men, completely invisible to Villa. Glancing over his own slope the *jefe de guerrillas* grinned with satisfaction. Not one of his own 100 fighters was visible either. With their big *sombreros* off and their leathery bodies burrowed into the rocks, cactus and earth, even someone who had watched them pick their places could not spot them now.

A sudden, shrill whistle snapped Villa erect. Far behind him, on a taller peak, a lone rider whistled again, then stood on his stirrups waving his *sombrero*.

"*Bueno muchachos, ya vienen*," Villa called to Eleuterio Soto and Pánfilo Solis. "You know what to do."

Both nodded, affecting a half salute. Their large hats flapped like wings as they turned and half-skidded, half-ran down the loose back slope into a draw where their horses waited. José Sánchez, Feliciano Domínguez and Lucio Escárcega were already mounted, along with the 50-odd men who would create the first diversion.

3

At 10:35, as the climbing sun slanted into the train windows from the east, the federal *soldados* saw the first enormous cloud of dust rising just behind the eastern ridge. Moments later they spotted another, and then another.

Puffing and laboring up the long grade, the troop train was moving at no more than 15 kilometers to the hour, and the racing clouds easily outstripped it.

The rank-and-file "Juan" was uneasy. Many of them came from these same mountains, and knew well that such clouds indicated hard-riding horsemen. Many horsemen. The ranks had also heard that small revolts had broken out among the people, all over Chihuahua, Coahuila, Sonora and other states. The thought of so much opposition and possible fighting unsettled them. Many would be shooting at cousins, nephews, uncles and brothers if the revolution should spread. Besides, *coronel don* Pablo Yépez had clearly explained that crazy men like Orozco, radicals like that little Jew, Madero, and blood-hungry *bandidos* like Pancho Villa were said to be the leaders of the rebels, and that any *federales* captured were sure to be hanged. *Demonio!* Who the hell needed all that trouble? The damned army was bad enough, with its stinking food, its mountains of lice and a million officers prancing around, all yelling orders at the same time. Now, savages and bandits!

With increasing dread the *soldados* at the windows studied the forming dust columns, muttering speculations.

"There are no less than a thousand, *por Dios!*" swore an old corporal who came from Parral, just up north.

"And a thousand on the other side," said a young private.

A young captain, tightmouthed and tugging nervously at his red-piped, blue *kepi*, walked through the train glaring at his men and pretending he saw nothing outside.

"What are you idiots staring at?" he growled.

"Sir," said the old *cabo*, "that dust—"

"Silence! Stupid fool. Don't you recognize plain dust-devils when you see them? Wind and desert, you imbecile!"

"But sir—"

"I said silence!" roared the captain rattling his sabre menacingly, as though he meant to lay the flat of it on the ancient corporal's back.

The intimidated soldiers bit their lips and were quiet while their company commander launched into a fist-waving lecture on courage, fidelity, and above all, good sense. He was still raging when a window exploded and the astonished officer staggered with a bullet through his thigh. He had just discovered what his men had been trying to tell him: that about 20 of his "dust devils" had materialized on a nearby cliff and were leveling their carbines at the train.

"*Alerta! Alerta!*" cried Colonel Yépez smashing out a window to fire his pistol at the riders on the cliff. But they were gone. Now there were riders on the other side, and they fired at the train rapidly, then rode off. Now horsemen came out of the rocks ahead of the locomotive, opened fire and were gone.

Yépez shouted furious orders to fire on anything that resembled a man. Shots came from everywhere. *Soldados* began to fall.

"Should we turn back, *mi coronel?*" asked the major who had run up from the rear of the train.

"Are you mad?" cried Yépez. "Give those dogs bullet for bullet. This troop started out for Guerrero, and that's where it's going."

"There must be five thousand of them," said a company commander rushing in from another car. "They've wounded *capitán* Hernández and at least a dozen men."

"To your post, Sir. Don't come here crying to me!" yelled Yépez. "Bugler, sound the alert again. Why aren't the men firing faster?"

4

Pancho Villa had never been a soldier, and had never trained as one. "But I've been chased by more uniforms than the town whore," he'd once told *don* Abraham, "and it's easier to know an enemy than a friend."

Life was simpler now that he was doing the chasing. Sucking a few pebbles to allay his growing thirst, Villa squatted by the boulder, keeping one eye on his lookout and another on the heaving puffs of sooty smoke which marked the snail's progress of the enemy locomotive, hidden by the descending hills. It was almost 20 minutes since Soto had ridden off with his group, and from the sounds below, they were doing fine.

Villa's plan had been to soften the train, and perhaps demoralize the soldiers sufficiently to make them turn back. To this end he'd revived some creaky bandit tricks, devised to simulate a large force. A dozen horsemen dragging brush at the end of their *riatas* could raise the dust of three cavalry squadrons. Forty riders, moving constantly, could appear on all sides of an enemy, giving the impression of battalions. Villa had never studied military science, but he'd been a bandit, a *vaquero,* and had the Indian's instinct for such things. You could teach a cow how to fly all day—but a sparrow needed just a little push. The bandit was the *guerrillero's* father, and the *Indio* grandfather to them both. Villa brought a tripartite personality to war. Quite confidently he expected to panic 500 *federales* and their train with 50 men. And if it didn't work . . . there was one final chance. The ambush of the hats.

When the train reached the top it stretched full length like a sleeping rattler in the sun. The engine poked its head around the curve as if probing strange territory, and at that instant the soldados saw the hats and opened fire.

"*Aya! Aya!*" cried the old *cabo* excitedly. "In the rocks, in those bushes by the ridge!"

One Federal captain fired his company by volleys, kneeling in the aisle and shouting his commands in a clear, controlled voice until the fire rounds in each Mauser were gone. Everything went into those hats until Colonel Yépez detected far more hats than bodies falling—and then he knew.

"You fool," he cried to the bugler, "sound cease fire! Can't you see what they're doing?"

That was when the main body of the rebels struck.

"*Viva* Villa!"

"*Viva la Revolución!*"

They poured down the slopes, 200 cheering, leaping men, catching the train in a murderous cross-fire that momentarily paralyzed all life within it. Led by Villa and Urbina, the army of peasants attacked without thought of self-preservation; their only desire to kill the hated *piojosos*—the lice-ridden ones—the *federales.*

Suddenly, from around the engine, Soto and his riders appeared, shooting and whooping until both fireman and engineer were down in the cab, and the great machine stalled. In a moment Eleuterio Soto had swung from his nervous mount into the train, waving his big hat and crying, "*Viva* Pancho Villa!"

This was the instant in which Colonel Yépez launched his counterattack.

Eleuterio Soto turned and received a volley in his face and chest. He fell without another word. A squad of *federales* had come swarming over the coal car, and into the cab to retake the engine. Two supply cars suddenly slid open and crews behind brand-new Hotchkiss machineguns swung into action, delivering a withering fire into the advancing ranks of yelling revolutionists.

Pancho Villa, pistols in hand, was caught completely by surprise and halted, momentarily puzzled. It was the worst thing he could have done. Halting, too, the others stared at each other in momentary panic, then broke and started back up the hillsides.

"Come back. Back, *amigos!*" called Villa.

Tomás Urbina, on the other slope, was having worse troubles. Thick cactus beds had impeded his downward progress and his men had suffered tremendous casualties in the final minutes of the charge. Now his people were stalled going up.

"*Cobardes!*" he screamed at them angrily. "*Coyotes.*"

The long-ingrained discipline and close fire-control of the regulars was beginning to tell. As the revolutionists retreated, Colonel Yépez ordered his officers to detrain and give pursuit. "Press them," he shouted angrily. "I want them wiped out. No mercy. No quarter. I'll teach these damned rebels the virtues of civil order!"

Desperately Pancho Villa rallied a dozen men around him and attacked, firing toward the Colonel. Yépez staggered, one hand groping for the car steps. His blue blouse turned red at the breast, but he wouldn't let anyone touch him.

"The rebels! Damn you, finish them!" he yelled.

In his own fury, Pancho Villa ignored the enemy bullets, discharging his pistol into the Colonel, until Yépez finally lay dead.

Then he turned and followed his men, dodging and retreating up the slope.

Hiding up there, trembling and covered with dirt, thorn-slashes and sweat, Villa watched the *federales* loading their dead and wounded onto the crawling train. A train still going to Guerrero.

It was a stinging defeat, retreat, and the humiliation of their highest hopes. Worse yet, for Pancho Villa it had brought an added measure of sorrow. Eleuterio Soto was dead. Nothing Villa could ever do would return to him this dearest *compañero* and friend who had shared with him, and with Urbina, the dangers and hardships of their mountain life.

Where had it gone wrong? What had he failed to do?

Villa could not imagine that Pablo Yépez, proud to the point of fanaticism, had been unable to accept defeat at the hands of "rabble." He had traded his own life for victory. This, plus years of preparation for war, had settled the issue.

Pancho Villa had done all he could; his men had given all they had but it had proved insufficient. Rebel cunning and recklessness had not been enough. Deep in despair, Villa turned to the gloomy Urbina.

"Tomás, we'll go back to San Andrés. We've got to raise more men. We've got to learn more about this military business. And we've got to try again."

"*No fué muy simple,*" said Urbina. "It wasn't very easy, was it? Not like fighting a handful of them."

"*No, compadre.* It wasn't," said Pancho Villa.

There were no *Vivas!* now as the soldiers of the revolution turned and rode away, leaving behind them the shallow graves of 40 comrades.

IV. THE MILITARY CHIEF

"I'LL KILL HIM, MAMACITA. *I swear it.* Te lo juro, mamá, que le he de matar!"

"No, mi hijito, por favor. *You mustn't. If you touch* don *Leonardo, the* rurales *will punish you. They will put a rope around your neck and drag you until you die.*"

"*He abused my sister—your daughter. He raped Martina. Now he'll marry her, or I'll kill him—no matter what.*"

He is armed and mounted. The hacendado *is also armed and out riding, surveying what he owns and rules. Dog. Spanish animal. Arrogant son-of-his-filthy-mother! I'll stop him now. Here. Look at his face. He senses it. He's afraid of me.*

"*I have to talk to you,* don *Leonardo.*"

"*Oh? Of course. I'm always available to my people. Ask the* mayordomo. *Maybe I'll find a few minutes tonight.*"

"*I want to talk now,* don *Leonardo. Right here.*"

"*What? Which one of them are you? Oh, yes. Young Doroteo Arango. I made the mistake of taking you out from behind a plow and letting you tame my horses. Now they tell me you have delusions of grandeur.*"

"*Let's forget my . . . whatever it is you called them . . . and let's talk about my sister.*"

"*I—I haven't time now. I have pressing—*"

"*You had time to rape her!*"

"*She's a liar! You indecent, foulmouthed Indians disgust me. I ought to have you flogged for—*"

Don *Leonardo's thin nostrils flare and his haughty lips curl. Involuntarily his riding crop rises.*

Yes. Now. Here. Pay them all. Pay them for the misery, for the death of your father. Pay them for your mother's wasted life, and for Martina's terror and pain and humiliation.

"*You think you can take any woman on this ranch and make her yours, because you're the* patrón. *You laugh at us, mock us, whip us, kill us. You think God's given you* hacendados *liberty to do what you like with us."*

He sees the gun under my shirt. He sees it. Look at his face. Where's your arrogance now, Gachupín? *Where's your courage and your superiority? What stops your hand from touching that nice, shiny pistol at your belt? Look, nothing stops me. Look right into this barrel, you sonofawhore. Justice is coming out of it. There . . . there . . . there . . . there . . . there!*

"Wake up, Pancho. Wake up."

"What?"

"*Hombre,* said Urbina, "you were having one hell of a nightmare. What were you dreaming?"

"I can't remember. What time is it?"

"It's nearly dawn. Do you want the men up? They're all worn out, they've slept like stones. Poor bastards. Three defeats in a row. They'll remember Cerro Prieto and Tecolote the way they did the train."

"And so will I," said Pancho Villa shaking out the horse blanket he'd slept on, and wrapping it around his shoulders.

It was dark, still, and it was unbearably cold. By night those desert stars sparkled like chips of ice, and even the coyote and the rattler sought warmth in the holes and burrows of the hills.

Villa rubbed his hard shoulders, wishing silently for a campfire, but he didn't dare. Not yet. Somewhere out there, in the plains below, General Navarro's scouts might still be hunting, and the tiniest spark of flame would betray them.

"*Bueno,* Tomás. We might as well rouse them. Get them up and ready to ride. I want to reach Guerrero before evening."

"And then, Panchito?"

"Damned if I know," said Villa dispiritedly.

He was thinking about his attacks on Navarro's positions, and how easily the old aristocrat had turned the tables on him. Again

Villa had sought to employ surprise, overwhelming the *científico*. But the old martinet had proven himself equal to any ruse the *guerrillero* could devise. Face-to-face the soldiers of the 20th Battalion, and the regular artillery, under Colonel Tamborell, had cleaned the field. And then Navarro's firing squads had started their vengeance on the revolution.

Men. Good, honest men. By the dozen. Lined up. Shot down. Lined up. Shot down. Endlessly, senselessly. Pancho Villa was no stranger to death, but his killing had always been defensive; in the line of self-preservation. Not bloodbaths. In his head he could still hear the interminable discharges which were killing his men. He knew Navarro would continue to kill until no prisoner was left. Failing with the train, Villa had hoped to assault the *federales* at Tecolote, thus replenishing his ammunition stock. But, failing again, he had been left without even sufficient ammunition to attempt a rescue of his comrades. That he would remember, too.

Tomás Urbina, a small, thin shadow under his enormous hat, approached, clanking with spurs and all the hardware of war. He was now a Captain, appointed by his *jefe*, Villa, to equal rank. Thief though he might have been, by upbringing and inclination, he was loyal, and brave, and as deserving of recognition as anyone in that *guerrilla* band.

"All right, *compadre*. They're up, but we'll have to sew their eyelids open. Can we light just a little fire?"

"No fires. What've we got to cook but our toenails, anyway? Tell them to mount up, and send Domínguez and his bunch out ahead. I've got to figure what the hell to do next."

"Well, *jefe*, there are ranches around—and they have cattle. And a gun in the right belly could get us some coffee, and even a few pesos."

"Tomás, we're not bandits anymore. The Revolution is our cause, and pays us a salary as soldiers," said Villa sternly. "That means we serve the people, not fleece them."

"Sure *jefe*. But just one little cow. *Una vacita*. For crissakes, we haven't eaten in four days."

"All right, one. But *one,* Urbina. And you leave the people alone, understand?"

2

"*Coronel* Orozco?"

"*Capitán,* please have a seat," said the tall, dry-voiced man, his jaw muscles flexing as his glittering eyes scrutinized the peasant soldier before him. "You received my wire?"

"Yes."

"And obviously you agree that a conference of band commanders would be beneficial to the movement."

Villa had heard sounds like Orozco's voice before. Burning wood crackled and popped that way; telegraph wires hissed and made such electric noises. Orozco seemed a man without a soul, all energy and business.

"You do agree?" the man insisted.

"I'm here," said Villa without arrogance.

Orozco's face was expressionless. He looked like a freight-boss. From his small-brimmed, campaign hat to his black, laced shoes, he resembled nothing so much as a freightyard boss walking around with two cartridge belts wrapped around his pants waist. A peg on the adobe wall of Orozco's Guerrero headquarters held a striped, blue coat which matched his trousers, and next to it hung a railroader's jacket with a massive pistolbelt bearing a .45 Colt. *Despite his looks,* thought Villa, *our Mister Orozco means business.*

"*Coronel* Herrera tells me you're a hellion, *capitán.* According to him you eat *federales* for breakfast."

"The last few bunches of them gave me a slight indigestion," said Villa. "Who else is going to be here?"

"Well, Herrera, Lucio Blanco, you and myself. Máximo Castillo and his band are up by the *gringo* border, waiting for *señor* Madero to cross safely back into Mexico. What I say goes for him."

"Do you have ammunition for me and my men?"

"I have ammunition for those who do us good," Orozco said. "You attacked that train and killed Yépez. But I defeated it, after it got here. The division is according to the labors invested."

Pancho Villa rose slowly, hooking his thumbs into his pistol belts. "Are you saying you called me here to inform me I don't get a thing?"

Pascual Orozco saw something he would never forget or forgive. Villa was capable of killing him. The peasant's face was red; he was breathing through his mouth. His whole aspect was that of a massive bull, driven by some inner goading. Orozco had never feared a man before. He feared one now. But in an instant, his nerve was under control. He held top card, not this smelly hillsman, and they both knew it. With 2,000 men behind him now, with a string of early victories, and with ample stores of ammunition, it was he, Orozco, who could call the turns. One bad move out of Villa and he would surround Villa's mangy army and smash it . . . but would Villa let him live that long?

"*Amigo*, you're jumping to conclusions," said Orozco, patting Villa's shoulder. "I didn't say that."

"Then tell me what you did say so we'll both understand."

"In attacking that train, you did more than the others and I'm not one to forget. These others talk. You and I fight. I'll be honest. When Herrera told me you'd hit that train, I thought you were a fool. But you didn't fight like a fool. The time you bought was the time I needed to clean up here, and be ready with my own ambush."

"What does all this gratitude add up to in terms of guns and munitions for me and my boys?" Villa asked, unmoved.

"How does 300 Mauser rifles and 200 rounds for each one sound to you?"

"Not as good as 500 rifles and 500 rounds each."

"Make it 400," said Orozco the businessman.

"All right. And 200 sticks of dynamite."

Orozco almost smiled. "My old man remembers when you

were herding mules and busting broncs. He said, for a snot-nosed kid, you were always hell to deal with."

"That's because he always tried to cheat me," Villa had started to say, thinking better of it. Orozco was a frugal, touchy sonofabitch whose pocketbook laid next to his heart. No use antagonizing him just for fun. This revolution business came first.

The "freightmaster" sat down behind the upturned crate he used for a desk, and was writing the order for Villa's supplies with a facility that made the peon-soldier envious. How many times had he promised himself that one day he would learn to read and write? But when? When would there be time?

"Well, I've got Guerrero now, and the *federales* can't stop me," said Orozco. Villa watched his fingers make those magic words. The city man wore a broad necktie. His fingernails were pink, clean and neatly rounded. Pancho glanced at his own hands. They were calloused, thick and brown. Fit only for the plow or currying animals or—

"There's your requisition. Just present it to Félix Terrazas or Marcelo Caraveo. They're my seconds here," said Orozco. "And, by the way, *don* Abraham González has placed Colonel Herrera under me, and that means you ride on the same donkey. This is mid-December. Before Christmas I'll hold Chihuahua City. By February, or before, I'll have the state, and present *don* Francisco Madero with Juárez City, so he can return to Mexico like a man, instead of sneaking in by night, like a thief."

He glanced at Villa and added, "No offense intended."

Villa made no reply, but thought: *Don't you worry, cabrón. I'll give you all the rope you want, but when the time comes, your toes may not reach the floor.*

"As *don* Francisco's First Revolutionary Army commander, I'm incorporating the others into my forces as soon as they arrive," Orozco continued. "Villa, I want you to put yourself directly under my flag, right now. What you got today is peanuts compared to what there is in this for men like us. What do you say?"

"I am pledged to the revolution," said Villa plainly, "not to personal ambitions."

"So am I," said Orozco brusquely. "And I let my actions speak for me."

Villa considered for a moment before nodding. "*Muy bien, mi coronel,*" he said. "So long as that's the case, you can count on me. But I'm going to say this, just so there'll be no misunderstanding: If ever you betray our Revolution—or my trust—I will kill you. Do I make myself perfectly clear, *amigo?* With this hand, with this gun, I swear to you that I'll kill you."

V. THE PEÓN LEARNS

PANCHO VILLA DIDN'T CARE for the petty court intrigues which were fast developing in the First Revolutionary Army Commander's headquarters at Guerrero. There was much talk and little action. Days and nights were consumed by drinking, arguing and making grandiose plans for attacking this city or that. To Villa, it seemed wasteful to devote so much energy to pure conjecture and to the framing of elaborate, if negative, messages to Francisco Madero—whose provisional government was still in El Paso, Texas—instead of doing something about getting Madero back into Mexico and immediate power.

Now, in the last days of the final month of 1910, the enemy's garrisons were being augmented. Federal troops and heavy equipment, under old firebrands like General Navarro (*compañero* and fellow patriot of Díaz in Mexico's war against the French), were arriving daily from the south. Crack units, under the leadership of youthful regulars, with considerable experience in Indian fighting and quelling minor revolts, were building a blue chain to isolate the Antireelectionist forces, and later to push and crush them against the *Yanqui* border, when *don Porfirio* should give the word.

As for the "benevolent" Papá Díaz: he seemed quite happy and unconcerned by all the noise up north. Just this December first, he and his vice president had been re-elected "by an overwhelming majority"—as tabulated by his joyful adherents— and had stated to an ecstatic public that despite his "ardent" desire to return to private life he would "humbly submit" to his people's demands and again take the office of *presidente*.

Such humility enraged Pancho Villa. He wanted to kill, to wipe every last *Porfirista* sonofabitch right off the face of the earth. Yet he felt helpless. He could fight, still he seemed unable to achieve even the smallest victory. This business of war was puzzling as hell.

"Those goddamn *científicos* know something we don't know," he told Urbina angrily. "They've buried the skunk, and we've got to smell him out, the hard way, before we can dig him up."

"If we kill enough of them, it doesn't matter what they know," opined the grinning Urbina, "because they can't use it."

"No, Tomás. You're wrong there. We'll have to catch them to kill them. So we'd better learn what they know."

1

Captain Villa's first opportunity to sniff that skunk, and to escape the confines of Orozco's camp, came with word that a federal mule-train was on its way to General Navarro's head-quarters through the Chihuahua mountains.

"Take your people," Orozco told him, "and don't let that convoy reach Navarro. And if you can do more damage—do it."

By now Orozco was certain he would have to assault either Chihuahua City or Juárez, and he reasoned that no man in his camp could soften the *federales* and harass them more effectively than the crafty *bandolero* who slept more comfortably in a coyote-hole than in a bed. So what if Villa's audacity far exceeded his witless, *peón* mind? No great loss if Navarro caught and stood him up against some wall. In the interim he could be of use.

Once in his hills again, Pancho Villa felt reborn. His nostrils joyfully sniffed the fresh desert winds, his narrowed eyes swept the peaks, the plains, the valleys. This was his classroom. He had come out here to learn. But this time it wouldn't be the university before the first grades.

The mule-train was no difficulty. He'd robbed enough of them, during his bandit days, to make it practically routine. This time the *federales* has made the mistake of trying to sneak supplies through Pancho Villa's backyard. In minutes it was done. Twenty dead *soldados*—and 10 mules loaded with arms, ammunition and food. Enough to launch the *peón* in his studies of the mysteries of military science.

2

By Christmas of 1910, Pascual Orozco's predictions went down a rathole. He didn't hold *Ciudad* Chihuahua. Nor did he have much hope of getting a good hold on the state. But within the confines of that Federal-held state one force moved at will, and struck with a regularity that galled the grizzled, old Navarro. That force was led by what the Federal Commandant disparagingly called "that bloody ignoramus, and scandalous bandit— Pancho Villa!"

The former outlaw was now, in truth, becoming the *guerrillero*. In his vast schoolroom equipped with the cactus and rocks, watched only by the eagles and lizards, led only by his probing mind and determination, Villa sought out small actions and carefully testing each vital if often minor lesson learned in some previous encounter.

He learned never to permit his men beyond the camp unless fully armed so that in case of surprise each man could act alone until rejoining his group. Now he understood that Yépez's counterattack had been possible only because he'd designated a reserve company—and that this force had risen as the main body had weakened, countering the rebel surprise at the vital moment. So Pancho assigned reserves of his own, drilling them in firing and maneuver under close control. Never again would the fatal mistakes of that train attack be repeated.

Beyond this, he'd borrowed the wisdom of the *vaqueros* who always took *remudas* on long rides, for assured mobility. One rider could wear out three mounts in a round-the-clock dash.

Clothes, food and equipment became infinitely more desirable than money. Even Urbina sadly admitted that fact. Rendezvous points were always assigned prior to any commitment, and these were generally near where extra supplies and ammunition had been cached. The value of orderly disengagement in small groups was preached to the *guerrilleros* by their *jefe,* and this lesson—as all the others—was rehearsed far in the hills, before employment.

In many, meaningful ways the former outlaw had, from the start, been well in advance of his enemies. His judgment of men and horses was superb, his knowledge of terrain was unmatchable, and his espionage system impossible to stop. Any farmer or mule-skinner, any sleepy old man or ancient *doña* Lupe might be a spy for Villa—and generally was. In his outlaw days Pancho Villa had paid off their debts, given them protection against the greedy *hacendados,* and always left a handful of *pesos* for a pair of new shoes or a bit of *melocha* candy for the *niñitos.*

Without knowing it, when he shared his windfalls with the poor, Pancho Villa had begun welding a single, unified force out of the peasants. And they responded. Because of the past, when the enraged *federales* came to their doors, the *peones* of Chihuahua could never recall from where the *guerrillas* had appeared—or how they had disappeared. Pancho Villa, it seemed, did not exist. Perhaps he had never existed. He was a rumor. He was a sudden, desert wind. He was the hawk behind the cloud. He was a thought and an idea . . . and that idea was growing.

3

"So," said Villa, the *cabrones* are laughing at me, eh? Who was it wrote you this note, Solis?"

"It was the major, himself, *jefe.*"

"Read it to me again. What does it say?"

Capitán Pánfilio Solis, one of Villa's original 15 *compañeros* from the Sierra Azul days, took the paper the *jefe* held out to him and read:

Sir:
If Pancho Villa has the courage and the withal to take the city of Camargo, step right up.

"And did you tell him I gave him an hour and a half to surrender?"

"Just as in your note," said Solis.

"And did you tell him nicely? That I wanted to spare their lives, and all that?"

"Exactly."

Villa grabbed the paper, spread it roughly between his bronze hands, then tore it to pieces. "Well, *amigos*," he said slamming his *sombrero* on his head. "We're going to have a little *tiroteo* here. Just a small skirmish to show those baldheaded, lice in-fested sons-of-their-towering-whore-mothers that we're not as funny as they think we are. Urbina!"

"*Sí, jefe?*"

"To your troops."

"Solis!"

"*Jefe?*"

"You commence this dance, *amigo*, as I instructed. I'm going to ride my little horse up on that hill, where they can see me, and I'm going to start cleaning my rifle, because I won't need it this trip. And by the time I finish, I want to see those lice-carriers flying for their lives. Is that clear?"

"*Sí, jefe. Perfectamente.*"

"Good! Start hauling."

Captain of Irregulars Francisco Villa had instructed his troops patiently, and groomed them carefully over the last month of campaigning. Now he intended to see whether they had ab-sorbed anything besides *frijoles*.

Pancho Villa watched his dismounted cavalrymen, under

Pánfilio Solis, extend their skirmish-lines and sweep down the plain which faced the federal trenches before the city of Camargo. As they ran, tiny puffs blew from their rifles, and seconds later the *crack-crack-crack* of fire reached his ears.

After many defeats, this was to be his first strike at a major center. Settled comfortably on his big bay, *Siete Leguas,* one booted leg over the broad Mexican saddle horn, Villa scarcely seemed concerned.

Solis' men advanced in the half-crouching, half-crab fashion he'd taught them, their weapons halfway to their shoulders, their conical hats flopping in the brisk wind as they kept levering rounds into their rifles and firing.

Two hundred of them charged the trench-defenses, and when they were nearly at pistol range, the federal officers' swords flashed upward, and the counter-musketry rattled in the wind obscuring the parapets with dirty smoke. The Villistas wavered. Villa could see Solis and Domínguez, among the ranks, arguing and yelling, but at the second fusilade the ranks broke up. The attackers turned tail and ran.

It was a clear-cut rout. The *federales,* following book procedure, rose with a general yell, their buglers sounding the exciting call for pursuit and annihilation of the enemy.

The blue-coated, bayonet-wielding *soldados* responded so marvelously, leaping recklessly out of their trenches in their eagerness to kill. At that instant, as Pancho smiled, a terrifying scream of "*Viva* Villa!" filled the morning air and the main rebel body broke from cover, charging both federal flanks with a volley of enfilading fire.

Surprised and surrounded, the Porfiristas balked under the saber blows of their officers. Cut off from their trenches, they milled in panic. Their flanks collapsed and, as the trap tightened on all sides, the beaten *federales* dropped their rifles, begging for quarter.

After months of work and near-despair, the *peón* had finally graduated. And with honors.

4

"This is a very good watch," said Pancho Villa flipping open the hunting case. It was a silver case, containing fine, railroad-accurate works. A small token of esteem sent to him by *don* Abraham González, and the only watch Pancho Villa would ever own. He loved the thing more for its mechanical beauty than for its function, for he could tell the time of day or night, almost to the minute, by simply glancing at the sky.

"This little hand here counts the hours," he continued, smiling pleasantly. "You see these little ticks here? They're minutes. You have just two of those little ticks left, so say your prayers, my friends. Tell God what dirty, crawling lice you were. Tell Him about the poor people you robbed. Tell Him about the babies you left without fathers, and the wives you left without husbands. Tell him Pancho Villa is sending you to hell."

"Please, *señor, no*." moaned the court clerk.

"You haven't the face for it, *señor*. Nor the manner. You are a compassionate man, *señor* Villa, aren't you? Aren't you compassionate, *señor*? Please answer me."

"You're talking away your time," said Villa.

The fat, middle-aged mayor stood very straight. He had a pink, rubbery nose, an enormous Teutonic moustache, and jowls that quivered when he swallowed. He wouldn't look at Villa. He would not beg or deign even to glance at the ropes which Urbina had swung from the oaken beams over the open rolltop desk.

"You stand convicted of profiteering, of abusing the people under your care and of denouncing innocent citizens to the police as rebels. Because of you they were murdered by firing squads," Villa said. "Your time is almost up. Is there anything you want to say?"

"Convicted by what authority?" demanded the mayor unexpectedly. "Yes, I ask it directly to your face, *señor* Rebel Chieftain. By whose legal right do you presume to judge me? I was the duly constituted authority here until you—"

"I'm going to tell you about a better authority than yours," Villa said. "There are nine new graves in your *camposanto;* two of them were women, and one a 16-year-old boy. I was talking to them, a little while ago—right after my own boys were buried there—and do you know what they said to me? 'Pancho,' they said, 'we didn't deserve this. We weren't criminals. Our crime was being poor, and desperate.' And then they said: 'Panchito, when you bring our fat mayor, and his pimply-faced clerk, and our ugly chief of police, and all those others here; put them far on the other side, alone. We had them on our backs, through all our lives, and it wouldn't be fair to have them on our backs again."

"You filth!" said the mayor furiously.

"No, *don* Cayetano," said the clerk. "*Señor* Villa, you are a kind, compassionate person. A humble person, yes sir, but intelligent, civilized and—"

"Shut up!" said the mayor. Then to Villa: "What do you intend doing with my son?"

"He offered to dig your grave, and his," said Villa. "After that we'll shoot him right there, what else?"

"Thank God I'm a widower," said the portly man as if to heaven. "You indescribable dog. You plague. You pox!"

"You bastard," said Villa, taking it up. "You fat, hypocritical pig. You play indignant with me—and all the time you *know* what you deserve. Don't you? Get up on that desk, both of you. *Arribá!*"

It took Lucio Escárcega and five men to get the fat man up, and it gave Pancho Villa pleasure to see the official's indignation at being shoved and goosed upward on Lucio's shoulder. The clerk was skinny as a quill-pen, but his rubbery legs kept buckling, and he had to be supported until Urbina could loop the rope around his chicken's neck.

But in the end, it was the irate mayor who cracked hardest, for his underling was beyond expressing himself, except in sobs.

"You cannot do this," stormed *don* Cayetano unconvincingly.

"I protest. It is murder. It is—" He couldn't go on, for he was finally paralyzed with fear.

"It is—*justice!*" Villa finished. "And *revenge!*"

Pancho Villa bunched his powerful fingers around their trouser-cuffs and yanked their feet free of the desk. They dropped six inches. The beam squeaked, and the ropes stretched. These were not hangman's knots. Their deaths came slowly, by strangulation. And all the time the dying men jerked and kicked convulsively, Pancho Villa stood staring, and said nothing, but his eyes were filled with grim satisfaction.

5

"*Señores,*" said Pánfilo Solis grandly, "you are in luck. No less personage than *capitán* Francisco Villa has come to see you off."

Villa dismounted and came up jingling, with that stifflegged, slightly pigeontoed walk which made people think of him as bowlegged.

He strolled along the row of open graves, peering in. Each held a dead man. There was no one left alive, save Pánfilo Solis and his eight-man firing squad. Solis, who was something of a joker, had been talking to the dead.

"*Bueno,* Pánfilo. How did they take it?"

"Pretty good, *jefe,* considering the breed. They were mad as hell about digging their own graves. They said they weren't common thieves."

"That's what *they* said," Villa commented ironically.

"One boy wet his pants. That young, blond lieutenant."

"Good."

"The captain slapped him, and said he should have done it in my face—."

"Two of a kind," said Villa. "What about the chief of police?"

"Not a word. Not a look. *Nada.* Like a damned statue."

"Well, I'll give him that, anyway," said Villa. "Good work, *muchacho.* Take your men to the nearest *cantina,* and have all you can hold. Tonight, and tonight only, I'm going to let you tank up. But remember this: don't bother the people. One brawl, one stink and I'll have the man back here by sun-up, digging a grave. With me waiting to put him in it."

Solis and the squad rendered their version of a military salute, and marched away, each mulling an almost identical thought. Something had happened to Pancho Villa which frightened them. Gradually, without a word being spoken, or an outward sign, Pancho had stopped being an intimate *compañero* and had become their commander. They could no longer walk up and joke with him. There was something different there.

6

"*Épa, Compadre,* look at this!" chirped Tomás Urbina, delighted as a baby. "You just pull this little chain, and you get water. There's enough in here now to make a good pot of soup."

"Some soup!" said Villa, who was busy shaving before the big, bureau mirror, washing his straight razor in a huge fruit-bowlful of hot water.

Urbina flushed the toilet again, chatting happily. "*Mira.*—Just look at that. Regular whirlpools. I'm going to make a paper boat, and sink that sonofabitch."

"Damn you, Urbina. You made me cut myself," said Villa. "When the hell are you going to grow up?"

"Hey, let's go get laid," said Urbina. "*Compadre,* what an idea, *qué tal,* eh?"

"*Nada de eso,*" said Villa seriously. "*Compadre,* none of that."

"But the town's full of *viejas,* for chrissakes. Listen, everywhere it's Pancho Villa *this,* and Pancho Villa *that,* and *such* and *thus,* and he *says* and he *did* . . . What the hell's wrong with a little *panocha* now and then? My horse gets more than I do, since I let you turn me into a damned patriot."

"You're a captain, and your horse isn't," said Villa.

"Well, hell, *compadre,*" said Tomás Urbina coming from the toilet into the mayor's livingroom, with a dejected look, and buttoning his fly. "People like us don't just change overnight. First no stealing, then no fighting, and now no women. What the hell's the good of being a captain? Next you'll have me working all day, and pulling my bellrope at night, like a Protestant priest. *Demonio!"*

"Look," said Villa turning from the mirror. "Today we got rid of a bunch of sonsofbitches who have exploited this city for over 20 years, *verdad?* Well, that isn't enough."

"I told you that myself," said Urbina perking up. "Let's go prong their wives, that'll teach them."

"Listen, *compadre,* I'm serious now," said Villa. "It struck me today that ridding the people of these lice isn't the whole answer. No. We have got to *work* these towns."

"*Now* we're getting somewhere," agreed Urbina. "Shake the bastards down!"

"You damned idiot," said Villa impatiently. "Don't you ever *think?* I mean work the towns for the good of the *people.* The common people. The only ones that count."

Urbina threw up his arms, and collapsed on the nearest chair, shaking his mane of black hair.

"Don't you see, Tomás. If the people prosper, the government will prosper. If the people learn, the government *must* learn, too. Because the people *are the government."*

"You're crazy, you know that?" said Urbina shaken out of his humorous mood. "*Completamente loco.* We're bandits. What do we know about the government? What do those *pelados,* walking out in the street care about governments? They want a little something for their bellies: a small pot of *frijoles,* a little stack of *tortillas,* a mouthful of *tequila* now and then. They don't want to be Porfirio Díaz. And if we come along and rob their bosses, just a little bit, now and again, do they think we're terrible? No. They get their share. How much do you have left of the hundreds of thousands of *pesos* you've stolen? Well, how much?"

"I want you to shut up."

"*Nothing,*" said Urbina. "That's how much. In Chihuahua you were the government of the adobe sections. You were a hard bandit, and a soft heart. Now, I'm going to go out, and I'm going to find me a willing *vieja* and pay her to get laid. And if you want to shoot me for that—well, all right."

"*Compadre*," said Villa very softly and sadly. "Please don't make things hard for me. Don't make trouble. I'm not very sure of myself, so please don't test me."

Urbina smiled, putting on his black hat and buckling the big-rawled spurs over his dusty boots. "*Compadre*," he said, "you're the best friend I have in all this world. And you know that, don't you?"

Pancho Villa nodded.

"Well, I am going to be careful. I'm going to keep one eye on the *viejas*, and one on the men. And I might even stay half-sober. Listen, that was some fight today, wasn't it?"

"We beat them," said Pancho Villa.

"I forgot to tell you. Nineteen of the privates wanted to get on the firing squad that shot their officers. They said they'd heard of Villa and wanted to join the revolution. There's something to keep in mind: recruits, already trained, and with their own equipment."

7

The capture of Santa Rosalia and its new industrial center of Camargo fell with ominous impact on the Díaz regime, for reasons which Villa, himself, was not sophisticated enough to grasp.

These twin cities, although numbering only 9,000 inhabitants, still ranked fourth in population and commerce in the state of Chihuahua—which happened, also, to be the key state to the northern campaigns because of its adjacency to the United States border. Additionally, while Santa Rosalia was an over-sized Indian *pueblo,* Camargo was a vital junction along the National Mexican Railroad, an important military post and the shipping center for cattle and mining enterprises out of the rich Conchos and Florida valleys.

On February 9, 1911, Pancho Villa withdrew his 500-man force from *Ciudad* Camargo when he learned that a powerful federal column (sent by the redoubtable General Navarro) was heading toward him.

Villa had held the city only two days, long enough to learn about flushing toilets, but not to plant his roots in the civil government as he had hoped. He had, however, distributed food stores to the poor, kept order, appointed committees of Anti-reelectionists to government posts and created what amounted to a revolutionary underground. He had also executed several of his men for looting or molesting the citizenry, thus re-emphasizing his break with banditry.

None of this seemed particularly remarkable to Villa. To him the chief virtue of this venture was that it had marked his first successful field engagement against the *federales*. By a fusion of native cunning with newly learned military principles, the former outlaw had assaulted a regular garrison—entrenched and supported by artillery and machineguns—carrying it by rifle fire alone. He was pleased, of course, but not elated. He lacked an experience-scale on which to weigh the brilliance of his military feat.

But the federal commandant did not.

8

Señor general Juan J. Navarro, Commander of the Forces of the North, a connoisseur of good cognac and a soldier of the old school, stood up behind his desk and brought a fist down on it angrily. It wasn't often that he lost his composure, but now he was at the limit of his patience.

"What are you men," he shouted, "a pack of idiots? Numb-skulls? You call yourself *cientificos—cientificos* of what?"

His staff members averted their eyes. General Navarro wasn't a man to accept explanations in place of achievements. True, Navarro's energetic columns had chopped Lucio Blanco to pieces when he'd tried to take Cerro Prieto. Then they'd driven that damned Orozco out of Guerrero on January seventh, leaving the vile traitor nothing to brag about. More satisfying yet had been Orozco's thumping defeat, at the hands of Tamborel, when he'd had the gall to assault *Ciudad* Juárez on February second. But what infuriated Juan Navarro beyond all measure was the uncanny manner in which one man, that dirty, ragbag bandit, Pancho Villa, seemed able to read his mind, to spring every trap before it was half set.

"Ever since Villa's withdrawal from Tecolote it's been the same story: supply columns assaulted, military posts raided. Finally a whole garrison and town overrun. And always excuses, excuses! 'It was Pancho Villa, my general.' 'The bandit surprised our troop, my general.' 'Villa wiped out our patrol, my general.' What is this man—a ghost?"

A major stood up hesitantly. "But, *mi general,* Pancho Villa—"

"If you say Pancho Villa to me once more, you stupid pig, I'll order you shot! Do you hear me?"

He held his breath with effort, pulling down on his trim, beautifully tailored grey blouse. His riding breeches were immaculate and tucked into tight riding boots. His white hair and neat beard were perfectly barbered. Juan Navarro was a very good soldier and very loyal to Díaz.

"I want the patrols doubled—tripled! Get me Villa. Locate Madero's band of traitors. Find me that swine Orozco, and that meddling foreigner, Garibaldi. I have a wall to stand them all up against. *Bring them to me!*"

He glared at them, picking up his smart, grey cap and placing it squarely on his head. Reinforcements would depart that day for his Juárez garrison: more artillery, more cavalry, more of the new Hotchkiss machineguns. His only satisfaction was that no other federal commander was any better off than he. Outbreaks in San Luis Potosí, attacks in Gómez Palacio. José María Maytorena, Governor of Sonora, calling on his people to support the Revolution. Gringo soldiers-of-fortune tearing hell out of his railway track. And that damned, damned *peón,* Villa.

Demonio! That man had created havoc with communications and morale. And where the devil was Madero?

9

On February 5, 1911, *coronel* Antonio Rábajo, enroute from Ojinaga to Juárez with reinforcements from General Navarro, encountered Pascual Orozco at Bauche—just south of Juárez— and soundly defeated him. Orozco withdrew southward and Rábajo proceeded unmolested.

In danger of internment by United States authorities for plotting against a friendly nation, *don* Francisco I. Madero finally crossed into Mexico on the night of February 13. Orozco, far from handing him *Ciudad* Juárez, was then in retreat. Villa had recently been driven from Santa Rosalia and Camargo.

Soon after, with 130 chiefs and men commanded by Colonel Giuseppe Garibaldi, Madero left Zaragoza (25 kilometers northeast of Juárez) and assaulted the town of Casas Grandes, where he was severely defeated by Colonel Samuel García Cuellar, one of General Navarro's best officers. Finally, with the world falling out from under him, Madero retreated to Bustillos, summoning all the rebel bands in northern Mexico to meet him there.

Of all his leaders, the chiefs whose exploits he knew best were Pascual Orozco and Francisco Villa. And it was on these two that *don* Francisco had already decided to risk his life and his cause.

An unexpected hope had risen on Madero's horizon. Disgusted by the atrocities and self-seeking "leaders" in his home-state of Morelos, Emiliano Zapata—townsman and farmer of Aneneguilco—had rallied a ragged group of peasants around Villa Ayala and given the Cry of War for southern Mexico. Leading 800 men, Zapata disarmed the local garrison on March 10, 1911, then moved on San Rafael Zaragoza, cutting telephone and telegraph lines as he went.

On the crest of Zapata's successes, similar uprisings were now taking place around Sinaloa and Zacatecas, and rioting was rampant in many more states. Thus the government found itself between two lighted powder-kegs—one to the south, one to the north.

Díaz's position was not as secure as it had seemed.

10

Unconcerned by the vulgar noise, and resplendent in top hat and tails, "Papá Díaz," the Indian's benefactor and the white Mexican's friend, laid the cornerstone for a monument to M. Louis Pasteur. Next day, February 26th, he attended an Air Exhibition, put on by aces Roland Garros and René Simon in their Bleriot monoplanes. Later he charmed his audience after receiving the Order of the Red Eagle from an ardent admirer, Herr Kaiser Wilhelm of Imperial Germany. But as another ruler, Czar Nicolas II of all the Russians, would presently discover, cheers could turn to curses when desperation and hunger curdled love into hate.

Don Porfirio Díaz knew about the uprisings, of course. He knew about that nasty, little traitor to his class, Francisco Madero, for he'd imprisoned him once for having the impertinence to campaign publicly—publicly, mind you—for the presidency. Now Madero consorted with all manner of scum and peasants, trying to convince them that they were equals, and inciting them to revolt. Well, General Juan Navarro would have something to say about that. For over 30 years he, *don* Porfirio had taken good care of his army. It was time, now, for his army to take care of him.

Díaz had no way of knowing it yet, but he had become a victim of his own corrupt system. Of the millions of *pesos* he'd poured into his *"científico"* army (each *peso* worth 50 per cent of the *Yanqui* dollar), nine-tenths had disappeared into the well-lined pockets of his generals and *políticos*. Surrounded by fuss, feathers, breastplates and sabers, *don* Porfirio had not yet noticed that—like his votes—most of his "regiments" were mere illusions in the ledgers of his corrupt military administrators. Jailbirds, dead men, barflies and town imbeciles filled the rolls of his army, his "splendid 50,000-man force." What he had bought was a fancy watermelon shell without the insides.

April would usher in the fifth month of *petit* revolt. But in a place called Bustillos, in that northernmost state of the nation, Chihuahua, something was happening which would alter all that had gone before.

A spark of inspiration was about to leap from a little dreamer to a warlike peasant, transforming the *peón*-warlord into an officer of integrity and incandescent fervor. Jealousy would now activate an ambitious wagonmaster to volcanic deeds, and in their giant steps would walk the armies of the poor. Even as the well-off and comfortable men in Mexico City disdained all talk of revolt, a peasant-fist was gathering which would smash *don* Porfirio's gaudy watermelon shell, exposing its emptiness to the Mexican sun. And under that sun it would lie, rotting and decaying into a rich, vast earth which had absorbed the Aztec, the Spaniard, the Austrian, the Frenchman—and now, the Mexican *Indio*, turned dictator.

VI. "SEÑOR, YOU ARE THE SAVIOR..."

THE CAMP HAD BEEN MADE at the Hacienda of Bustillos, on the sandy plain around the large, comfortable adobe dwelling, not quite a day's journey south of Juárez. It was a fine, defensible position, and *don* Francisco Madero had complimented his Chief of Staff, Giuseppe Garibaldi, on it.

From around the vast desert and mountain regions, the many independent rebel bands gathered, until more than 3,000 fighting men filled the sprawling bivouac area that lovely morning, late in March, 1911.

They lay about, munching warm *tortillas* stuffed with meat or *frijoles,* listening to guitar-strumming minstrels, cleaning weapons of all descriptions, currying horses or sipping bitter-black coffee boiled over their smokeless fires of desert brush.

Most of them were plainsmen and mountaineers, with a sprinkling of miners—happy and confident despite the odds they faced. There were a few city fellows who were intellectuals . . . whatever the hell that meant. *Don* Francisco Indalecio Madero, provisional *presidente* of the Republic of Mexico, sat in a huge wicker chair with his small body slightly hunched over his plate. He was a vegetarian and an idealist, and the first *revolucionario,* and he was eating American canned beans with salt crackers and water. At 37, the tough game of Mexican politics had already ruined his stomach, and a nervous twitch frequently jerked his bearded chin toward his left shoulder.

Opposite him sat his brother, Raoul, a young man of the same slender, aristocratic type, but physically strong and not so temperamental. He was less the dreamer, more the soldier, and his cultured voice never reached Francisco's shrill peak of excitement.

Beside Raoul sat Giuseppe Garibaldi, handsome, blond, polished and very European. Where the Madero brothers had been educated in Mexico City and Paris, the Italian was a product of the world. He was the grandson of the "Great Liberator" of Italy, and at 31, this was his fifth war. He had given but one reason to Madero when he had come to volunteer: *"Señor,* we Garibaldis do not believe in tyranny." That seemed reason enough.

A soft breeze blew warmly across the plain.

Garibaldi sighed. "Your country, *señores,* reminds me of Italy and Greece," he commented in his limited Spanish, which, like his English, he spoke with an Oxford accent. "Warm and voluptuous, like the Latin women."

"What would you give for a bottle of champagne right now?" asked Raoul Madero smiling.

The Italian smiled too. "With ice—or without?"

"Ah, well! You want too much, *coronel!*" said Raoul, amused.

The *sombrero*-wearing Mexicans looked at their tiny circle of officers and roared lustily, slapping their skintight riding pants. "Ha! Champagne!" laughed one of them. "That foam is for girls to wash in. Give a man some *aguardiente*—there's a drink!"

A half-hour after breakfast there was the sound of fast riding. Through a cloud of sand, a square-set, heavily armed stranger leaped from his lathered horse, tossing the reins to one of the men riding behind him.

"*Buenos días,*" he said above the clanking of his spike-rawled spurs. ".Which one of you is *el señor* Madero?"

Garibaldi and Raoul stiffened, imperceptibly feeling toward their guns, mindful of possible treachery.

"*Eiy,* none of that," said the man.

For a moment no one moved as the stranger pulled off his floppy *sombrero,* smacking it against his leather pants which were caked with dust. He and his *vaqueros,* in their knee-leggings, crisscrossed ammo belts and large-brimmed hats were an odd contrast: they seemed rougher, barely half-tamed, and far more fierce than those rural fighters already in camp.

"And who are you?" asked Garibaldi, rising slowly.

The newcomer ignored him. His quick eyes had already found those of the revolutionary leader, and he was walking hesitantly toward him. Their communication was instantaneous, and as mysterious as it was unmistakable. Madero rose, nodding.

"I am Francisco Madero, *señor.* Whom have I the honor of addressing?"

The stranger noted how diminutive the leader was: no more than five feet, two inches. Perhaps a bit over 100 pounds. His tan campaign hat, whipcord Norfolk jacket, tan riding breeches and fine English boots labeled him citybred. He carried no weapons in sight. And that labeled him foolhardy.

Madero, too, appraised the other, noting his unusual height, the large frame and easy grace; the way he wore guns, as though they were as essential as trousers and boots; and the arresting quality of those glittering, brown eyes and reddish hair. Beneath the instantly apparent savage, the crudities and brutality, there was a second aspect about him—a frankness in his unwavering gaze which Madero liked. This one could be a friend even though Orozco was the greatest asset the Revolution could pray for.

"*Señor presidente,*" he said. "I think you sent for me. I am called—"

"*Por favor,*" said Madero smiling. "Permit me one guess. I believe, gentlemen, we have the rare pleasure of addressing the great *guerrillero* of our cause, *el señor capitán don* Francisco Villa."

That simple act had been a diplomatic coup. From that instant, whatever reservations the rough hillsman may have entertained simply melted in the paternal handshake, hug and welcome which *don* Francisco Madero gave him. Future generations, and the entire world would feel the consequences of that meeting. It would raise and destroy armies, dissolve governments, save or sacrifice thousands of lives, and culminate in the creation of one of the greatest small-troop commanders since Genghis Khan.

2

"*Bueno señor,* I was only a snotnose *chamaco* of 17, and I'd been in the *sierra* only five months after ringing López-Negrete's bell when the *federales* caught me. *Pero, por Dios!* I was so stupid, you wouldn't believe it. *Pues,* they dragged me by my skinny neck to the San Juan del Río *calabozo,* near my *hacienda* (I mean, where I'd been raised. *My hacienda!* What a laugh). So, there I was, dumped into a cold cell, under sentence to swing for killing an *hacendado.*"

"Barbarous," said Madero. "Without even a trial!"

"Trial? For a *peón?* Ha!"

"Incredible!"

"Well, when I was loose again—"

"They freed you, after all?"

"Freed me?" chuckled Villa. "I was a *burro* when I ran off into those hills, and didn't know anything. But I learned in a hurry. Those dogs taught you fast. But it's funny you should mention that. I remember meeting the great bandit, Ignacio Parra (well, I thought he was great in those days). He was looking for promising material to add to his gang, and there we were, face to face in Soto's house—and I couldn't spit out three words. But he spoke plain enough: '*Eiy, muchacho,* people don't just float out of jails. What did you give those lice-ridden *federales* to get loose?' And I said: 'Give them, *don* Ignacio? Well, I gave one of them eternal peace, that's what.' 'Eternal what?' yelled Parra. 'Well,' I said, 'one morning they opened my cell and dragged me out with kicks and pushes, and I thought: Hail, purest Mary, make room for Pancho! (You see, I'd changed myself from Doroteo Arango to Pancho Villa so that my family wouldn't suffer if I got caught—and good thing!) I thought it was time for a firing squad, or the rope, or an antpile was just my head sticking out, or some other kind of clean fun for the *federales*. But it just turned out I was assigned to grind corn for the prisoners' *tortillas*. So, playing it stupid, I got the soldier to move closer . . . And suddenly—*tras!* I leaped forward and crushed his skull with the heavy stone roller. 'There's your *tortillas,* you *pinche piojo!*' I yelled. 'And I'll save some for your friends, too!' "

"Good heavens!" said Madero recoiling.

"Well, now you know how providence helps the poor," said Villa. "It makes them with a good, right arm and lots of desperation. And it makes the mountains. And hope. Always hope."

"I could weep when I hear you say those things, *mi capitán,*" said Madero. "God help me to eradicate such injustices. But please go on. I must hear more. I should know, so that I *can* help."

"Well, it's not much. *Don* Ignacio looked me over, and I told him I'd already killed seven *rurales.*"

"At 17," said Madero sadly.

"*Bueno,* I really stretched it a bit. It was five *rurales,* that louse-bag *soldado,* and López-Negrete. But the old coot wasn't impressed. Not that he let on, you see. 'Look,' he said. 'We're not talking now about killing some stupid *rural* who's coming after you, boy. We're talking about robbery and killing to get what we want. Do you understand me, boy? I'm talking about murder. That's a bandit's business.'

" 'I'm disposed to do whatever you want,' I told him. 'You give the orders, and I'll do whatever it is.' "

"But *why,* Panchito?" asked Madero aghast. "In heaven's name, how could you enter into such a bestial bargain?"

Villa laughed ironically. "You wouldn't know that, would you, *mi señor?* Well, I'll tell you what I said to Parra. I said: '*Don* Ignacio, I'm a man who surely was born to suffer. Who cares about me, except my sainted mother, whom I can't touch; and the buzzards, who sit up there sharpening their beaks? This is the only destiny I see. My enemies pursue me, and God knows what other suffering waits ahead. If it's between being a *bandido* or a dead dog . . . my choice isn't hard.' "

Villa rose, still laughing, and took a fresh orange from a bowl. That main room of the *hacienda* which Madero used as headquarters was the most beautiful place Pancho had ever seen. And the idea of simply reaching out for fresh fruit delighted him. He was peeling the orange, tearing peels with his strong white teeth, and spitting them into the same bowl, when Madero, left the table and placed his arm about the bandit's thick shoulders.

"Oh, my poor, poor friend," he said, his gentle face contorted with deep emotion. "If only I could have aided you. If—"

"*Pues,*" said Villa moved. "Listen, *don* Francisco. We did fine. Parra was all right. Sure, we weren't the big *bandidos* everybody thinks. No big horses and silver spurs. We walked or rode mules. But we lived. The storytellers have us holding up trains. So, instead, two or three of us ran off a few mules. But my share of the first job was 3,000 *pesos.* Well, that's no trainload of gold,

eh? But more than a *peón* could make in years of slavery. And on
my second job my share came to one-third of the 150,000 *pesos*
we'd found under the saddle of a mining boss' horse. Fifty
thousand *pesos* for me. Think of it. I was rich! *Demonio!* I could
have bought my family a house, except that I didn't dare show
my face. So . . . I gave it all away. *Si, señor.* Gave money to anybody who needed it. So I cheated more *hacendados*, storekeepers,
grocers and other respectable thieves out of their chance to
grind the poor, than you can shake your—. Well, it was a good
feeling. The old women used to cry: '*Dios te bendiga*, Panchito!
God bless you!' and the little kids would shout excitedly when I
came into a village tossing candies at them. And the young
girls . . . Ah, life has it's own rewards, *don* Francisco. Even for
a bandit."

"And your mother, Pancho? What did she say to all this?"

"God bless her. She lived—and finally died—thinking I was
working for a mining company up in the hills. My brother,
Hipólito, told her the money came from the earth. Which it
did, but once removed. Removed out of the mine bosses'
pockets."

"My dear friend," said Madero, sighing. "If only I could come
to grips with the grim realities of my life, as you have with
yours."

"Life is simple," said Villa. "A man lives. A man dies. It's
that business in between that makes one *loco*. But I've invented
a little rule: Don't hurt anybody. But if they come after you,
nail them first, and nail them permanently."

"But doesn't the idea of violence ever bother you?"

"Sure it bothers me. Do you think my mother dropped me
with a gun in my hand? I kill because I don't have any other
answers. I'm not educated. I'm a *peón*. I don't understand men
who fight with their tongues and moneybelts. You show me a
better way, and I'll think about it."

"You're right," said Madero sadly. "You're right. I never intended to use force. I never thought it would come to this."

"Do you know what I am?" said Villa. "I'm a heart with a

gun. You're a heart with a brain. Between us, somewhere, there
should be one whole man. There should be a hope for us, and
for what we're trying to do. I say it because I understand completely what you've told me—and it must be done."

Madero nodded. "God grant it, Pancho," he said.

"You know something else, *don* Francisco?" said Pancho
Villa sitting beside the little man. "My father died when I was
a little boy and—Well, I never had anybody after that. Nobody
to teach me. Nobody to tell me things. Nobody ever asked me
anything or cared about all the things that were here—inside
my mind, and inside my heart. Nobody ever listened to me in
my whole life. You're the first one I've ever said all these crazy
things to. Even a peasant doesn't want people to think he's
stupid. You see? I'm just a man—like you. I'd feel it if you
kicked me. I'm human. I want to be something . . ."

"Panchito, are those tears? Are you weeping?"

Pancho Villa nodded putting down the half-eaten orange and
pushing a big hand across his eyes. "I'm a baby. I can't stop
myself. I cry like a stupid baby sometimes."

"*Lágrimas del corazón son como una bendición del cielo,*"
said Madero patting the big man's shoulder. "Yes, *mi querido
amigo.* Tears of the heart can be like a benediction of heaven.
They can wash away many sins."

Villa glanced up, red-eyed, and taking Madero's small hand
in his own two, he held it tightly. Only three years separated
those two, yet in that frail, already graying man of 37, Francisco
Villa knew he'd found the strength he needed. In those eyes so
deep and sad lay the answers he sought. In that soft voice he
heard unspoken commands which he was ready to obey.

In the days which followed Villa's arrival at Bustillos, and the
integration of his forces into Madero's Revolutionary Army, the
two men spent much time together—each learning something
from the other—and in the process of mutual education came
respect, and a lasting trust.

Villa was more outgoing than he had ever been, making no
effort to hide his veneration. But if Madero, at times, found it

necessary to maintain an air of public aloofness, the former bandit understood and accepted the fact that before friendships must come the professional relationship of commander and commanded. For in Pancho Villa's eyes now, *don* Francisco Madero had grown to the stature of a father and a saint, and could do no wrong. Moreover, he knew finally that no matter what, no one, nothing would ever threaten or ever hurt Madero while he, Pancho, was by his side.

Villa did not see that in his devotion he was like a huge and silent animal, watching, waiting, casting sullen eyes on all who grouped around the little leader. And he did not know that his reputation and quiet manner worried many in that camp, and that his curt ways could cut like the razor-edge of a *machete*. He paid no attention to such things. For him, Madero and the Revolution had become all.

3

"Very well, gentlemen," asked Madero, studying the assembled leaders. "Is it to be Chihuahua City then?"

Villa watched the nodding, then rose with an air of determination. He had listened to all the talk; to all that interminable nonsense and indecision; and he was sick of so much ignorance parading as knowledge. Sick of pomposity going for patriotism, and ambition thinly buttered over with big words.

Pascual Orozco sat in a corner of the room saying nothing while waiting for a mandate from the *jefes políticos* (political leaders), among whom were the men selected to fill Madero's first cabinet—if the Revolution ever succeeded. *Don* Abraham González was no military man, and neither was *el señor* José María Maytorena, the Antireelectionist chief of Sonora. But they at least were willing to listen. That bearded, old bastard sitting next to Maytorena—the one named Venustiano Carranza, whom Madero had designated Minister of War—that one acted as though there was nothing anybody could teach him about anything. He was a cold, unfeeling, self-satisfied old fart. His hypocritical tongue rasped across Villa's nerves like a carpenter's file across a bar of soap. Yet, for Madero's sake he had to be endured.

"I'm not a *jefe político, señores,*" Villa began hesitantly. "I don't understand about political embarrassments. But I do understand that we have decided to free the Mexican people from the strangle hold of Díaz and his cheap *científicos,* and all those other pigs who are feeding at the trough."

"Quite correct, quite right," smiled Madero encouragingly.

"Well, what does Díaz understand—words? He tossed you in the *calabozo* because you told him five turns at *presidente* was enough for any man, am I right *don* Francisco?"

"Well expressed, *mi capitán,*" said Madero.

"And I found out an *Indio peón* didn't have the right to kill the sonofabitch who had abused his sister—if the other man was an *hacendado's* son. Drunkard, perverted, brutal—and despised by the people. But still an *hacendado's* son."

"I was an *hacendado's* son," said Carranza half-rising, "and so was *el señor* Madero."

"I know that," said Villa quickly. "But I was not. And neither was Orozco. So what are we doing here, comparing parentage, or fighting a revolution?"

"I am certain *capitán* Villa meant no insult," said Madero, patting the irate Carranza's shoulder.

"Well, I won't waste any more of your time," said Villa. "We're cockroaches, all of us now—little *cucarachas*—grabbing for our little bit, our crumbs. But our crumbs. Not the ones Díaz throws us from the goodness of his heart. Crumbs we have the balls to take. And then bread. Yes, and land. And plows and seed and the fruits of what comes out of this Mexican ground. Our ground, *señores.* Bought with our blood and our balls and our hot sweat. Ours."

"Please get to the point," said Carranza coldly. "We have numerous things we must discuss yet and time is short."

Villa stared at him murderously. But as he realized he'd let his thoughts and feelings go without control before these strangers, he flushed with shame. He stumbled back and sat down. "I've finished," he said.

"That is not all you wanted to say, Panchito," said Madero. "I think we should hear the rest of it."

"So do I," said Maytorena ignoring Carranza who sat back combing his grey whiskers with the fingers of one hand, satisfied with having squelched Villa.

Urged by the majority, glaring hatred at Carranza, Villa turned, straddled his chair like a saddle, and said: "I don't think we can attack Chihuahua City and laying siege to it would be a waste of time. I think we should attack Juárez."

"Absurd!" said Carranza standing and triggering a general babble among the revolutionary leaders which finally forced Madero to demand order. Even Orozco had come alert on that suggestion.

"Why Juárez?" asked José María Maytorena, a big, shaggy man to whom Villa had promptly taken.

"Why not?" Villa countered. "We've heard talk here of demonstrations, or strikes, of—God knows what. But battles, *señores*. Talk of battles to a soldier like Díaz. Defeat him. Take Juárez, seal him off from the gringo border. That he understands. From Juárez you control what goes in, and what goes out. You, *señor presidente*—not Díaz.

"I like the way you say *you*, Panchito," said Madero. "It somehow gives me the confidence I need."

"Juárez is too well garrisoned," said *don* Abraham. "General Navarro had been preparing for just this decision, *capitán*. A month ago—perhaps. Now . . ." he shook his head sadly.

"And the *norteamericanos* have already warned us—both sides—about stray bullets striking their ground," said Madero. "Any mistake could mean intervention."

"We don't have to fear the *gringos*," said Villa emphatically. "They're on our side. They've had their problems with maniacs. They've had to fight for their freedoms. Didn't you tell me about *democracia*? You, yourself, *señor presidente*—didn't you tell me the gringos had fought many wars for their ideas?"

"I did, Panchito," said Madero beaming as if on a bright student.

"Well, then. Are they so stupid, and so blind, that they'd die for freedom over there—and leave slavery right across the line? I have several gringos with me, as dynamiters and machine-gunners. A fat, little Jew named Samuel Dreben, and a big bastard named Tracy Richardson. They chew nails and spit bullets. Garibaldi has a redheaded *loco* dynamiter named Creighton, with balls like a stallion. Why are they here?"

"*El capitán* is right," said Maytorena. "The *norteamericanos* are sympathetic to us, even if their Wall Street manipulators are cheek-to-jowl with Díaz. I wouldn't fear them."

"*Coronel* Orozco," said Madero turning to the silent man behind. "We have not heard from you in this discussion."

Villa watched the dry, lean man sit up, chewing on a whittled matchstick. "Well . . ." he said, "It was me that proposed Chihuahua . . ."

"Absolutely!" said Carranza triumphantly.

". . . But now I'm for Juárez."

"For Juárez?" asked Madero as if afraid he'd misheard.

"If we took it, it would shake Díaz out of his boots," said Orozco glancing at the astonished Villa.

"But—could we hope to win?"

"*Para todo, hay tiempo y modo,*" said Villa. "For everything there is a time, and a way. We must prepare one blow—*un solo golpe terrífico*. One terrific blow that will rock them. One fierce rush on Juárez—and victory, *señores!*"

"I wish I knew," said Madero troubled. "If only I knew."

4

Still undecided, Francisco Madero, nevertheless, moved his headquarters northward, to the edge of the Río Bravo, sending his forward echelons ahead by April First.

Under a six day truce, peace delegates from *presidente* Díaz had offered to negotiate certain reforms which *don* Porfirio was willing to institute. Villa had not much hope for things.

In mid-April Pascual Orozco, described by Madero as "the soul of the revolution in the North," was elevated to the rank of general during an impressive ceremony before the rebel trenches. In the same ceremony Francisco Villa was raised to colonel, and Raoul Madero to major.

The rebels were inactive, and *don* Porfirio's reforms had come to nothing. Villa had been right. Words were not the weapons the old dictator understood.

"We must attack Juárez!" both Villa and Orozco were telling Madero more and more often. But Madero was afraid to risk everything in that single combat, and had come up with an alternate plan. On April 19th he dispatched a formal request to General Navarro, in Juárez, asking for the surrender of that city to his Revolutionary Army. The following day, before the revolution's National Palace had been properly established in the tiny, flag-draped adobe-house on Rancho *Las Flores,* Madero's offer was politely rejected by General Navarro.

"He means to fight," said Orozco. "Villa and I have scouted the city. That *piojoso,* that lice-ridden Tamborel, has the place bristling with machineguns and cannon."

"All the more reason, *señores,* why we should not risk disaster," said Madero. "We shall have to devise another plan."

Over 3,500 Maderistas were camped around Las Flores by now, awaiting their leader's "other plan." But hemmed in by his fears of American intervention and facing that ferocious, old soldier, Juan J. Navarro, Francisco Madero straddled his painful dilemma unable to fall either way. General Jan Viljoen, hero of the Boer War, had lately joined Madero's staff, and concurred with the little *presidente* that attacking Juárez could only spell suicide.

Across the Rio Grande 20,000 *gringo* soldiers were taking positions behind barbed wire and machineguns, sent there by President Taft—a Díaz sympathizer—whose orders were to "safeguard American soil." A northward assault on the city would surely make Madero's troops responsible for any accidental casualties on the United States side.

The remaining days of April wore on pointlessly in prolonged talks with more of Díaz' "Peace Delegations."

Coronel Villa grew restless and touchy. He responded waspishly to Garibaldi's European fastidiousness, and on one occasion threatened to "kill that foreign buttinsky the first time he gets in my way!" Because many *hacienda* owners were Spaniards (who spent most of the year in Europe, enjoying themselves), Villa hated the *gachupín*—those high-strutting Spanish bastards—passionately. And to Pancho, the Italian Garibaldi, with his European manners and accent, smacked of the same breed of cat. Pancho Villa also hated the Chinese, who were the storekeepers of Mexico, and the small moneylenders. (In his entire life, however, Villa evidenced no anti-semitism. One of the incongruities of that enigma born Doroteo Arango was that the man he was to venerate above all others was physically frail, indecisive, an *hacendado,* European-educated, half-Spaniard, half-Jew.)

Something had to be decided, and fast. Villa fell to brooding over the men General Navarro had executed at Tecolote, and claimed "first rights to Navarro's carcass" when Juárez should fall. Orozco agreed with Villa, for he, too, had felt the old federal General's vengeance.

The impending "Battle of Juárez" had received so much publicity in American newspapers, and drawn so many sightseers to the border city of El Paso that one writer described it as "a glorified Barnum and Bailey circus." Tourists with box cameras, college girls, newspaper correspondents, movie camera men, salesmen, self-styled soldiers-of-fortune (most of them bums who ran at the first shot), and little old ladies from Peoria—all bent on a peek at "those Mexican *bandidos!*"—flocked to the streets of Juárez, daily, hoping for that ultimate thrill . . . a "real" battle.

As if to mock Madero's indecision, Coronel Tamborel, technical designer of Navarro's formidable Juárez defenses, and an ardent hater of all rebels, now wrote an open letter to the American press, accusing the revolutionists of cowardice and incompetence, and calling them "a gang of bandits and cut-throats."

It has been said that "Pancho Villa's absorption of an idea" was "always catastrophic in its force." Whatever his idol, Madero, may have been planning, Villa believed that only the fall of Juárez could suffice.

In his own encampment, in a small ravine, along the eastern outskirts of the city, Pancho Villa set to translating the processes of his mind into action. He knew that if the Madero Revolution was to triumph, he would have to convince Madero of the Juárez objective. Then if it failed, he alone would bear the brunt.

In a small, jerrybuilt armory a group of Villa's smithies had spent the past few days—and nights—practicing an odd occupation. Stuffing old tin cans with powder and tiny chunks of metal, they capped these, stuck a short fuse through an opening, then stored them in a nearby dugout. When they'd run out of tins, they cut pieces of fresh cowhide, rolled a stick of dynamite in each, sprinkled in nails, screws, or any metal scraps and sewed the hides together. These highly indigestible *tacos*, when dried and shrunk, made a batch of firm, hard bombs.

5

"General Navarro has refused me," said Madero sadly. "I have all but humiliated myself, but he is totally unmoved. I have therefore decided that our sole hope lies in marching southward, on the capital of Mexico."

The announcement, while not completely unexpected, left Madero's military advisors aghast. Only General Viljoen, the Boer hero, seemed to consider it a good idea.

Madero, clearly depressed, then proceeded to draw a glowing —if somewhat strained—picture of a mighty "People's Army" marching "triumphantly" down the length of the country, gathering to itself thousands upon thousands of ardent followers until—irresistibly—it appeared at the gates of the nation's capital . . . toppling Porfirio Díaz' government.

Another outburst of protests only brought Madero's sad refusal to listen. The outraged advisors were cut off by Madero's: "My decision must stand. Tomorrow we commence preparations for our withdrawal. That is all, gentlemen!"

When the small, adobe headquarters had been emptied, only one man remained with *don* Francisco.

"Yes, *coronel* Villa," asked Madero. "Is there something?"

"*Señor*, you are our savior," said Villa. "You have brought us hope. If by giving up my life I could win your cause, I would be ready this moment."

"Thank you, *mi coronel*," said Madero, deeply moved.

"But I tell you again that unless you have Juárez, you have nothing. Nothing, *señor*. Will you attack?"

Madero looked at him, dismayed. He twitched, then turned his face away. "You have my orders, *coronel* Villa."

"Yes, my president. Thank you."

Francisco Villa hesitated, started to speak again, then left the president alone. That was it. It was up to him now. Right or wrong, it was Villa's move now.

VII. "OH, THE VILE, SCURRILOUS DOGS!"

IT BEGAN like a soft rumble; like a gradual expression of growing outrage. An occasional shot, here and there, from the rebel trenches surrounding Navarro's fortifications. A burst of enemy fire in reply. An insult shouted over the short distance. A counter-insult.

"*Eiy, piojosos.* Where did you learn to shoot?"

"Your sister taught me in the barn! *Cabrón!*"

"You need balls to meet my sister—father of whores—and you haven't got them."

Tomás Urbina's gleeful hand was in the provocations. Since Pancho's return to their encampment, and following his explicit orders, Urbina, Solis, Domínguez, Escárcega, and the other captains had been out visiting the trenches, circulating among the Villista ranks the outspoken Colonel Tamborel's comments to the *gringo* press.

"So, he says here in this paper that Colonel Villa is nothing but a cut-throat, and us a pack of *cobardes,* eh? Right there?"

"Right there, *compadre.* And, listen, it also says we're all going to hide under the skirts of our *viejas* the first time we hear a federal sneeze."

"In that paper that everybody reads?"

"Right on it, and almost in those very words, *amigo!*"

"*Cabrón* of a lying *piojoso. Mi capitán,* he'll eat his dirty words before we're done!"

"Make them eat them now. Kill some of the bastards. What are you waiting for—them to come after you?"

Fanned by Villa's captains, the rumble grew. From one rifle 10 took the challenge. Then 20, 50, and 100. The *federales* ripped off angry replies, and a seething fury broke into the open along the half-moon system of trenchworks.

"Come on, rat-eaters—are you coming after us, or are you the pack of *mierda*-eating, blowhards Colonel Tamborel says you are?"

"We'll be pissing in your faces before the night is out, *pelones.* And we'll send Tamborel to hell without his balls!"

A restless night approached. Crackling bursts of automatic fire came from the federal side as trees and brush covered the shapes of big-hatted men sneaking up into position. Agitated movement in both camps betrayed the fear of sudden all-out attack, and hour by hour, the possibility of this increased.

Madero's aides rode about, frantically, searching for Orozco, Villa and Garibaldi with orders to quell the firing.

"Where is Colonel Villa?"

"*Quién sabe, jefe?* He's probably up front chewing hell out of our men for firing without orders."

"*Demonio!* It's got to stop. Immediately!"

"*Sí, jefe.* I'll tell Pancho when I see him."

At headquarters, Madero was frantic, threatening to court-martial any officer who let his troops get out of control; sending messages to Navarro, asking for suspension of hostilities; and trying to call a conference of chiefs.

"Where are they? Where is everyone? *Dios mío,* has everybody gone insane?" he cried helplessly as reports of expanding hostilities reached him. "Someone will pay for this!"

The *guerrillero* had planned well. By the coming of dawn nothing could have stopped the determination of those in the trenches, for each side had teased and infuriated the other beyond recall. If it was a battle the *other* sonsofbitches wanted —by God, they had one now! The petty hatreds, the fears, the weeks of waiting, the insults—all of them—had suddenly formed into a grim showdown before Juárez. Just as Villa had expected. The ranks wanted to fight. All they needed now was leadership. And Villa was ready.

In the confusion of crossfires, that morning, the ninth of May, Colonel of Irregulars Francisco Villa suddenly appeared at the lines with Major Urbina and a troop of 50 men, all heavily girded with extra ammo belts and canvas pouches stuffed with homemade handbombs. These were the big, *charro*-hatted, rifle and pistol loaded, terrible hillsmen whom Madero and Garibaldi had first viewed with awe so many weeks before.

Immediately Villa called his minor officers and sergeants together. "*Bueno, amigos,* me and my men are going over there to blow those sonsofbitches out of their holes. But we're carrying too much hardware to move fast, so you've got to support us. When you hear the bugle, you start a general fire. Paste hell out of them. Shoot low, right into their trenches. Make them duck. When you hear my second bugle—come out of your own holes as if your pants were on fire. Charge them hard, understand?"

"Muy bien, jefe."

"The rest of you, light up," said Villa distributing cigars to his bombing squad. "When you see me signal, light your fuses from the cigars—and throw. You've got five seconds, so don't stop to scratch your behind. Fall flat, then keep throwing until our second line comes over. Any questions?"

"Sí, mi jefe. What happens if I forget to throw?" asked Urbina grinning at the men.

"We'll bury your little pecker with military honors," replied Villa chuckling. *"Bueno, muchachos.* Places. Bugler, play me 'Commence Firing'— And play it loud."

For five minutes, as the bombing detail stood poised, the Villista trenches released a drumroll of rifle fire that completely paralyzed all movement in the federal lines. Under this tremendous small-arms barrage, Villa led his men over the parapets, crawling beneath the crack of bullets until they lay in position, halfway between the two lines.

"All right, *muchachos . . . now!"*

"Viva Villa!" *Viva la revolución!"*

Rising behind their audacious leader, the bombers loosened a rain of tin-grenades as the rifle fires died and the *federales* suddenly awoke to the ruse. Machineguns opened up, but their fires were erratic. More bombs, and more. Black cans sputtered through the morning air, and fell. Stunning blasts tore open the trench-line, leaving terrible gaps and dazed, red-spattered men. The bugle sounded the charge, and the main line came sweeping forward, firing and screaming *"Viva's!"* for their leader and the *presidente.*

It was man-to-man then, in the trenches, as the Villistas closed. Colts and *machetes,* riflebutts and knives worked against bayonets, and as the *federales* found themselves outfought, they gave ground, then began boiling out of their positions, racing for the rear in complete panic.

By brute courage, Pancho Villa had achieved his first objective, and had gained command of the main part of Navarro's first defense perimeter. He was ready to send his column against the city, itself, and he had a plan for that, too.

Another sort of panic had seized General Pascual Orozco. That damned *pelado*—that ignorant savage, Villa—had stolen a march on him, and now was racing up the Acequia Madre—the empty irrigation canal which led from Hart's Mill Dam, in El Paso, down through Juárez, and behind the very trenches Villa had just taken. That black devil—he had plotted his attack down to the last details! This was no accident.

Without orders from Madero, Orozco threw his own troops into the battle, advancing simultaneously from south and north-west against stiff federal machinegun fire. By then, Madero knew there was no holding back and had committed Colonel Garibaldi's forces and those of Colonel José de la Luz Blanco, who charged by the southwest.

But it was Pancho Villa, himself, leading his men with smoking rifle and deadly grenades, who inspired the fight. He who set the crushing pace that swept the *federales* from every position.

Along with Villa, by his own request, fought the *Yanqui soldados*, led by Captain Sammie Dreben—know to his friends and enemies as "The Fighting Jew." Dreben, born in Poltroe, Russia, had come to the United States as a boy, enlisting in the Army, where he served two hitches, then became the greatest of all soldiers-of-fortune. Before joining Villa, he had fought in the Philippines, Nicaragua and the Boxer Rebellion.

Under Sammie fought Captain Tracy Richardson. Together with a mysterious redhead, Captain Oscar C. Creighton—better known as "the Crazy Dynamiter"—and a young man named Tom Mix, from El Paso. All told, the American contingent numbered close to 100, and this day they were gaining the respect of the wildman, Pancho Villa.

"I had heard of this guy," commented one *Yanqui* later, "but to see him fight was not to believe your eyes. My God! That man didn't know what fear was."

High on the rooftops of El Paso, and in the upper windows of the skyscrapers, hundreds of Americans trained their fieldglasses on Villa's spectacular advance. The betting was all on the Government troops. They numbered nearly 3,500 men, with automatic weapons, artillery and emplacements—commanded by a veteran officer of the war against the French. Opposing them was a makeshift army of civilians led by amateurs, with no more than a handful of machineguns, and a stovepipe antique of a cannon, which had promptly broken down. Although the rebels also numbered around 3,500, only half of these had been committed to the attack under the three ranking commanders, Orozco, Villa and Garibaldi.

Now Colonel Tamborel's artillery opened fire, trying to disperse the rebels with shrapnel. But Villa had chosen, cunningly, to launch his attacks from east and north. To his back lay El Paso, Texas; and Tamborel dared not fire directly on him for fear of killing Texans and risking United States intervention. Hugging the steep east bank of the Río Bravo Ravine, the Villistas, spearheaded by their chief and the bombing squad, quickly infiltrated their way north, then west, around the city.

Ahead they could see the International Bridge, sandbagged and lined with machinegun nests.

Deploying his bombers, Pancho Villa crept forward under an outburst of enemy fire, then opened a barrage of grenades, directly on the federal positions. For nearly a minute hellish explosions and chattering machineguns turned the scene into a smoking inferno.

"*Adelante, compañeros!*" called Villa charging over the sandbags. "Don't give the bastards quarter!"

Under the unremitting assault of Villa's bombers and riflemen, the bridge became a clutter of human flesh and smoldering ruins. Villa had breached Navarro's secondary line. He now had a clear run into Juárez itself.

But Technical-Colonel Manuel Tamborel—the rebel-hater, and Navarro's master architect of defense—had planned well, too. Not only had the tops of all commanding buildings been turned into sandbagged machinegun nests, but every strategic street crossing had been similarly barricaded. Against this imposing network of mutually-supporting pillboxes, Pancho Villa charged—and was stopped cold.

The battle raged from mid-morning until sundown. As darkness halted the firing, the *federales* still held their city and many revolutionists had been killed.

Pancho Villa remained awake through the night planning the next day's strategy and evacuating his casualties. Runners brought him word that Orozco and Blanco had succeeded in their assaults in the south and west quarters of Juárez and that Major Raoul Madero, *don* Francisco's brother, had made headway up the center section. *"Menos mal,"* said Villa to Tomás Urbina. "At least we're not in this soup alone."

By dawn Villa was eager to resume his attack. But Navarro and Tamborel had taken advantage of the opportunity to reorganize, too, and were ready for him. Without artillery, and with few machineguns, the rebel advance would have to be made the hard way.

His officers ordered their troops forward along the building fronts. Villa saw the machineguns open fire, catching their first men. They jerked about in the crossfire then sprawled across the pavement, dead.

"Those dirty sons of lice-ridden mothers!" yelled a strawhatted peasant firing from a nearby window. "I'll nail them, by God!"

Before anyone could stop him, the man had jumped through the open window, firing his Mauser as he went. In the middle of the street the machineguns caught him. He stumbled, clutching his leg then dropping the rifle he pulled a grenade from under his shirt and hobbled forward, cursing the *federales* and trying to light the fuse.

"You'll never make it!" yelled Villa, "come back!"

The machineguns opened up again, knocking the man down. Another Villista jumped through a doorway, trying to drag the fallen man off. He, too, was hit. From above, on the rooftops, Villa's Winchesters snapped at the machinegunners. Then the roar of a cannon, and Pancho saw the shell explode against the roofs, sending up a shower of men, rifles and adobe dust. The machineguns rattled again, tearing at the walls around the *jefe,* and away. More revolutionists fell.

It was a madhouse, a slaughterhouse. Someone high in the opposite roofs cried: *"Viva México! Viva* Madero *y* Villa!" and two tin-can grenades arced slowly through the air, toward the bunker. Two dull explosions filled the streets and one machine-gun was done for.

A company rose out of houses and doorways with a thunderous chorus of *"Viva la revolución!"* and charged, firing toward the intersection, where the *federales* were entrenched. But they never got there. As Villa, Urbina and the others surged out to join the advance, Tamborel's artillery countered with cannister at point-blank range, then the machineguns came alive. They couldn't miss. Choked with charging, screaming, firing rebels, the streets became rivers of broken bodies and blood. Braving the bullets to control his men, Villa ordered a retreat, and under the panicky bleating of a bugle, the beaten rebels fell back. Sweating and soaked with blood from helping the wounded, Tomás Urbina joined him. "We can't break them, *jefe!"* he panted. "They've got us this time!"

"The hell," yelled Villa in a fury. "Give me one of your bombs, and stand back. I'm going to blast a hole through this goddamn wall, and move under cover. Those stinking *pelones* have slaughtered the last of my men."

Buildings standing wall-to-wall lined both sides of the street and Villa's keen mind recalled how the *gringo* dynamiter, Creighton, and Raoul Madero once looped their way through the houses of Casas Grandes. Why not through Juárez?

So, wall-by-wall, Pancho Villa cut his way around the federal positions, outflanking, and surprising the enemy gunners before they had a chance to retreat.

The city jail was Villa's first major victory. The beaten *federales* were driven east, toward the *Plaza de Toros,* with Urbina's wing pursuing, while Pancho Villa freed the prisoners, most of whom chose to join him on the spot.

"General," Tracy Richardson cried riding up on a liberated

horse. "The feds have captured Tom Mix up by the bullring. They're getting ready to pop his cap."

"We'll see about that," said Villa. "Give me that horse, friend. I've got to get my *gringito* back."

Within minutes of his arrival, Villa's presence had so energized the battle around the *Plaza de Toros* that the ring was taken, and Mix—on the point of execution—was saved.

"General," Tom Mix said. "I ain't cut out for this fighting business, and I just learned it. There must be *something* I can do better."

Still laughing, Villa proceeded to *Avenida Juárez*, where the streetcar tracks turned west on *Avenue 16th of September*. There *Coronel* Manuel Tamborel had been located, fighting a desperate action with the last of his headquarters. It was a climax Pancho would not have traded for all the gold he'd ever stolen.

"Ese gallito—" he said happily, "that little rooster belongs to me, boys."

Sam Dreben and some Americans and Mexicans had placed captured machineguns across the street and were firing steadily on the *soldado*-lined rooftop, and into the sandbagged windows. "*don* Samuel," called Villa jokingly. "What is holding you up? One would think the *federales* were mad at you."

The pudgy soldier-of-fortune grinned back. "Well, they sure are touchy about something, all right. They keep shooting real bullets, and tossing bombs off their roof."

"Got any *granadas* left, Sammie?"

Dreben handed Villa two tincan-bombs, his comical face beaming with deviltry. "Have *mucho bueno* fun, *general,*" he said in his horrible Spanish.

"Well, keep those *piojos* busy, *amigo,*" said Villa remounting with a grenade in each hand. "I'm going around the side to see if I and my *muchachos* can make a new door."

The dead lay everywhere. Pancho Villa galloped down the Juárez street, ignoring the sniper fire which struck around him. Commandeering the remnants of a rebel platoon and their young lieutenant, he made his way on foot now, to the side of

the headquarters building where Tamborel and the exhausted
survivors of the once proud 20th battalion were barricaded—
determined to die at their posts.

"*Muchachos*," said Pancho Villa, "inside is the man who
called us all thieves and cowards. What do you think we ought
to do?"

"Let's go in and kill the bastard, General," said the lieutenant.

"Just what I had in mind," laughed Villa. "Here, *teniente*.
Light this little fuse, and let's get started."

The explosion burst in the wall, and Villa was through it,
pistol in each hand, before the others could move.

It was dark inside, with all the windows barricaded, but
Villa's platoon deployed quickly, cleaning out the first floor and
starting upward. Sharp firefight came from the stairways, but
Villa overran the defenders. Beneath Sam Dreben's hot machine-
gun support, more rebels breached the building's front to join
Villa's tiny force in cleaning out resistance.

Upstairs, where Tamborel was barricaded, an aide burst in,
shouting, "*Mi coronel*—they're inside the building!"

Tamborel's aristocratic face was tense, his uniform torn, his
delicate *pince-nez* awry on his slender nose. But at the news he
turned like a tiger. "Oh, the vile and scurrilous dogs!" he cried
full of contempt and loathing.

The next cry was from the young rebel lieutenant, who had
burst in beside Villa. "*Rindase, cabrón federal!*

"Surrender, you Federal son-of-a-goat-pronger!"

"Not to pigs, by God!" Tamborel shouted back, opening fire
with his pistol.

In seconds the shooting inside the cluttered office was deafening. Then it was capped off by the last of Sam Dreben's tin-
grenades, tossed in by General Villa.

The blinding flash of flames and terrible concussion tore
everything loose from the walls, obscuring the defenders.

When Pancho Villa charged in, pistols leveled, there was
nothing to oppose him. Colonel Tamborel had proven the

magnitude of his hatred, and of his manhood, in the bitterest
way.

But Pancho Villa was a man of his word, too. "Cut off his
balls," he ordered the lieutenant, "and throw them out the
window, so everybody can see them. I said he'd go to hell without them. Maybe this city belongs to the people now. But
Tamborel belongs to me!"

2

At 1:15 P.M., May 10, 1911, Francisco I. Madero, *presidente
provisional* of Mexico, picked up his telephone for a three-way
conversation with General Navarro and Colonel E. Z. Steever,
commanding the United States border forces, and what he heard
left him trembling between joy and disbelief. General Navarro
was offering to surrender with 500 remaining *federales,* and un-
conditionally. Was it possible? Dear Lord, was it possible that
his ragged fighters had actually overcome the most "perfect
defenses" in Mexico with only rifles and courage? An hour later
Madero stood flanked by Colonels Villa and Garibaldi as the
silent, old warrior drew his sword and passed it to the Italian.
Then Villa took charge.

Grimly, glaring into the Federal Commandant's face, Villa
conducted him to his guarded quarters, then posted additional
sentinels. "Rest well, *mi general,*" he said ironically. "Pancho
Villa will be back for you. He hasn't forgotten you."

For Pancho the long months of waiting were over. The
moment had come for evening accounts with Navarro: autocrat,
martinet, refined butcher. Pascual Orozco had also expressed a
profound interest in Navarro's future, so Villa stopped by to
invite the dour wagonmaster along. But as they entered the
Customhouse, where Madero had set up his new Provisional
Capital, neither man was prepared for what occurred.

"I am sorry, *señores.* What you ask is simply impossible."

"*Imposible?*" said Orozco, staring from Madero to the set faces
around the presidential chamber. Villa's mouth hung open, his

eyes uncomprehending. For a moment he seemed more a comical wax dummy than the fierce soldier of legendary deeds.

He had changed his filthy, blackened and torn peasant clothes for a tweed suit, hiplength charro leggings, and a white Stetson, peaked like a gringo soldier's hat. But beneath the unaccustomed oxford coat two enormous bulges gave proof of one habit Villa hadn't changed: the big, deadly Colts were in their usual places.

"*Imposible* . . . ?" Villa echoed.

"Quite impossible, gentlemen. I am truly sorry."

Pancho Villa's hands were beginning to shake now, his eyes to grow red and bleared. He stared dumbly at the quiet, dignified assembly. Venustiano Carranza, just named to Madero's new cabinet as Secretary of War; Doctor Vásquez Gómez, just appointed Secretary of Foreign Relations F. González Garza, the new Secretary of the Interior; Pino Suárez, new Secretary of Justice, and a dozen others—all busy with the business of constructing a new government, knowing that Díaz was all but finished. All important, astute, educated men. Even Raoul Madero looked alien now. Even José de la Luz Blanco, once a peasant himself, and Giuseppi Garibaldi, now Provisional Mayor, and head of Madero's personal bodyguard, respectively, seemed remote and foreign.

"Impossible?" asked Villa again. "How can it be impossible? He is my prisoner. You, yourself, promised Navarro to me if ever I took Juárez. And I have taken it."

"Colonel Villa," said Madero patiently, as to a child. "General Navarro is a most important prisoner. He was a hero once. A fighter, under President Benito Juárez, for Mexican freedom. He is 80 years of age; a proud, harmless old soldier . . ."

"Harmless?" cried Villa enraged. "Proud? Who the hell has been filling your head with such . . . *mierda!* Navarro is a butcher! He slaughtered my men, and I want him so I can do to him what he did to them at Tecolote. Right this minute, Urbina has a wall for him—ready and waiting."

"With your permission, Mr. President," said Garibaldi standing forward. "Colonel Villa, may I remind you that you are addressing your commander-in-chief? It is your place to—"

"Will I have to kill you?" roared Villa flushing terribly. "Will I have to pop the cap on this pimp-faced sonafabitch—or will somebody keep him quiet?"

"Please, *coronel!*" said Madero, as Garibaldi stepped back whitefaced and undecided. "Your conduct, *señor.*"

Villa also stepped back and got himself under control.

"I am truly sorry," said Madero after a moment. "But these gentlemen and I have discussed General Navarro's fate at length, and we feel common decency demands that we parole him. It would be uncivilized for me to decree his execution. I have therefore given the general my personal assurances of safe conduct across the American border. I cannot go back on my word."

"And what about your word to me?" asked Villa.

"Things were different then, *coronel*. I am a gentleman. A civilized human being. We are no longer at war. I have already received word that *presidente* Díaz is preparing his resignation— all thanks to your loyalty and courage."

"You're using words on me," said Villa desperately. "Orozco, remind him. Did he or didn't he promise us Navarro?"

But Pascual Orozco, already seeing the shift in wind, had mentally calculated his own opportunities. "We can't go against President Madero without being judged traitors," he said. "You should see that, *coronel*. We were wrong to come here."

"Does a President owe his people something or not?" asked Villa disregarding Orozco's saccharine speech.

"*Señor coronel . . .*"

"Does he, or doesn't he? Yes or no?"

"Yes, of course, Panchito," said Madero in a kindly tone.

"Well, I'm one of your people. *Me*. Pancho Villa. I fought for you. Not Navarro—me. Navarro was the enemy. Now, all of a sudden I am the enemy . . . Orozco, tell him what you said to me. That he has Juárez because of us. Yes. Because we had the balls to take it on ourselves—to risk our lives—while that pack of do-nothings you call your staff and cabinet stood around scratching their asses and shaking their heads."

"Then *señor* Carranza was right," said Madero downcast. "You deliberately disobeyed me. You attacked against my wishes."

"Tell him, Orozco," said Villa. "Tell him why we did it."

"I acted because of circumstances and not due to any personal choice," Orozco said.

"You treacherous liar!" said Villa. "Liars and fools! But I'm the biggest fool of all, for having trusted you. For having believed the words out of your black tongues."

Villa stared at all of them, as they sat back in stunned silence, then he looked directly over the small desk, at Francisco Madero and shook his head slowly. "*Mi jefe,*" he said almost pleading. "Look around you. We fought for the people, but where are those people? Not in this room. Where are the *peones?* Show me the good, honest blacksmith here. Who is the *soldado* on your cabinet? *Hacendados,* yes. Lawyers, yes. Also a Secretary of War who's never fought a battle or fired a shot. What have you done, *señor presidente?*" he said trying not to cry openly before those astonished men. "Tell me, *por favor.*"

"Oh, my friend. My dearest Panchito," said Madero walking around to embrace the *guerrillero,* both men now weeping without shame. "My loyal, and good Panchito. You mustn't condemn me this way. I do only what I must!"

"And so do I," said Villa. "I can't stay here anymore. There's nothing for me here. I'm going home."

Shortly after the meeting, *coronel* Francisco Villa made arrangements to turn his troops over to his friend, Major Raoul Madero. He was then given the sum of 10 thousand *pesos,* and his release.

On May 25th, just 14 days after the surrender of Ciudad Juárez, President Porfirio Díaz resigned the presidency, boarded the German steamliner, *Ipiranga,* and sailed into exile in Paris for the remainder of his life. He had ruled Mexico, according to his own whim, for 31 years, 3 months and 18 days.

With Díaz, went the stately and oppressive Victorian way of

life. A new era waited beyond the horizons of Chihuahua. The
20th Century, stillborn for 11 years, now flickered to life. But first
the ancient tyranny would have to be cut out, like a malignant
thing. An operation for which Colonel of Irregulars, Francisco
Villa—at the moment striving happily to become a peaceful
farmer in San Andrés—was the one, the absolute, the perfect
surgeon.

VIII. THE SILENT THUNDER

FOR FRANCISCO VILLA, ex-*bandolero* and one-time *guerrillero*, the
days from May of 1911 to January of 1912, were among the
happiest, most peaceful he would ever know. The Madero revolution had triumphed, Mexico's savior was newly elected to the
presidency, and Pancho was home, with his vivacious and loving
Luz, the girl he'd met and married in San Andrés, and had
scarcely found time to know in the intervening months of
battle and strife.

Returning to San Andrés with only a few of his trusted
followers, Pancho launched himself into raising crops and babies
with the same zeal he'd once devoted to fighting.

"*Por Dios!*" he'd say happily. "Just look at me, Pancho Villa,
the farmer. This is what my little *jefe*, Madero, meant. This is
what it was all about. Freedom, *amigos*. Peace. Smell that air. No
rurales. No gunpowder. Only life."

In love with democracy, that man who had known less freedom than anyone within his circle of acquaintances reveled in
every moment, every nuance of it. Whatever the necessities of the
rebellious Pancho Villa; the inner man, Doroteo Arango, was a
cheerful, and surprisingly gentle, husband, father and friend. He
learned to play the guitar, passably well, and he had a better-
than-average voice which he happily exercised at the slightest

request. At the many community *fiestas* (for good Mexicans are never short of Saints' Days or baptism parties) Pancho *yiiiped* and danced as energetically as any youth. He still didn't drink, nor did he smoke; partly because both made him sick, partly because long years of evading death had demanded that all his faculties remain alive; but this never got in the way of his enjoyment. "We were rather surprised that his repertoire included so many of the current Mexican songs in El Paso . . ." one new acquaintance recalled. But Pancho explained that his soldiers had taught him the words and that he "just naturally learned the tunes."

Pancho's idyllic existence was interrupted twice, and each time to answer the summons of his *presidente,* Francisco Madero, who had called him to Mexico City for consultations. Following the second visit Villa returned to announce that he would leave his *rancho* in little San Andrés to open a business in Chihuahua City.

"But why, Panchito? I thought you loved it here," said Luz unhappily.

"You do what I tell you, Lucita, and don't ask so many questions," he replied testily. "We're moving to Chihuahua, and that's enough."

He couldn't tell her about Madero's mounting fears and difficulties. Nor could he tell her about the Chief of the Military Zone in the garrison of Chihuahua, who was the source of President Madero's greatest worries.

"Here they are," *don* Francisco had said flipping over the files, his wizened-child's face wreathed in sorrow. "Reports, complaints, warnings. Who are his closest companions? Why, none other than Juan Creel and Alberto Terrazas, a notorious pair of Porfiristas."

"I'd heard rumors," Villa had replied.

"He, of all people, Panchito! My own right hand. Grown ambitious and insolent. How could he, Panchito?"

And Villa had thought, and finally answered quietly: "One cannot always explain life, *señor.*"

"But Pascual Orozco, of all men!"

"Well, my president, Judas, too, was an apostle."

2

Francisco I. Madero reached the capital on June 7, 1911, to be cheered wildly by over 100,000 joyous citizens of his newly-liberated nation. Meeting with Francisco León de La Barra—the former Secretary of the Interior, under the deposed Díaz—who had stepped in as President *pro-tem*, pending the coming elections, *don* Francisco had duly announced his candidacy and embarked on a hard campaign to win, by democratic process, an office which could have been his by right of conquest.

To no one's surprise, Madero's victory proved overwhelming. He was inaugurated on October 2, 1911, and assumed his duties on November 5, of that same year. And from that moment, too, he assumed a load of chicanery, jealousy and deceit which was to weigh him down into his grave.

While not apparent to the Mexican public, within three months of *don* Francisco's election, it was abundantly clear to political sophisticates that Mexico's "little savior" was no statesman, but rather a theorist and idealist, filled with good intentions, but disconcerted more each day by the hard realities of public life. Weakened by an old infirmity—epilepsy—he was a man fast reaching the limits of his endurance. Caught on the one side by the demands of his own morality, on the other by the snide opposition of the Porfiristas, *presidente* Francisco Indalecio Madero found himself bordering on failure at the end of his first 90 days of power.

There was no one he could turn to within his vast and gaudy *Palacio Nacional*. *Don* Abraham González, loyal and as idealistic as Madero, had gone to assume office as new Governor of Chihuahua State. *Señor* José María Maytorena, decent and a friend, had similarly won governorship of Sonora, and *don* Venustiano Carranza had resigned as Secretary of War to become governor of his native Coahuila.

Around Madero glimmered a confusing aura of obsequious smiles. Half-remembered faces danced out of a past murky with evil. Strange intonations sounded in voices parroting his orders. Names which evoked frightening memories loomed out of corners. Out of the darkness re-echoed a dim, peasant voice, desperately trying to warn him against the men around him. Pleading with him to save himself, and thus preserve the nation. "You must turn to the people, *señor* Madero," the insistent voice warned over and over again. "Who are these strangers around you, *mi presidente?* Look at them. They are the enemy. They are the oppressors. We drove the pigs out. Now you've let them in again!"

Whose was this voice, so soft, so worried, so gentle; yet so angry? Was it the Puma from the Hill? Was it the Tiger? Was it the Wind? Was it Pascual Orozco, or Carranza or González?

In those cruel days, Francisco Madero—suffocating in silent panic, had wanted to cry out: "Save me! *Socorro! Por favor!* I am dying!" But he never permitted himself the luxury of self-preservation. He had a nation to preserve. A solemn oath to keep. And, if he felt inadequate, he must never show it; frightened, he must never flinch; confused, he must master that confusion; hemmed in by phantoms, he must dominate.

He had refused to discharge many of the *científicos* he'd found in office. To discharge them would have meant discharging years of experience, without first evaluating the individual man. He believed that a good clerk *could* have been hoodwinked by Díaz, just as he believed that a good judge or a good general *could* have acted for Díaz under extreme duress. He believed, for example, that a kind and efficient officer like General Victoriano Huerta most surely had been a victim of the cruelest circumstances. Here was a splendid soldier, at this moment trying to bring about the surrender of the eternal rebel, Emiliano Zapata. Risking his life as ardently for the new government as he had for the old. People called Huerta a drunkard, a coward, a base conniver, but where were they while that loyal, old warrior performed his duties so modestly? And *who* were they? Former revolutionists, sour on all Porfiristas. Disgruntled office-seekers. Men like Orozco and Villa, despite their undeniable worth, were suspicious of any former antagonist. Upon Madero's assumption of office, one of the first men to walk through his door to congratulate him, and to offer his considerable talents to the new Mexico, had been none other than *señor general don* Victoriano Huerta. God bless him! Never a thought of reward, never a word of apology for his understandable loyalty to his former president. There was a man.

But why do I feel myself sinking: Why this fear? Why am I always insecure, so naked to adversity? Things are not right. Why, dear God? Why?

While the questions were never answered, in his mind *don* Francisco bore the comforting picture of his "good, right hand . . . The Soul of the Revolution in the North. Of Orozco. Nothing could touch Madero—would dare touch him—while Orozco lived.

That thought had comforted him through the darkest hours. Orozco, his paladin, his bright sun. Twice, during those trying months, *don* Francisco had sent for Pancho Villa. He didn't really know why. Perhaps out of gratitude. When he had spoken with Pancho, it had been a relief to unburden himself to that genial-brutal child of the hills. A strange and inexplicable relief. But Orozco was his true pillar. Villa had seemed delighted, and had shed tears of joy and gratitude on learning that his *presidente* bore him no ill-will, but only the same paternal love he'd always felt for him. And the rough hillsman had said: "If ever you need me, *don* Francisco . . ."

Madero loved him for that. But Villa was moody and unpredictable. A bull, a tiger, a savage soul who could fight like 20 devils when the chips were down. But nonetheless, a savage. If one of them had to go, let it be Pancho Villa. The nation now needed cool heads. And thank God for Orozco's stability.

How could the world turn like that? Pascual Orozco bordering on treachery? And the one man in all Mexico who could perhaps contain him—the Chapultepec-trained Huerta—just then fully occupied in trying to pacify that incurable rebel, Zapata.

President Madero sought counsel within his government, but found none. Poor Pino Suárez, his Vice Presidential choice, had turned out to be as impractical as he was aesthetic. And the others, confused obstructionists all. In one sense, at least, the earthy Pancho Villa had been something of a prophet: the men around Madero talked tall, but acted short. The thing was to recall General Huerta from the south immediately. To order him north to Chihuahua, in case General Orozco did prove a traitor.

And what of Colonel Villa? Would he work under Huerta, a former Federalist? Poor Pancho, so honest, so . . . well . . . a peasant, pure and simple. Limited to courage and to a peasant's view of life. A killer, if angered. A tiger. A puma.

Nevertheless, if Pancho Villa were willing to keep a sharp eye on Pascual Orozco until things were decided . . . Sometimes Madero suspected that General Orozco might be a little afraid of the *guerrillero*. But who wouldn't be? In the face of such uncontrolled strength, who wouldn't be?

Thinking about it, Madero liked his idea better and better. Why not draw Villa from his retreat? In war the puma—the mountain lion—was better than the subtlest fox. So why not awaken the Puma?

3

And so Pancho Villa was jarred awake during his second visit to confer with his President. Villa agreed to the move to Chihuahua City where Pascual Orozco, Chief of the Military Zone, kept headquarters. And Villa in one of those small ironies of life, had decided to open a butcher shop.

In his outlaw days Villa had learned a bit about butchering other people's cattle. With *don* Abraham González' aid, and the fat Terrazas herds under confiscation of the new government, Pancho was able to prosper, to watch and to fulfill one of the ambitions of his peasant heart: to sell meat to the poor at a price they could afford. It really wasn't hard for Pancho to succeed in any business. Thousands of people knew the bandit, thousands wanted to see the famous *guerrillero* who had captured Juárez. The curious, alone, could have made him rich. But Pancho Villa didn't want wealth. What he wanted was happiness and peace. And these he couldn't have. Not just yet, for he had once made Pascual Orozco a promise—and by God, now he meant to keep it. If Orozco betrayed Madero, he would find Pancho Villa waiting.

Villa became moody once more. The soft arms, the kisses, the warmth of his Lucita no longer moved him. More and more of his time was spent among the men. Long discussions were held around the shops and the corrals, and the eleven men Villa employed at butchering now spent more time bearing messages than tending meats. Villa, himself, returned to a habit of long, solitary rides through the neighboring *ranchos,* and he once more carried a pistol and a saddle carbine.

"Look at that sky, Lucita. What do you see?"

"See? Why nothing," said Luz Corral de Villa holding close to him.

"Storm-clouds, Lucita. Right there, above Mexico."

"It's perfectly clear, Panchito. The rains have passed."

"*No, niñita,*" he said shaking his head. "*Ya quisiera que fuera verdad.* How I wish it were so. Listen. You'll hear thunder."

Luz turned her lovely eyes to him, puzzled. Either he was in one of his straightfaced joking moods, or—*Pero, demonio!* Damn it all. What was wrong with Pancho these days? What was this nonsense about thunder, without a cloud in the clear, blue sky?

IX. "VIVA OROZCO!"

IN THE LAST DAYS of January, 1912, a communication dated the
26th, from Chihuahua City arrived at the National Palace and
was delivered directly to Madero, who read it and turned pale. It
began:

> *Most esteemed Sir and Friend: Today I permit myself again to
> raise the question of obtaining my release from duty that I may
> dedicate myself to my former affairs . . .*

And it ended:

> *. . . I am one of those who would give his life with pleasure for
> the happiness and well being of his fellow citizens. I am, your
> most affectionate friend, Pascual Orozco.*

Viewed without its fullest implications, the letter was a simple
soldier's resignation, a friendly and respectful restatement of
Orozco's faith in Madero and Madero's policies.

Yet, examined against the background of unrest in the north,
it carried ominous possibilities. Even if Orozco were still loyal,
that "good, right arm," which had sustained Madero's hopes for
peace, was now being cut off. Then, too, what hidden meaning
lay behind Orozco's sudden desire for a pursuit of his former
affairs? Did the foremost General of the Revolution really plan
to return to his mules and wagons?

2

In Juárez two days later, 300 soldiers of the garrison unexpectedly turned against their colonel, commandeered a train
and turned southward, destroying bridges and rails as they went.

At six A.M. February second a detachment of soldiers under
Captain Refugio Mendoza revolted, assaulting the Chihuahua
Penitentiary and attempting to arm the prisoners. Meanwhile,
from San Antonio, Texas, Emilio Vásquez Gómez, Madero's one-

time Secretary of Foreign Relations, promptly launched a manifesto "accepting" the provisional presidency "offered" him by the rebels of Juárez and Chihuahua.

Madero stood naked. The revolts had been triggered by news of General Pascual Orozco's resignation.

Those whose politics transcended borders had already detected an unusual, and ominously silent, *Yanqui* interest in the Madero administration's difficulties. Ambassador Henry Lane Wilson in Mexico City was said to be quite busy keeping President Taft (*don* Porfirio's good friend), and certain Wall Street interests, informed of conditions.

What possible inter-relationship could these varied and farflung interests have? Seen from the inside, the sprawling jigsaw puzzle of Mexican strife made sense. The picture which evolved showed a dollar sign, superimposed on a presidential sash, draped across a purple background of putrid politics and ambitions.

The chain of manipulations linked up this way: Ambassador Wilson to Taft—Taft to Wall Street—Wall Street to the exiled remnants of the *científicos*. And the surviving leader of these *científicos* was *don* Luis Terrazas, once owner of half the state of Chihuahua, with its immense cattle and mining regions. If Madero, the *peón*-lover, could be dislodged, and a *científico* returned to power, *don* Luis might then reclaim his properties, and Wall Street would once more find the welcome sign spread over the wealth of Mexico.

Several men were perfectly willing to spearhead the return of the old party in exchange for the presidency. Among the readiest were Félix Díaz, nephew of the former dictator; General Bernardo Reyes, whose white, imperial whiskers seemed more tailored to Imperialistic France than to Democratic Mexico; and the mousy, eager Doctor Vásquez Gómez, who was ready to dump electoral procedures for halfbaked revolt, if it suited his cause.

One final link remained to be appended. A competent military leader who was respected by the rank-and-file. But perhaps *señor* Juan Creel, and young Alberto Terrazas had achieved this. They certainly seemed to have much in common, of late, with the very "soul of the Revolution," who happened, happily, to occupy the most important military post in northern Mexico while awaiting acceptance of his resignation.

Would Orozco go?

3

Pascual Orozco, himself, had waited impatiently for another man's answer. Now he had it, and it had thrown the tall, grim man into a fit of almost unrestrained anger.

"That stinking bandit!" he snarled. "How dare he? Who the hell does he think he is?"

Once more he read the note Pancho Villa had sent in reply to his own letter; the one in which he'd subtly suggested that he and Villa, together, would constitute an unbeatable force were they to "sink personal animosities for the good of the Republic." This had been Villa's answer:

> *Señor* Pascual Orozco: In reply to your letter let me say that I am not a prop for shameless opportunists. I am now withdrawing into the desert, from where I'll return soon to prove to you that I am a man of honor.
>
> —Francisco Villa

"Well, he sure smelled the deal out fast," said José Orozco, the general's younger brother. "You should have seen his face when I read him your letter."

"What did he do then?" asked Pascual.

"Nothing. He told me that he'd sold everything. That he was out of the meat business, and that his wife and family were gone, and that now he was also gone. Then he had this note written. And he went."

"He went? What do you mean?"

"Listen, Pascual. I mean he went. He whistled for his men, mounted his horse—and he went."

"Dirty, greasy meatgrinder!" hissed Orozco. "Let him go. Who needs him?"

"But, *Dios mío*," said José again. "You should have seen that face. You know I'm no coward. But that face made me shiver. He had the look of a maniac."

"How many men did he take?"

"About a dozen, maybe."

"Let him go," said Orozco still fuming. "The crazy sonofapig. Let him bury himself in the desert. Meanwhile, I'm the man here. I rule. And before I'm done, they'll all be yelling, '*Viva* Orozco! *Viva* Orozco!' "

4

Official word, on March third, that General Orozco had actually revolted, calling on all his garrisons to disavow Francisco Madero, struck the President like a physical blow. Stunned, despite Villa's repeated warnings that it might happen any day, the "little Savior" sank into a melancholic stupor from which he only stirred momentarily to shake his head and moan: "It isn't possible. *No es posible*. How could Orozco desert me?"

In his grief he forgot that other man in Chihuahua—the one whose deep-rooted loyalty had led him to up-end his own life, to send his family away, to dispose of his livelihood, his home, his friends.

Pancho Villa was not in Madero's thoughts. He didn't believe the ex-bandit was really important. This task called for something more than a simple *guerrillero*, an illiterate. What was needed was an organizer, a man of scope and training.

Frantic and heartbroken, Madero recalled the former Federalist, General Victoriano Huerta, who had fought in the southern campaign against Zapata, and placed him in command of the Division of the North in Chihuahua to oppose Orozco.

Huerta, a leathery, squinteyed Indian (whose father had served under Juárez, then Díaz) seemed delighted with the assignment. Although his predecessor, the illustrious General Salas, had been so disgracefully beaten on his first encounter with Orozco that he had committed suicide after the battle,

Victoriano Huerta was not dismayed. Before he left the Capital
for the north, he smilingly assured Madero of a speedy victory
over the Orozquistas.

This rebellion was no more than Huerta—a not-so-secret
cientifico—had expected. Dogs will fight over bones. Only a
political baby like Madero could fail to perceive that defeat and
victory were laced with malice; idealism lined with corruption;
reform undermined by personal ambition. Madero was a rank
fool.

Huerta's appointment came on March 24th. From then till
April 10, Huerta's new power could be seen in the trains
departing from the Capital almost daily loaded down with
infantry, artillery and cavalry.

No man since Díaz, himself, had wielded such strength. No
one who despised the Revolution as Victoriano Huerta did could
ask for more help from his enemies.

Mexico was again caught up in bloodshed. Only this time it
was between rebel and rebel. With the former allies divided, an
unregenerated *cientifico* (the last man to grasp *don* Porfirio's
hand in friendship as he boarded ship for exile) *general de
División, señor* Victoriano Huerta, stood directly in the center
of action. The Mexican revolution was split apart. First he would
smash one faction then the other, swooping down like an eagle
on his prey.

The "eagle," too, had forgotten the Puma.

X. PARRAL

PANCHO VILLA pushed the white Stetson to the back of his head.
Rising on his stirrups he adjusted the binoculars and squinted
against the noonday glare. Parral looked like a miniature town,

scattered over a white, shimmering sandpile in the distance, under the pressing sunlight.

If he attacked, what were his chances? He had only 60 men, while Parral was garrisoned by 400 regulars, under crafty, old General José de la Luz Soto, a turncoat sliced from the same rancid cheese as his boss, Orozco. The hell of it was that food and water had become more important than flesh and blood. If Villa didn't attack, his small troop had no chance at all.

This was the 24th of March. Twenty-two days ago he'd ridden out of Chihuahua City to learn that telling Orozco to go to hell was easier than making it stick.

Each of those 22 days had been an unceasing struggle to stay alive. From his original dozen, Villa had quickly multiplied his army into a scarecrow force of nearly 500.

But these were measures of pure desperation, and he'd known it. A means of bluffing Orozco's patrols into thinking him stronger than he was.

Caught between the stresses of unending movement through the hot lurid sun and freezing nights, of starvation and thirst and bloody ambushes, his makeshift army had morally and physically disintegrated. In one night alone nearly half his men had deserted him, and Villa had almost cried in the morning.

One consolation sustained him: every one of those still loyal to him was an old *compañero* of the early days at San Andrés, the Train, and Juárez. His hopes rested on this loyalty and on their superb combat conditioning.

Then a second hope appeared. The spies he'd sent in returned with information that among the garrison officers was a former subordinate of Villa's, Colonel Maclovio Herrera, and in the Puma's agile mind a plan began to take definite form.

Nightfall. The silent figure in the white Stetson moved swiftly past the unsuspecting sentries, slipped through the compound, and into the colonel's quarters. On his bunk Colonel Maclovio Herrera lay dozing, his khaki tunic open, his harness with the pistol and saber nearby. The unmistakable click of a Colt's hammer cocking awakened Herrera with a nervous start. "Pancho! What's that gun for, *amigo?*"

"Will I need it here, Maclovio?"

"With me, *mi coronel?* God, put it away. I've been half expecting you, with all the frantic messages from Orozco."

"Maclovio," said Villa prudently laying the pistol across his knees as he sat down. "I haven't time to play games today, so I'll tell you what it's all about. And you can tell me how it's going to be. *Bien?*"

"Certainly, *mi coronel.* You know that."

"Outside this compound I've got 60 good boys. You'll remember most of them from San Andrés. Well, that's all I've got. Between the desert and Orozco, the others have gone home or to the buzzards. Tonight it's got to be Parral—or the end of Villa."

Herrera sat up combing his long hair with his fingers, and rolling sleepballs out of his reddened eyes. "It's that bad, eh?"

"It's worse, *compañero.* Now, you've always been a friend, but I can't read these friendships anymore, because half of you are still wearing Madero's uniform and fighting for Orozco."

"Do you think that in my heart I've betrayed Madero?" asked Herrera. "Even if I don't know what to do next, do you think I'm a traitor, *jefe?*"

"That's what I am here to find out," said Villa catching the word *jefe.* "How many men do you command here, *amigo?*"

"Two hundred. Jesús Yañez has 200, and Soto is in overall command."

"You know that I still can't read or write."

"Yes."

"All right, *viejo.* I'm going to let you prove whether you're a friend or a traitor. I want you to write a note that will bring Colonel Yañez here, alone. If you do it, we've got his men and yours. And that means you're with me, and we've got Soto and the town. If you don't, if you trick me, I'll only know it when Yañez comes to take me. And then some of us are going to die, right here in this room."

"You can trust me, Panchito," said Herrera earnestly.

"I am trusting you," said Villa. "With both our lives. Because I know you're not a man who would hesitate to die; if he really wanted to get me. Write your note, *amigo*. I want to find out."

Herrera smiled at his former chief as he took the pen.

Thirty minutes later Colonel Yañez eyes widened as he opened the door and stared down the barrel of Pancho Villa's pistol. He was alone. Villa's gamble had paid off. Yañez was put under guard and Herrera's men, accompanying their new leader quietly surrounded General Soto's quarters and took him prisoner in the name of Madero's government. In one hour Villa's audacity had netted him Parral, the most important military center south of Chihuahua, and a new army, complete with machineguns. And all without firing a single shot. For all of his initial advantages, Pascual Orozco had lost the game. The illiterate peasant had proven himself the better strategist. In that deadly King-of-the-Mountain play, the Puma was now the hunter.

2

When the telephone in Villa's Parral headquarters rang, Herrera was the first to answer. "*Mi general,*" he said covering the speaker, "it's that sonofabitch, Emilio Campa. He says Orozco has sent him to combat us, and he wants to talk with you."

Villa's eyes flashed with delight. "With me?" he said taking the instrument. He had always wanted to talk on the telephone. Now he was being paged.

"Is this Pancho Villa speaking?"

"Yes. This is me."

"Well, this is *el general* Emilio P. Campa," said the young and efficient voice on the other end. "Emilio P. Campa."

"All right, I believe you."

"I am calling from Sombrerillo. I just want to say that I'll be in Parral tonight to knock some of the vanity out of you."

"You'll be around Parral, but not in it, sonny. And as for my vanity, I don't know why you'd want it. You seem to have plenty of your own. But you come around, anyway. We'll receive you with a lot of kindness, because you know me."

Villa heard the sharp click on the line, then smiled and stood clicking the connection, just to hear it.

"*Tick, tick, tick,*" he said delightedly.

"For crissakes, *general,* what did he say?" asked Huerrera.

"He'll be here tonight. Listen: *tick, tick, tick.*"

"*El demonio!* And what else, *mi general?*"

"And we'll defend the plaza. You know, I've never defended. But I've attacked enough of them, so I ought to know something. *Eiy!* What's this *general* business? How did I get promoted so fast?"

"Well," said Herrera, "Campa's *un general.* I didn't think it right to have that pink-faced little pimp talk down to you, just because he owns a pair of leather puttees."

Villa laughed, putting down the telephone. "*Épa,* Maclovio, since I'm *un general* now, tell those bankers and the others that my loan will be 100,000 pesos more. I'd like to pay the boys before tonight. They'll fight happier."

"*Jefe,*" said Herrera worriedly, "the bankers are crying already. They say the loan is illegal."

"I don't know 'illegal' from guava jam, *señor,*" Villa said, flaring suddenly. "You go tell those fat bellies they'll make that loan within two hours—or I'll put them all out in the outposts, where Campa's men can hold target practice."

"*Sí, mi general.*"

"And listen, Maclovio, we'd better demote me back to *coronel.* I don't want to make Campa feel bad."

Herrera grinned, saluted and went out to tend his duties.

3

The coming of night brought Emilio Campa. And for Campa the attack brought many surprises, all of them unpleasant.

The young Orozquista general knew only of Villa's reputation as a cavalryman. Campa's plan was to pepper the town with light artillery fire from pieces he'd placed in the hills, then crush Villa's weak defense by overpowering it with infantry. It was clear that cavalry would be useless in the defenses of a close-knit garrison where movement was greatly restricted.

In a sense, Campa was right. But in the broader, more vital sense, Campa was disastrously wrong.

Villa had a remarkable grasp of organization. He placed the Federal-trained soldiers in well-positioned barricades, supporting them with machineguns. His cavalrymen were formed into small companies of heavily-armed shock troops which could be easily shifted into any part of the battleground to deliver a small, localized attack. The illiterate *peón* who had never heard of Generals Sheridan or Jeb Stuart was now employing dismounted cavalry with equal brilliance, drawing solely from intuition.

As the fan-shaped Orozquista attack developed, Pancho Villa's infantry positions opened fire and contained them. Campa withdrew, shelled, then resumed his attack. Again he was contained. His last attack came just as dawn was breaking. That was when Villa moved. With enough light to see his enemy's hasty fortifications, Pancho Villa's cavalrymen launched a fierce counterattack which smashed right through Campa's center, then crumpled one wing, while Herrera and his infantrymen charged the other.

Before noon the mopping up was over, and not a horse-hair of Emilio Campa's army was within miles of Parral. Villa had fought his first defense, and had won it with laurels. He had once more defeated Orozco's forces, he was now more powerful than ever. This was the sweetest touch of all.

Two days later, this message arrived from the beaten Campa:

Graceless bastard. Within four days you will have me back there to knock some of that vanity out of you.
—Emilio P. Campa

Within two days Villa knew the repetitious General Campa wasn't bluffing. The *guerrillero's* farthest-flung spies—those tele-

graph operators in his pay—began reporting that three trains,
filled with 5,000 Orozquistas, supported by cavalry and field-
pieces, were on the way to attack Parral. Villa considered his
position carefully. Outnumbered six to one, and outgunned, he
had little hope of holding the city against Orozco's furious attack.
Yet he couldn't let it go without a fight.

"*Compañero*," he said to Herrera that evening. "Whatever the
consequences, I think if Campa wants us out, he's going to have
to kick us out—*a balazos*. With bullets."

"The merchants and bankers are up in arms, Panchito," said
Herrera. "They say you're going to get them all killed."

"Screw them," said Villa scornfully. "They are the same piss-
ants who ran things under Díaz. Money and their clammy skins
is all they think of. I wish their mothers had sat on them when
they were born."

"Then we're going to defend?"

"Until they throw us out, *amigo*. That artillery's going to hurt,
believe me. Listen now, and carefully. Because if they take the
town, we're moving out of here damn fast. I've two plans:
one for winning, and one for losing. Does that make sense,
compañero?"

"That's what those barracks generals do."

"Good," said Villa pleased. "Good. Now, listen."

Drawing lines on a piece of old wrapping paper, Pancho
plotted Chihuahua, Parral, Jiménez and Torreón with ticks running down to indicate the railroad.

"Orozco controls the rails from Juárez to Jiménez," he said.
"But the desert is mine. With a start, we can march farther from
their tracks than they'd care to follow. Then through the hills,
and southward to join Madero's main body at Torreón, the
government's railhead. Then we can do what Campa's done—
return in force."

"But what if Campa decides on pursuit?" asked Herrera.

"*Pero, hombre,* what a question. If I was a praying man, I
would stay up all night praying for nothing else. I am the king

there, *amigo*. That desert is my wife and mistress. Those hills are my daughters."

"Your wife and mistress almost killed you, Pancho."

"And so did Lucita a couple of times. But that was a lovers' quarrel, *viejo*. The more bitter the tears, the sweeter the kisses. Let that *cabrón* Campa try my desert."

"Well, he will be here tomorrow, and then we'll know."

"Yes, *mañana* we'll know," said Villa. "Now, to business."

Methodically, drawing Indian pictures, instead of writing, the illiterate soldier outlined his campaign, again following instinct. Instinct had been the *maestro* from whom he'd learned escape, survival and, more recently, bloody retaliation. Villa's battles had been a product of trial-and-error, filed in his mental ledger which, so far, could show no debit, only a profit column. This worked—use it again. This failed—force it on the enemy. For the uneducated peasant productive thought was a joy he couldn't yet completely explain. But it was there.

4

"One needn't collapse the house," went the ancient proverb, "in order to evict the fly." Yet this was exactly what Orozco meant to do, not knowing that his fly had already found an open window.

On the morning of April third, after an intensive artillery barrage, General Emilio Campa's reinforced columns struck Parral.

After four hours of ceaseless attacks, under the overall command of General José Inez Salazar, the Orozquistas swept into the town. But by then Pancho Villa had vanished, along with an entire army. What Salazar and Campa had been combating for the last hour, they discovered, had been a tiny rear-guard of volunteers. These were quickly rounded up. Then, to relieve his rage and humiliation, Campa had them summarily executed.

This cowardly act, combined with Orozco's basic treachery, was more than Francisco Villa could ever forgive. Henceforth the red flag of the Orozquistas was to turn him into a raging avenger. Never again would he offer a captive "Redflagger" the usual choice of death or embracing Villa's cause. For them there would be but one choice: "Where do you want the bullet, *cabrón?*"

Pancho Villa was unable to think, to act, to feel by degrees. To the very end, life would forever be all love, all hate, all war, all peace, all loyalty or all defiance.

Momentarily life was all mystery and chagrin for the co-commanders at Parral who couldn't understand how Villa had escaped them. The defenders' disengagement had been masterfully subtle, and their withdrawal from the combat zone could only be described as miraculous.

Neither Salazar nor Campa, though efficient, could be characterized as great generals. Yet they recognized genius in their opposition, and this puzzled as much as it infuriated them. Under whose plan and guidance had Villa acted? To attribute it to Herrera seemed unrealistic. But who, then? Perhaps, after all, it had all been a fluke. But whose fluke had defeated Campa four days earlier?

Deep in the heart of the Mexican desert rode the answer.

Moving always southward; now toward the settlement at Villa Coronado, then on to Escalón, and beyond, to Buendia and Jaralito; Villa led his remaining irregulars and his loyal followers of Parral through nearly 200 miles of a western Sahara. After the second day they had left Chihuahua and were passing down the state of Durango; the ground from which the *guerrillero* had sprung: where he had first loved and hated, feared and killed. The earth in which his father lay buried, on which his mother had borne and suckled him and in which she, too, lay buried now. Buried with his childhood, and his innocence, and his dreams of peace.

XI. "LIKE MANY VILLAINS . . ."

"THERE ARE HORSEMEN AHEAD, *mi coronel*," said the young captain galloping up to Villa.

"Well, what are you waiting for? Deploy your point."

"*Sí, mi coronel!*"

But the other group came on without suspicious actions, and presently Villa recognized a slender man with the brown face of a happy rodent, galloping just ahead of the revolution's fluttering standard.

"Urbina! *Mi querido compadre!*" cried Pancho reining up to embrace the grinning *guerilla*. "Where in hell did you drop from?"

"*Panchito, mi compadrito.* Come to my arms," said Urbina.

In the midst of the war, they had to pause to beat each other's dusty shoulders; to laugh, to shout, to hold one another at arm's length and to comment on the loneliness each had known without the other.

Knowing Villa, Urbina had expected his arrival in Durango after learning of his battle and ultimate defeat at Parral, via their common agents and the telegraph line.

"So now, where?" asked Villa. "Where is the army?"

"First to Mapimí, where our forward echelons are," said Urbina. "And, you'll never guess who is there."

"Who?"

"Guess."

"*Ah, demonio.* You're still a baby."

Tomás laughed his little boy's laughter, delighted at having provoked his *compadre*. Truly, no two men had ever been closer since their first meeting. And it was wonderful being together again.

"Who would you like to see, of all people, beside me?"

"I'm going to cut your nuts off."

"Raoul Madero. That's who!"

"*Raoul?* You don't tell me!"

"And listen. You're a General. The President learned of your little brawl at Parral, and there's a message from him waiting for you at headquarters."

"From *don* Francisco? Is he pleased? He's not sore, is he, Tómas?"

"Sore? *Compadre,* he's delighted. And now, since you are *señor general, don* Francisco Villa, maybe you'd better take command here. Do I salute you, or bow?"

Villa laughed hard at his friend's absurdities, realizing how much he had really missed him.

"You're the one who went regular army on us," he said. "So maybe I'd better watch how you do it."

"You're absolutely right, general. It's the army's duty to protect its civilians—and irregulars. With your permission, now, *mi general* . . ."

"Go to hell!" laughed Villa digging spurs to his horse.

2

In the broiling, desert misery of Mapimí, Pancho Villa found ample cause for happiness and satisfaction. Old friends, lost in the tides of war and peace, had once again been reunited by circumstances of a new conflict. Ancient and sacred loyalties were reaffirmed by the presence of familiar faces. There were many hugs and expressions of joy from Raoul, the president's younger brother, who like Urbina had elected to remain with the army. And Villa's pleasure had been doubled by the handshakes of Emilio Madero, another brother of the president, and by the warm reception from Lieutenant Colonel Guillermo Rubio Navarrete.

"I am very much impressed with your campaigns, *mi general,*" Navarrete said on meeting him. "I know of no officer who has accomplished so much with so little."

"Well, it's true," Villa laughed good-naturedly. "There's damned little under this *sombrero* besides hair."

"My reference was to supplies and troops, General Villa," the handsome, young regular replied slightly embarrassed. "I would say that your tactics at Juárez were brillant. I should know. I was then on the other side."

"We all make mistakes," Villa replied without malice. "And I'm glad you weren't there. You don't look like Navarro—or Tamborel's kind. You have an honest face."

"I warned you the general was plain-spoken, didn't I?" Raoul chimed in.

Young Navarrete, with his waxed mustache, tailored khakis, puttees and pith-helmet, was a new breed of companion for Villa. He was a *científico* to his fingernails, yet, because he made no effort to hide it, or to impose his more sophisticated views on those around him, it was impossible to dislike him.

As chief of artillery for the Northern Division, under Huerta, he was perhaps the closest man to that strange, ambitious, little Indian. And yet, the two were like white and black in personality and nature.

Through the first half of April Pancho Villa remained in Mapimí, and was able to learn much concerning the employment of field guns from the young *artillerero*. Despite their differences in background and manner the two had found a middle ground in the respect each held for the other. Since Tamborel's death Guillermo Navarrete had become the most promising artillery officer in the army—but for one. And that one was an almost legendary figure named Felipe Angeles, whom Navarrete venerated and regarded as the greatest artillery officer in the world. "Did you know," Navarrete explained enthusiastically, "that General Angeles was sent to Paris, to study the French 75—and then turned around and wrote the manual which all the European armies now use for that piece?"

"You don't tell me," Villa replied, not bothering to ask what a *manual* did, or a French 75 was.

During those days Pancho Villa relaxed, ate well, and reorganized his forces, while awaiting a summons from General Huerta at Torreón. What he'd heard of Huerta, thus far, failed to delight him. Yet, he didn't permit himself to prejudge the man. After all, Colonel Navarrete was a *científico*, too, and he was *"un hombre muy decente."* A very decent man. Additionally, the message from the president, which had so pleased Pancho, had also instructed him as to the chief executive's wishes:

> Pancho, I congratulate you on your loyalty, and may you never change your ways. You may requisition any supplies from *señor general* Huerta; and it would please me enormously should you reach some understanding with that gentleman.
>   —Francisco Madero

To Villa this left no question but that his president meant him to serve the cause under Huerta's command, and what Madero wanted was, to Pancho Villa, tantamount to a direct order.

The *guerrillero's* hopes were doomed if he had expected a pleasant relationship with General Huerta. On April 17th, summoned at last, Pancho arrived at Headquarters of the Northern Division in Torreón to confer with his new chief. It turned out not so much a conference as a painful farce.

"So, you are the famous Pancho Villa—" said *el señor general don* Victoriano Huerta peering up at the *guerrillero* from behind a pair of dark glasses.

Villa's stance was awkward; a poor attempt at emulating the Chapultepec snap which *coronel* Navarrete so easily assumed before superiors. He stood rigidly, his hands thrust down stiffly, his self-conscious face trying to look blank, his toes pointing in like a small boy's. He'd removed his Stetson, draping it over his pistol by the chin-cord. But his attempts at military bearing were ill-at-ease and ludicrous.

"Yes, my General. I'm Villa, sir," he stammered.

Huerta squinted and sniffed, as though he had stepped on something distasteful, and when he spoke again Villa's alert nose and ears told him that General Huerta was not exactly sober.

"So you are the famous *guerrillero* Pancho Villa—" he said

again. "Sit down, go on, you're, after all, a general, are you not? Go on, sit down. You and I have to talk . . ."

Huerta watched Villa pull a chair under him, and sit uncomfortably. The division commander's black-bead eyes took in every aspect of his new officer, from behind the cover of those dark lenses which everyone hated and which so many men had come to fear in themselves—as though ground glass, could think, and plot, and penetrate men's minds, and generate evil above and beyond the evil of the wearer.

"Come, let me look at you, Pancho. Let me hug you, my dear friend," said Huerta suddenly rising and lurching toward Villa. "To my arms, sir! My valiant comrade!" he said grabbing the *guerrillero* roughly and with surprising strength, considering the size and condition of the man.

Villa submitted to the alcoholic excesses of the old *cientifico,* but was revolted by the maudlin tears, and by the vile smell of whatever Huerta had been drinking so freely. Liquor didn't annoy Villa but the stupidities and loss of self-control brought on by drunkenness always did. He was embarrassed for Huerta, and because of this he lost all respect for the man.

For an agonizing hour the foolish performance went on; Huerta crying or sneering or laughing, as the mood struck him. And Villa was forced to sit, observe it and be scrutinized. Methodically, as though studying some strange creature from another world, Victoriano Huerta fixed his tinted glasses on Pancho's dusty clothes, his crossed belts, his gun, his hat. Even on the black bandana which Villa wore loosely about his neck. "*Señor general,*" said Huerta drunkenly, "where can I get a pair of leggings like yours? Big, leather things, goddamn! Big buckles . . . that make you look like a big—sonofabitch—a real man, you know? *Muy macho!* Lots of man! I want you to tell me where I can get those big—. What . . . was I talking about? Do you remember? Oh, sure. Listen. We're going to finish off that dirty, traitorous whore's-son, Orozco! Right?"

"I'm at your orders, general."

"All right. Listen, Panchito. Listen now. You *listen* . . ."

"I'm listening, general."

"What were we saying?"

"You were saying you'd like me to come back tomorrow."

"That's correct. I'm glad you're listening."

"Well," said Villa finally rising, "I'll be back tomorrow, then, to listen some more."

"You're all right, Villa. Goddamn you. You're better than some of these pimpy, little sonsofbitches around here."

"Well, I'll be back tomorrow. All right, general?"

"You're all right, boy. A little sloppy in your uniform. But then, you're an irregular. You want to be a regular?"

"No, thanks, General. I'm happy."

"You're a little sloppy, Villa. You spruce up your uniform before I see you tomorrow. I don't like sloppy soldiering, you hear? Get an orderly. I like my people to be sharp."

"Fine, General. With your permission, then."

3

Villa's disillusion with Victoriano Huerta amounted to distrust and active dislike. He didn't like being pawed or wheezed on. He didn't like drunken hypocrisy. And he didn't like a man who made stupid and improper use of foul language. One was not responsible for what he thought, but for what he said. Villa shuddered to think what might have happened had Huerta called him a sonofabitch, even in jest. He might have had to kill the old bastard—in jest—and then there would be hell to pay.

But if Villa had thought General Huerta a harmless old fool the first time they met, he was in for a surprise. On their next meeting, the man who greeted Villa was sober, suspicious and hard-eyed. Even through the dark glasses Pancho Villa could detect the glitter in those eyes; and the brittle voice and impatient manner of the Commanding General bordered on sheer rudeness.

"General Villa," Huerta said crisply. "I am moving my command forward to attack General Orozco. Are you ready to fight?"

"As ready as we'll ever be, General."

"And what does that mean, General? I interpret readiness in terms of supply, troop organization, training status—"

"We're ready, General, in whatever terms."

The small, wiry man squinted suspiciously at Villa. His skull-like head, under its crescent of white hair, had a leathery sheen.

"You're not a regular, my General," Huerta said pointedly. "There's much I must excuse in our relationship. But one thing I never excuse is insubordination. Do I make myself clear to you, sir?"

"*Sí, señor*. Perfectly clear."

"You don't know how a clear understanding relieves a commander's overburdened mind, my General. You're new to army duty, so it might be worthwhile to observe how we do things around here, eh?"

"Anything you say, my General."

"So. One thing an army profits and learns by is constant self-scrutiny. Tell me, do Irregulars inspect their troops, sir?"

"I usually make sure my men have footgear, food and plenty of ammunition," said Villa, pretending not to have understood the slurs. "If they want for anything else, they usually have the brains to ask for it. And I get it, one way or another."

Huerta flared. Already he was beginning to hate this arrogant *peón* who always seemed to say what was right on his mind. On the other hand, he couldn't afford to alienate him for two very good reasons. One: he was an intimate of Madero's—and of that simpleton, Raoul, Madero's brother. Two: No man in the army knew the Durango-Chihuahua territory as well as Villa; nor had any of them been there more recently.

"I think you'll find my inspections a bit more thorough," said Huerta disguising his anger behind efficiency. "Meanwhile, as senior Irregular officer in this encampment, you will assume command of all non-regular units, including those of Colonels Urbina, Madero, Benavides and Robelo."

"That's been done, *mi general*," said Villa.

"What? On whose authority?"

"Well, on yours, general. You just told me so. I only tried to think ahead to what a smart commander would want me to do—and I did it."

"And did you also 'think' that I might want your troops ready for inspection this afternoon, General?"

"The minute a little bird told me we were going to go north, I asked myself: 'Pancho, what would the general want to do?' Wasn't that a lucky guess, *mi general?*"

Victoriano Huerta sniffed and adjusted his glasses. He was hard. He was sharp. He was a field soldier, not a tea-room dandy, as many of his Chapultepec classmates had become. He was a thoroughly obnoxious old man, ugly and unreasonable. But he was, above all, a commander whose medals had been earned in campaign against the enemies of his government. Because of this he'd come to know men, and could evaluate them at a glance—when sober. He'd misjudged Villa. This *peón* was not a fool, like Madero. He couldn't be cajoled, flattered or intimidated. Nor could he be won, in any way, by someone like himself. He would have to be killed. Purely and simply, he would have to be disposed of when the time came. Perhaps, with a little luck, fate and Pascual Orozco might just take that small problem off his hands.

4

The body of the *División del Norte* was commanded by regulars, but its head was controlled by General (Honorary) of Irregulars Francisco Villa. The *guerrillero's* job on the advance was to provide security to the front and flanks. And this security would be enforced by an aggressive policy which called for mounted combat patrols to probe the northern routes and clear the railroads and other approaches of Orozquista activities. Villa went further. From Bermejillo on, he began clearing all the small towns.

With a grasp of organization which even the shrewd and demanding Huerta had to admire, Villa split his command so that the Madero brothers worked flanks, Herrera remained at General Huerta's headquarters (with the main body), and Villa led the advance, with the point directly under Tomás Urbina.

Villa's contempt for Huerta didn't lessen a bit, despite the *federales'* competent handling of his forces. To the forthright peasant, Huerta was just "a goddamned, warmed-over *científico don* Francisco dug up somewhere after Díaz vomited him."

But Raoul Madero was deeply concerned. "Be very careful of him, Pancho," he cautioned. "Like many villains, Huerta's nothing of a fool, and less of a coward."

Yet Villa laughed, feeling that he was more than a match for an old conniver like Huerta.

XII. THE FIRING SQUAD

VILLA'S DUTIES were perfectly suited to his temperament, particularly since his sole escape from Victoriano Huerta's tiresome moods was to remain at the head of his troops. At Tlahualilo, on May 10, his mounted guerrillas overran Orozco's rearguard, forced a fight and scattered the Redflaggers. Villa then ordered all prisoners shot, and all supplies and captured mounts sent to the rear.

This day General Huerta's happiness called for a celebration. The substantial booty delighted him, and his whiskey-buoyed spirits demanded that he personally congratulate everyone.

Villa, who had learned to dread Huerta's drunken affections as much as his sober abuses, bore up under the old man's mewings, then returned to his men as quickly as possible.

It was a different story next morning, when Huerta again cornered him following a war conference. Villa's dispersal of the Reds had opened the road to the plains of Conejos, where a large Orozquista force was entrenched. Since the Reds had ripped up much track—delaying the regular army's main source of transportation—Huerta had decided that General Villa's Irregulars, supported by elements of Colonel Navarrete's artillery, would deliver the attack on Conejos.

"*Señor general*," said Huerta, fixing Villa with that suspicious stare which characterized his sober days. "Tomorrow, at first light, you will initiate the battle. And I want you to understand that I will not tolerate one step backward."

Villa's astonishment was scarcely less than that of the others present. Then his face flushed. "When have you known me to take a step backward?" he said. "Me, who's led every one of your actions. By what right do you talk to me this way?"

"*Señor*, I'm certain General Huerta didn't mean his remarks the way they sounded," Navarrete interjected quickly.

"I meant exactly what I said," replied Huerta glaring. "I'll tolerate no evasion of duty. Nor will I put up with any further impertinence from anyone. Is that clear, gentlemen? I want to hear an answer."

"You'll have my answer in the field," said Villa walking out, followed by his staff, Urbina and Herrera.

Huerta's remarks had been well calculated. At dawn of May 12, Pancho Villa launched the attack with all the fury which had seethed in his heart throughout the night, and that anger, translated into terms of action, swept before it the Orozquistas.

But now his rage turned on Navarrete, whose artillery fires seemed to fall dangerously close to his charging cavalrymen.

"Go and tell that *cientifico* idiot that he's about to kill our men," he ordered Maclovio Herrera.

Navarrete's calm reply was that his fires were placed exactly as they should be, for a successful barrage.

It took Villa several charges before he began relating the whistling shells, just overhead, with the systematic disorganization of the enemy positions, and to see that as his men moved, the shells kept just ahead of them, sweeping the way clear.

"I have wronged and misjudged you, *señor coronel*," Villa told

Navarrete when they met after their victory. "It's the curse of being a stupid peasant."

"If you're an example of a stupid peasant, *mi general*," replied Navarrete graciously, "I wish I could be one, too. I'll wager Napoleon had a bit of such stupidity in him."

"That fellow must be with Zapata," said Villa. "I don't think I know him. But listen, *mi coronel*. I want to hear more about these barrages. Are there many kinds? Can you teach some of them to me?"

The courteous *científico* could—and did. After Conejo, Pancho Villa's interest in artillery would forever be keen. He learned his cavalry by instinct, his infantry at Camargo and Juárez. At Parral he'd practiced defense and disengagement. Under Colonel Navarrete, the third and most complicated arm at his disposal was becoming skillful. It was the last step toward the goal of being the total soldier. And before his role in the Orozquista uprising had reached its abrupt end, General Francisco Villa would have passed the category of *guerrillero* into that of full-fledged Field Commander—an education won, *magna cum laude* on the field of battle.

As Villa's personal fame spread along the holocaustic path to Chihuahua, his relationship with Huerta deteriorated rapidly. The aging martinet's drunkenness became as insulting as his sobriety, and his remarks were usually accented by shouts and curses which Villa found hard to tolerate.

Reluctant to initiate the break, Pancho's anger sought other outlets. His savage pursuit and slaughter of the Redflaggers intensified. He shot or hanged all Orozco prisoners, and let his fury extend to those who might try to protect them. The enemy retreated to Jiménez, ripping up the rails, and slowing Huerta's main force, but Villa's highly mobile cavalry needed no tracks. In 14 days his powerful thrusts harassed the Redflaggers out of Jiménez to Escalón, a distance of 100 kilometers. Huerta rebuilt the track, day and night and kept his regulars as flush to the ranging Villa as his trains could bring him. To the rank-and-file "Juan" (the conscripted or enlisted regular soldier), who understood shouted orders, bolt-action rifles and methodical advance, better than the free-wheeling tactics of the *guerrilleros,* Pancho Villa became at once a hero, an enigma and an unseen terror who won distant victories before the regulars could even get on the scene, and who kept "Juan" busy replacing tracks and uprooting camps almost daily. This was the picture of Villa which would be imprinted indelibly in the *soldado razo's*—the rank private's—mind, and would greatly influence the course of Mexican military history for almost a decade to come.

At Escalon the Orozco rebels massed, determined to hold, but Navarrete's shrapnel and "Juan's" rifle work pried them loose. The regulars had finally gotten a taste of battle as Orozco's main body entrenched. On May 21st, Orozco's forces evacuated Escalon. Next day it was Huerta's unhappy task to assemble his senior officers to announce the promotion of Honorary General Francisco Villa to Brigadier General, for his outstanding services against Orozco. For Pancho, who had thought himself forgotten by his old commander-in-chief, it was an unexpected honor, and his eyes filled with tears.

The long-sought confrontation of the two armies finally came on May 24th, as Huerta's regulars attacked Orozco's heavily-entrenched rebels at Rellano. Commanding the Orozquistas were Pancho's old enemies, Generals Salazar and Emilio Campa. General Huerta sober, and confident, hurled his 6,500 well-armed, French-uniformed "Juans" against the 8,500 Orozco rebels, notwithstanding the fact that Villa's scouts had just reported the approach of 2,000 Durango Irregulars coming down the mountains to Orozco's support.

"There's your mission, General Villa," Huerta barked disdainfully. "Stop the reinforcements, while I smash their main line. If you don't stop them, I'd like to hear that you died trying!"

"Thank you, *mi general,*" said Villa, considering it the first honest order he'd received from the old *cientifico.*

Outnumbered three to one, Pancho Villa ambushed the Orozquistas in their own mountains and ravines. He slashed their advance guard to pieces, thinned the main column down, by feigning retreat, then doubled back and annihilated it. That night he crept around the exhausted Rebel camp, fell on it, and scattered them in panic.

Villa's intuition had summoned up a new dimension to warfare in Mexico: one practiced by the Indians of America for centuries, but disdained by the "Civilized Armies"—night warfare. Without knowing it, he had anticipated the tactics of a war still 40 years in the future. For not until World War II would this practice find general acceptance among recognized armies.

Meanwhile, at Rellano, General Victoriano Huerta was proving his own qualities as a soldier by scattering Orozco's main forces into bloody pieces, aided by Navarrete's deadly artillery. By the 26th Orozco and his staff were retreating northward, completely on the defensive, while in a nearby sector of the smoking, body-littered battlefield, the returning Villa ordered his men, red-eyed and numb from fatigue, to stop for a brief rest.

Exhausted, feverish, Villa lay against a shattered tree, trying to nap, when the sound of hoofbeats aroused him with a start. It was a moustachioed federal lieutenant-colonel, followed by several junior officers. Pancho recognized him as García Hidalgo, Huerta's chief of staff.

"*Oyiga*—you! What are you doing?" Hidalgo called rudely from his saddle. "Don't you know the battle's over? What are your men doing, still here?"

"I'm General Villa," said Pancho sitting up. "Maybe you don't recognize me, *amigo*."

"I recognize you," said Hidalgo loudly. "But my orders are to clear the battlefield, and that's what I'm going to do."

"Listen," said Villa standing, "I'll tell you what you're going to do, you Goddamned chocolate-drinker. You're getting the hell out of my camp—and I mean this minute."

Hidalgo saw Villa's face transformed from a pleasant oval to a flushed, tense circle of anger. His eyes had gone red—bloodshot with rage—and his gunhand automatically crept toward the white handle of the Colt.

In that instant Hidalgo's arrogance was replaced by near-panic, and his voice trembled slightly as he said: *"Señor,* I have a friend in General Huerta. I have his full backing."

"And I have a friend right here, Mr. Federal," said Villa half drawing the pistol. "Now, you son-of-a-crosseyed bitch, are you leaving, or am I going to blow a hole right through your God-damn head?"

"You'll regret this, sir!" said Hidalgo.

"A la chingada!" yelled Villa. "Move!" and Hidalgo moved, and kept moving right out of sight.

"I don't like it," said Urbina, staring after the retreating federal. *"Compadre,* that *piojoso* was trying to provoke you."

"Well, he succeeded," said Villa sitting again.

"I don't like it," said Urbina. *"No señor.* Not at all."

"Then go to sleep," said Villa closing his eyes.

2

"Panchito," she whispered. *"Ay, mi* Panchito! You don't know how much I've missed you! Hold me, *mi querido.* Tightly."

"Is this tight enough, little cat?"

"Tighter. *Tighter!"*

"Can you feel me now?"

"Yes. *Ay, si, mi* Panchito."

"Everything?"

"Yes."

"Is that what you waited for? Is it, kitten?"

"Oh, yes. Kiss me again. Touch me again. Pancho. I feel like an animal when you're near me. I can't get enough of you."

"Were you faithful, little cat? Did you wait for me?"

"Yes. Yes. I thought sometimes you'd never come. I kept hearing about you, fighting. I was afraid, but I knew you'd come back to me. You wanted to come back, didn't you, Pancho?"

"Always and always, kitten."

"I dreamt about you, almost every night."

"What was I doing?"

"You know . . ."

"No, what? Tell me what, kitten."

"*Pancho!*"

Laughter. Giggles. "Every night, really?"

"*Almost* every night, I said." And: "Pancho . . . Were you faithful?—Why don't you say something? Were you?"

"Sure."

"You weren't—damn you. Were you?"

"Kitten . . ."

"Damn you, you treacherous stud!"

"Kitten . . ."

"You were laying everything in skirts. I know you!"

"Kitten. You're wrong! Oh, you're so wrong. How can you misjudge me so? I was fighting. Dirty. Tired. Lifeless. How could I think of women, kitten?"

"If I know you, you conniving son-of-a-seed-bull—you *managed.*"

"Little cat."

"Yes, Panchito?"

"Lie back, and shut up."

"Yes, Panchito . . . Oh, Panchito . . ."

3

"And how was your stay in Parral, *mi general* Rábago?"

Brigadier-General Jesús M. Rábago removed his pith-helmet, dampened his chapped lips, and shook his head.

"As my report stated, *mi general,* the Orozquistas had evacuated upon hearing we were enroute. General Villa and I occupied the city without incident. Without *military* incident, that is."

"What do you mean?" asked Huerta leaning across his desk and peering suspiciously.

"Well, sir . . . The people of Parral—well, they're more than fond of General Villa, it would seem."

"Treachery?" hissed Huerta.

"Well, no, *señor*. Mass hysteria, I would say. They regard Villa as a—well, a savior. A hero. Not that Villa had any part in it, to tell the truth. But from the moment we entered the city the '*Viva* Villa's!' were deafening."

"Only *Viva* Villa. No one else?"

"Only Villa, *mi general*," said Rábago. "And it was difficult to say who were the worse—the men or the women. Women of all sorts, rich and poor, followed us down the streets, tossing flowers and kisses . . . And there was one girl in particular. Villa swept her up and carried her on his horse, as though such public familiarity were the most natural thing in the world. In fact, he rode right into a hotel with her."

"Horse and all?"

"Horse, woman, cheers and all."

"He has a wife, somewhere in those parts. In Parral or San Andrés. Somewhere. Perhaps it was she."

"Perhaps. Although I'd envy the man whose wife could still look at him the way she did." Rábago smiled in recollection, despite himself. "What a woman she was! Those azure eyes. Those milkwhite arms . . ."

"Please, enough!" snapped Huerta humorlessly. "So he'd be a little dictator, eh? That glorified stablehand. Where is he now? Why isn't he here to report to me?"

"He said he was sick, and needed sleep. I told him I'd—"

"Yes, I can imagine he'd need a little sleep—after spending a week plotting and giving vent to his disgusting instincts."

Victoriano Huerta clenched his fists, staring with fixed fascination at the top of his desk. He was in a fury; a silent fury such as Rábago, a close associate, had never seen him in before.

"Did he try to corrupt you, Rábago?" he asked urgently. "Did he attempt to draw you from me? I want to know!"

"Truthfully, *señor,* we seldom spoke of you, save in an official sense. We were there to carry out your orders. To take and garrison Parral. And this we did, sir."

"Why did you leave Maclovio Herrera there?"

Captain Francisco (Pancho) Villa, in 1910, shortly after emerging from the hills to join the Madero revolution. From the beginning, even as an outlaw, he showed great dash in his clothes, his methods, and his personality. At this point he was 33 years old.

General de División, don Porfirio Díaz, President of the Republic of Mexico, shown in 1909, the year before the start of the Madero revolution. Díaz had been a hero of the war against the French and Austrians.

Don Francisco I. Madero, the idealistic scion of an *hacendado,* whose demand for free elections launched the 1910 revolution. He is shown here in 1911, at 37 in Hacienda de Bustillos, where he first met Villa.

Two leaders of the Madero revolution shown just before the attack on *Ciudad* Juárez, in 1911. At left: Colonel Giuseppe Garibaldi. At right: Colonel Pascual Orozco, First Military Chief of the Revolutionary Army, then 31 years of age, taciturn and tough.

Early leaders of the 1910 revolution shown in the field, somewhere in Chihuahua State. Front Row, Sitting: Major Roque González Graza, Major Eduardo Hay. Back Row, Standing: *don* Abraham González, Unidentified Noncombatant.

A detail of the famed *rurales*, performing one of their most common duties. This corps of Mexican Rural Police was composed of hard-riding, hard-fighting men, intensely loyal to Díaz. They were often compared to the Cossacks.

*uis Terrazas
owned the largest
attle Ranch in
Chihuahua*

Two types of army uniforms, under Díaz were the French (extreme left) and the German, as seen in this photo of Federal officers circa 1910.

Revolutionary Infantry engaged. Note excellent shooting positions.
Most of these men had learned to shoot by hunting in these same hills
and plains. Note the officer with fieldglasses, directing fire.
Discipline among Villa's men was splendid.

These early revolutionary
troops display a variety
of rifles, but their enthusiasm
and intent is uniform
enough. Note the tired
expressions of men who have
recently been embattled.
Pancho Villa led men like
this into Juárez.

This remarkable photo shows a famous American soldier-of-fortune
servicing one of the few pieces of artillery used by the Rebels
in their attack on Juárez. The man who has turned his *sombrero*
backwards for better visibility, and is about to load a shell,
is Captain Tracy Richardson, who participated in many Latin-American
revolutions before joining Villa.

Venustiano Carranza—whom Villa called "the Old Badger of the revolution,"—shown at the Juárez racetrack while he was "primer jefe." Through the revolution Carranza affected the plain uniform, with gold buttons, although his efforts were largely political, and not military.

General Felipe Angeles, the great artillerist of Mexico who shared Pancho Villa's dream. He was born in Zacualtipam, Hidalgo, on June 13, 1869.

This is General Álvaro Obregón who defeated Villa at Celaya, lost an arm, won a war, and later became President of Mexico. He was assasinated by a young art student, long after the revolution's end.

An extraordinary and rare photo of Pancho Villa advancing
(center, in white Stetson) with his entire staff, behind his
deployed cavalry. It is clear that enemy contact is imminent.

Rugged fighters of Villa's "American Legion" pose outside
of Juárez in early 1911. Note older type Colts machine gun
at extreme left. Many Americans adopted Mexican *sombreros*.

A sniper in Villa's guerrilla army, outside Juárez in 1911.

The Fierro Brigade, headed by Villa's "Butcher," triumphantly
enters a captured town.

"Redflaggers" on the march. This flag, rarely photographed, gave Orozquistas their nickname. Its white lettering reads: "Reform—Liberty—and Country."

Revolutionary officers, believed to have belonged to Villa's famed Dorados, taken before these shock troops had adopted their khaki uniforms by which they were later identified. Notice fine pistols and abundance of ammunition.

"But—" said Rábago astonished. "It was your express wish that *coronel* Herrera remain there."

"You're lying, damn you!" shouted Huerta furiously. "It's part of Villa's deviltry, and you fell in with it!"

"Sir," said Rábago rigid with outraged dignity. "General Villa and I executed your orders to the letter. Exactly."

"Where is that other devil—Urbina? Plotting with Villa?"

"Enroute to Torreón, *señor*, for reinforcements."

"*Ah, sí, sí.* I recall now," said Huerta as though emerging from a mental fog. "I—I wasn't feeling well that day. Too many duties. A man can only handle so much, eh?"

"*Sí, mi señor general,*" said Rábago who was abundantly familiar with the nature of Huerta's chronic ailment.

Several days passed, and Pancho Villa did not report to General Huerta. The rigors of campaign, and his hurried trip to Parral (with its attendant pleasures and duties) had been complicated by a recurrence of fever. Without Urbina or Herrera, and with Raoul Madero temporarily pinned to urgent paperwork, the Guerrillero found himself at loose ends for a confidant. He didn't know that Victoriano Huerta, ever conscious of a slight —real or imaginary—was fuming in his headquarters because "that bandit" seemed bound to ignore him.

At this time, Huerta received a personal visit from a prominent citizen. *Señor* Marcos Russek charged that while riding the countryside, Villa's men had rounded up a mare; a very beautiful, valuable animal for which *señor* Russek had a special fondness. Russek, owner of the largest mercantile store in Jiménez, and a horse fancier, had apparently claimed his mare from Villa, whose blunt reply had been, "You go to hell!"

Now *señor* Russek was personally appealing to *señor General* Huerta, a gentleman like himself, for justice—and his horse.

"You have my personal guarantee, don Marcos," Huerta replied, rising to the heights of his indignation. "I shall see that justice prevails." And then he called for his Chief of Staff, *coronel* García Hidalgo, to go summon "that unruly *peón.*"

Villa was sleeping peacefully when the arrogant Hidalgo entered to announce that General Huerta wanted him.

"Tell him I'll be there when I'm up to it," said Villa.

"General Huerta directs that you present yourself immediately!"

"*Bueno.* In that case, tell him to go to hell. And you go with him. Now, I'm going back to sleep."

It was perhaps the most incautious and foolish move Pancho Villa ever made. When he awoke again it was to an insistent shaking, and to the gradual realization that Colonels Hidalgo and Navarrete both stood beside his bed, and that a squad of regulars stood with fixed bayonets just behind them.

"I regret this deeply, *mi general,*" said Navarrete. "But you are under arrest."

"What are you talking about?" said Villa irritably, rubbing sleep out of his eyes. "What hour is this for jokes?"

"I only wish it were a joke, sir," said Navarrete. "My orders from General Huerta are to disarm and convey you, under guard, to General Headquarters, where you are to be detained until tomorrow morning."

"And then?"

"Then . . . you are to be shot. By a firing squad."

Villa sprang up, his face gone white. "Shot? Shot for what?"

"The charges, sir, are insubordination to a general officer, and the theft of a horse. By General Huerta's direction, you have been tried in absentia . . . and were convicted."

4

"Get me Mexico City, immediately," said Raoul Madero. "Direct wire to the President. Quickly."

"*Coronel,* my orders forbid—"

"Damn your orders!" he said gripping the telegraph operator's shoulder roughly. "Send the following: '*Pancho Villa sentenced by General Huerta to be shot at five tomorrow morning. Stop.*

Wire immediate reprieve or execution will be carried out.
Signed: *Raoul.*

"*Ay, Chihuahua!* You mean Pancho Villa—?"

"Send it, and keep your mouth shut!" said Madero.

The desperate message was transmitted at 6 P.M. By ten, when Raoul returned there was still no reply. Raoul then instructed the operator to raise the Mexico City telegrapher and charge him personally with seeing that the message reached the President's home.

Still no word at midnight.

At 3:30 A.M., just one and a half hours before the scheduled execution, word finally ticked in. The message was on its way by special military courier. By then Raoul was extremely nervous. Colonel Navarrete had tried to intercede with Huerta, who refused to reconsider. "I'm afraid General Villa will die unless the President intervenes," Navarrete had informed Raoul by telephone.

"For God sake, keep sending," Raoul urged the operator. "He's probably at one of those damned diplomatic parties."

At 4:45 A.M. there was still no reply, and the early bugles were already awakening the encampment. Raoul was frantic.

5

A few moments before 5 A.M., the door to Villa's room was opened by a tall, gaunt captain. "*Mi general.* I am *capitán* Hernández, in command of your firing squad."

Villa sat up, smoothed his rumpled hair, and pulled on the Stetson. He was in poor humor after a night under guard, and being kept incommunicado from his own men.

"Son," said Villa softly, "how would you like to be a major tomorrow?"

"I'd like it very much, *mi general.*"

"Good," said Villa. "Look. I'm sick of this little game. You just get word to whoever's in charge of my brigade at the moment. Tell him I want some action. Do you understand, captain? But quietly. And fast."

"I'm sorry, *mi general*. There's no more *Brigada Villa*."

"No what?"

"Last night our people surrounded your encampment, by General Huerta's orders. Your officers were placed in temporary arrest, and the brigade scattered among other units. There is no more *Brigada Villa, mi general*."

"You're crazy!" said Villa desperately.

"I'm sorry, *mi general*. I have to carry out my orders now. Have I your word that I don't have to handcuff you?"

"That old sonofabitch is going to play this farce out to the end, is he? *Bueno*. I can play it, too. Let's go."

As Pancho Villa walked between the two files of stiff-faced regulars the grotesque thought struck him that this might not be a joke, but a real execution he was going to.

"No," he thought. "The stupid, old drunkard wouldn't dare. *Nunca!* He's trying to throw a scare into me. To make me cringe."

In the large courtyard he pushed the hat over his eyes to ward off the rising sun, and stepped through the halted squad, up to the adobe wall, with the captain beside him.

"*Mi general,* I'm to offer you a blindfold."

"For what?"

"Then I'm to offer you a last, reasonable request."

"Fine. Let's get on with this stupidity. I'm hungry."

Villa studied the stolid Indian face of the captain, waiting to catch a glimmer of a smile. But the man remained grim as he drew his sword, wheeled, and strode briskly to his post beside the firing squad.

"*Atención!*" he sang out. "*Listos . . . Apunten . . .*"

As the sword flashed upward Villa's breath choked in his throat. *Santa María purísima*, he thought. *It's true. They're going to do it!*

Hanging in that instant between life and death, Villa raised his arms. "No, wait! I want to know why you're doing this. *Capitán,* that's my last wish!"

"I only know my orders, *mi general,*" said the captain as the soldiers hesitated. "I'm sorry, but I must proceed."

"I demand to know!" cried Villa trying to forestall the final order. "I've had no trial. This is assassination!"

As the six rifles leveled again with his chest, Villa heard shouting, and a clatter of hooves approaching, then a man leaped from his horse, calling to the captain. "Wait. Don't fire! I have authorization here to halt the execution!"

It was Raoul Madero—followed closely by a breathless Colonel Navarrete—invading the scene in the most ridiculous motion-picture fashion, waving the telegram in which the President had granted Pancho Villa's last minute reprieve.

Slowly, as the squad was ordered to ground arms, Villa's entire body sagged against the earthen wall behind him. "My God, Raoul," he whispered. "I was *that* close to it. That close, *amigo.* And it really shook the hell out of me."

It was an experience the *guerrillero* would never forget or forgive. Even after he was on a military train, enroute to Mexico City as a prisoner, he couldn't get it out of his mind. He could think of nothing else. He swore that never again would he trust any man against his instincts. And he determined that never, so long as he lived, would he let himself be caught unarmed and helpless. Nor would he ever surrender to anyone. Not if he died. Not if he had to go down fighting to the last bullet, the last breath, the last instant of consciousness.

It was an oath he would never break: that covenant between himself and his guns, that deadly anger which would cause so much blood to flow in the streets, in the hills and along the plains of Mexico. To be slaughtered like an animal, a worthless, meaningless *peón,* a nameless nuisance, was more than that flaming nature could endure. It hadn't been death, itself, which had frightened him. It had been the thought of dying for nothing. For nothing at all.

XIII. THE BEAST INTO MAN

FRANCISCO VILLA's outward calm concealed a gathering storm of angry plans. Unshaven for days, shaking from tension and little sleep, he was like an animal caged, silent and dangerous; knowing that when his moment came he would tear and claw his way to freedom over the bodies of his tormentors.

Any thought of Huerta infuriated him. He longed for the day when he should see his dearest friend, and President, again to right the wrongs and the indignities. When Madero should release and restore him to rank, he was ready to head north once more, to drag that miserable drunkard from behind his desk, goldbraid and all, and show him how a man could win a war in a hurry. When he and *don* Francisco met, by God, things would be set right!

Villa never doubted the support of the people. The *charro* pants, the white cotton shirt and the *sombrero* of straw were their uniform, and his; and the cornstalk, the puma, the free soaring eagle their coat-of-arms and flag. He talked their talk, cried their tears, felt their pain. He knew and loved and needed them. They needed and loved Pancho Villa. They, the people: the despised peasants, the landless peons, the old women begging by the church-doors, the sweating plowman, the girl fat with child, the *niños* playing in the fields and streets: the multitudes; poor, hungry, angry, tired, humbled, exploited, cheated and indignant. They were Pancho Villa, and he was all of them.

If he needed reassurances, he received them, and loudly, during the train's stopovers, particularly at Torreón and San Luis Potosí, where the 50 man guard escorting him to prison was forced to hold back yelling crowds which had turned out to cheer the *guerrillero*.

"*Viva* Villa!" they shouted gathering around the prisoner's window. "Death to the *pelones!*"

"Silence there!"

"Silence your mother!"

"*Viva* Pancho Villa! The baldheaded Federals have fleas!"

"Free Villa! *Viva* Villa!" the growing crowds shouted.

"Pull out! Move, you imbecile. You want a riot?"

On the morning of June 7, 1912, Pancho Villa arrived in Mexico City and was driven, handcuffed, directly to the Federal Penitentiary. On the 11th, Military Judge Santiago Mendez Armendariz formally charged him with "Disobediance, insubordination, and robbery." To wit: Ignoring the lawful order of a superior during time of war, attempting to subvert the army forces under his command, unlawfully appropriating 260,000 *pesos* while "looting" a city. No one considered that the troops had been recruited by Villa, himself, or that his "loot" had been raised to pay these same troops in the interest of the government, and in defense of Madero. The mare had been forgotten. An ever better trap had been happily furnished by the bankers and merchants of Parral.

On the 18th of June, aided by his appointed counsel, Attorney Guillermo Castillo Najera, Villa entered a plea of not guilty. But his ardent hope was that his friend, President Madero, would soon move to dismiss the absurd charges and censure Huerta publicly.

Weeks passed in loneliness. Pancho Villa struggled with an ever growing fear that Francisco Madero had abandoned him. "I've planted sweet wheat," he told Najera sadly, "but *amigo,* I am harvesting bitter weeds."

On July 13 he was formally declared a federal prisoner. The Parral bankers were suing him for their money. "I used it to fight the Orozquistas," he cried impotently. "Doesn't anybody care?"

By July eighth Huerta's troops were in Chihuahua City. On the 30th, as Villa lay in prison minutes away, Huerta made a triumphant visit to Mexico City and was promoted to full General of Division by the beaming *presidente,* himself. Villa refused to believe it. Was the whole world crazy? Did they mean Madero had time for Huerta, but not for Villa?

His letters to the president received no answer, but orders came for Pancho's transfer to the Military Prison of Santiago Tlaltelolco, a sort of penitentiary deluxe for wayward generals, gentlemen plotters, deposed *políticos,* and other privileged classes. It was a bitter appeasement to the *guerrillero* who saw now that no pardon would be forthcoming, and that his enemies would have their day in court at his expense.

But why? *Why?* he kept asking himself constantly. Why should his dearest friend forget him?

Soon after his arrival at Tlaltelolco he had a visitor who tried to answer that question for him.

"The truth is," said Gustavo Madero, the President's older brother, "that he is afraid to come visit you, general."

"Afraid? *Hombre,* he's the president. How can a president be afraid?"

"He is afraid, I tell you. Afraid of the *científicos,* afraid of the plotters and plots behind them. He is afraid of Orozco and also of Zapata, who will not recognize the government until we agree to give land to his peasants. And to a soldier, *señor,* life is black or white. The enemy is clearly labeled, and his weapon is the gun or bayonet he bears. But the life of politics, *señor,* there is naked savagery. A morbid ant-heap in which your friends may fight you hardest, and the one who smiles broadest may want your head. And where the weapons are gossip, treachery, soft words and—God knows what, *señor!*"

"Yes," said Villa sadly, "that may be true, *don* Gustavo, but cages are not paradise either."

"He's wanted to come see you a thousand times," said Madero. "But he doesn't dare offend Huerta. He can't, with a war still raging north and south. Can you understand that? Who else could save my brother and preserve the democracy, *señor?* Who but General Huerta?"

Villa's heart seemed to shrink inside him and his eyes filled with tears. He wanted to cry out: "*I* could. *I,* Pancho Villa, who gave him the presidency in Juárez!" But instead he bit his lips and replied: "It can't be easy to be a president. It isn't as if *don* Francisco was free to do what he liked."

"No, General Villa. It never is."

"When I was a little boy," said Villa, "I used to think sometimes that if I were king, or emperor, or even just a president, that I would be able to tell the whole world what side to mount on. I'd have fat, old rich ladies washing clothes for my mother, and ministers or *hacendados* giving their biggest cigars to my father, because they wanted to say they knew him. And I'd eat candy all the time, because I love candy. But it's never like that, is it? Is it, *señor?*"

"No," said Gustavo adjusting his glasses to cover his embarrassment.

"It's never quite that simple, or that good. I know that now, *amigo*. But I halfway wish I didn't."

"Well, *mi general*," said Madero extending a slender hand anxiously. "I must go. I am aiding the President, and there are a million things to be done. But fortitude, *señor*. Things will go well. And in the interim, anything you want here, to make you more comfortable, is at your disposal. You need only ask the warden. Clothes, special foods—"

"Freedom?" asked Villa smiling ironically.

"I must go, *señor*," said Madero again. "Really. And the best of luck at your trial. My brother . . . Well. I think you understand."

"*Sí, cómo no?*" said Villa. "Thanks for coming, *amigo*."

When Gustavo Madero had left, Pancho Villa turned to the wall, and the tears leaped from his eyes. For a long while he stood hunched over, his flushed head hidden in his arms, his massive shoulders shaking. But when he had cried himself out, and turned again, he knew what he would do.

There would be no degrading trial, no chance for Huerta to crow publicly, no conspicuous absence of his friends who were too busy elsewhere to defend him. If he must face it alone, he would face it as he chose, for he was heartily sick of turning one cheek, and then the other, only to have them both slapped. He had plenty of time, so it simply narrowed now to a matter of planning and the right opportunity. Then—*adiós pájarito!* Farewell little bird!

2

"*Perdóneme, señor.* Forgive me. But are you not *general* Francisco Villa?"

"At your orders, *amigo,*" he replied sizing up the pleasant, copperhued face and the slight but muscular figure of the man who had stopped him in the prison garden.

"I am Gildardo Magaña, aide to General Emiliano Zapata. May we sit together, *mi general?*"

"*Cómo no?*" said Villa happy to converse with someone. "But I have to warn you, it might ruin your reputation."

"*Ha!*" said Magaña bursting into ironic laughter. "Don't you know, *mi general,* that we people of Morelos are nothing but sunbaked savages and bastards? Or so they say. So they tell it. To need land is a crime. And to want freedom is a worse crime yet. We've heard you're something of a criminal yourself. And sometimes a bigger devil than our Zapata."

"How do you know this?" asked Villa laughing.

"Oh, I've read a bit about you, *don* Pancho. In fact, it was I who used to read to Zapata about your activities."

"You . . . you read?" asked Villa no longer laughing.

"Me? Yes. My father kept a store, and I went to school, and studied many things: geography, history—"

"*Amigo,*" said Villa urgently. "Could you teach me?"

Magaña finished licking a cigarette, twisted the ends, and lighted it thoughtfully. "Geography, history . . . ?"

"To read. Only to read, *amigo.* Maybe to write a little."

"*Con todo mi corazón,*" said the southerner smiling. "With all my heart."

"But you must be patient with me. I am a *burro* of the first calibre."

"The man who took Juárez?"

"*Ah*, Gildardo, if words were as simple and direct as bullets we would all be such wise men. I've wiped out armies, but I can't sign my name, so what good is it? What good am I if I'm treated like a fool? Listen, *amigo*. A dog can feel a kick, even though he can't tell you about it. And even an idiot can cry, if you hurt him hard enough. But complaint only makes fools funnier. Little boys throw rocks, and men throw slights, and the idiot moves on to make others laugh. I'm 34 years old, *amigo,* and all I know about my country is what I've seen with these eyes, or heard with these ears. There are babies in school who know more than I do."

The Zapatista shook his head, snuffed out his cigarette, and grinned. "Come on, *don* Pancho. The sooner we wring this rooster's neck, the sooner the pot will boil."

3

"*Tomás,*" he says, "*they're coming. Wake up, Tomás. They're almost here,* compañero. Óyeme. Dispierta! Demonio, *wake up. They're almost here.*"

But he can't awaken him. Nothing wakes the sleeping Urbina, damn him. Damn him! Lying there, in the loose dirt, like a dying lizard. "Tomás, for crissakes, wake up!"

He's been watching the rurales *winding down the foothills, hours away, then galloping, by twos, across the plain which separates the two ranges. Their horses had been specks then, their large, brown hats and uniforms only buckskin smudges. And he'd let Tomás sleep on because neither of them had slept in four days and nights.*

"You want me to take the first watch, compadre?" *Tomás had asked. But he couldn't have, and both knew it, so he'd replied: "Viejo, I'll take it and wake you up in two hours." "Good," Tomás had said. "Then I'll watch and let you sleep, Panchito. Do you think they'll be here before noon?" "No, not likely.*

They haven't slept much either, and they're tracking as they come."

Now four hours have passed, and Urbina can't awaken. The squadron of rurales *isn't more than a half hour off. In desperation he saddles their horses and pours water in Urbina's face, but Tomás can't awaken. He shouts and slaps Tomás, but his face remains immobile, his breathing regular, his mouth slightly open. What is this terrible power called sleep?* Dios mío! *The tenacity of it frightens Pancho Villa more than he can admit to himself. What if Tomás never awakens again? Is this death?*

Desperately he shakes Tomás, then pulls him to a sitting position, but the sleeper's head lolls back, like a dead man's head. Sleep won't release him. It holds him. He doesn't care that the enemy is almost on them. That they will be captured, and ordered to dig their graves right there, and shot into them. No, not for Villa and Urbina. Nothing merciful for them. The captain of rurales *and his sergeant will loop lariats over their necks and drag them a bit. Just a bit through the rocks and cactus. Just enough to rip the flesh off their faces and their eyes out of their heads. Only enough to strip their chests to the bone. Listen,* compadre. *Wake up, for God's sake. Look. I'm just as tired as you. More. But they're already starting up the hillside. There, see them? Damn you!"*

Struggling, nearly collapsing, he picks Urbina up on his back and drops him over the horse. He ties him on, then mounts. He begins riding up, up, higher into the mountain, away from the rough trail, into the thick, trailless wilderness of the lizard, the snake and the vulture. He rides, pulling Urbina's animal behind him; both their jackets, pants and shirts ripped by the razor-edges of the brush and cactus and their bodies covered with blood. But Urbina still sleeps on.

It is late afternoon now. It is twilight now. It is night at last. Urbina still sleeps on. Pancho Villa unties his friend, and lays him tenderly on the ground, still asleep.

There is a sound behind them. Then another to the left. The rurales! *They've found them!*

Villa leaps to Urbina's side and comes up with a pistol in each hand. He can feel them moving in on him now. That dark and sinister circle closing in. He waits, but Urbina sleeps on, not caring or knowing. Then a small coyote breaks into the clearing. Only a stupid, hungry, little animal—searching, like themselves, for something.

Pancho Villa's arms drop. The guns fall out of his hands and lay in the dirt. He knows, now, the difference between life and death. Life is fear. It is flight and pursuit. It is struggle, terrible exertion and endless desperation. It is needing and wanting; hurting and being hurt; hungry days and long nights filled with spectres out of pasts and futures.

Urbina has discovered, for them both, what death is like. It is letting go. Hoping it will end. Not wanting to come back to it. Not wanting to know or feel anymore. Villa is so tired that he could die. But he will not sleep. He is afraid of it.

4

Pancho Villa's hours at the speller and blackboard were long, and so his days seemed shorter. Painstakingly, smiling happily at his work, the *guerrillero* who had destroyed battalions of armed men sat beside Magaña attempting to destroy his own ignorance with a small, dull pencil. And during the evenings, when the light grew dim, the bronzed, little man would sit explaining schoolroom theories to the warrior, or opening his mind's eye to the vastness of their universe.

"You mean that little star up there is a million miles away? *Hombre,* I can't believe that."

"But it is, Pancho. It says so in every book of astronomy."

"Listen, I don't give a damn what that Astronomy says in his books. If the damn thing was as big as El Paso, Texas, even as big as all the State of Chihuahua, I couldn't see anything a million miles away. Could I see a horse 100 miles away? Could you, or that crazy bookwriter? Hell no! And I've got good eyesight, too. So he's crazy."

"Now, what if I told you that that star, Venus, is as big as our whole earth?"

"And I suppose somebody went up there and measured it, eh? This *loco* Astronomy?"

"But, you don't understand, Panchito. Astronomy is not a man."

"A woman, eh? Whew!" and his arms went up in horror. "Worse yet! I think we'd better forget stars and go on to something else."

Within that melting pot of thwarted ambitions and intrigues, the Military Prison of Santiago Tlaltelolco, educations of another sort were to be had for the listening. Every corner held its group of earnest planners; every clique held a hopeful candidate for the job of *presidente,* and every candidate was good for at least 10 reasons why he should have been in Madero's place, or as many explanations of how he'd been cheated out of his rightful due.

Chief among these plotters was the bearded and bombastic old General Bernardo Reyes whose abortive plot against the Díaz regime had earned him his first trip to Santiago Tlaltelolco, and whose subsequent attempt against the Madero administration (after Madero had freed him) had earned him his return.

General Félix Díaz, claimed Reyes, would soon raise his own revolt in Vera Cruz. Orozco would soon be beaten. Madero would fall, and he, Reyes, would then step in to save the nation from the infernal rabble. Would General Francisco Villa care to join him, in return for a good government post?

General Villa would not. But thanks, anyway.

"What's the matter with that old man," Villa asked his *maestro,* Magaña. "Is he crazy, too?"

"They're all crazy. Crazy with the lust for power, *amigo.*

"But does he know what he's talking about?"

Magaña shrugged. "Time will tell, Panchito."

Time did. Amid the political blizzards of shifting factions and fickle loyalties, word came that on September second, Huerta entered Juárez. Ojinaga then fell to him on the 4th. General

Pascual Orozco, inexorably pushed against the northern-most borders by the fierce drunkard, had but one hope left—and he took it.

During the night of the final battle he and the beaten remnants of his staff had crossed the American border and delivered themselves into custody of the U.S. authorities. Huerta had triumphed, and the Orozquista revolution was totally crushed.

But peace was shortlived.

On October 16th, Reyes' second prediction came true when General Félix Díaz declared himself in revolt against President Madero. Badly beaten, Díaz was summarily sentenced to be shot, and Pancho Villa breathed easier. Then Madero ordered the sentence commuted to imprisonment.

"He has learned nothing," said Gildardo Magaña sadly. "Nothing at all, and that will be the death of Madero. You mark my words, Pancho. This place is filled with men Madero has forgiven—and just listen to the plots that go on here."

"*Bueno,* Magaña," said Villa. "But his heart is good, and what can a man do, go against his conscience and heart?"

"You sentimentalists!" cried the Zapatista. "You talk of hearts. Haven't you learned anything either, from the things I've told you about Miguel Hidalgo, the priest, or about Maximilian, the would-be emperor? *Hay, demonio!* But can't you see? Their hearts were good enough; it was their political naivete which finished them off—which put them between the firing squad and the wall!"

"*Pues, es verdad,*" Villa admitted. "That much I know."

"And if you had to do over again, would you trust Huerta?"

"Never. That manipulating bastard," said Villa hotly. "I used to think he stank of booze. But what he stank of was the little worm's taste of power!"

"Well, let me tell you where your little worm is now," said Magaña cynically. "He is back in Mexico City. Right in the National Palace, by your little *presidente's* elbow. Your conquering boa-constrictor, wrapped around your quivering, little rabbit, telling him what's best for him. Whispering in his ear."

"You're lying!" said Villa explosively. "Damn you, Magaña, you're lying to me!"

"Am I, Pancho?" replied Magaña cooly. "Then go ask that old windbag, Reyes. Ask him what he and Huerta have been communicating about while you're at it. That should be interesting."

"Reyes and Huerta?" asked Villa aghast.

"Ask him point blank. Tell him you'll join him, too."

Pancho Villa sat back on the garden bench, his eyes staring at the trembling hands on his lap. That snake, Huerta, beside the President. Huerta and the incurable, old plotter, Reyes—and Reyes somehow tied in with Félix Díaz, nephew of old *don* Porfirio. The whole air of this so-called prison—this Plotters' Club—was foul with open treachery. And no one the least interested in warning Madero!

He wondered: What if I did warn *don* Francisco? What if I wrote, or called for Gustavo to tell him? Would they believe me? Would they act? He recalled Gustavo's words: *"He doesn't dare offend Huerta. He can't . . . Who else could save my brother and preserve the democracy. . . ?"* Who else, indeed? thought Villa bitterly. And then he thought also of those other things Gustavo Madero had said: *"The life of politics . . . a morbid ant-heap . . . your friends may fight you hardest, and the one who smiles broadest may want your head . . . treachery, soft words and—God knows what, señor!"*

It was a horrible, insane feeling this: everything going downhill, like a runaway train, headed right for a crossing full of people: and no one able to stop it. He, least of all, shackled here, like an animal; locked away from the world and from his friends. But what if he were free—right now? What if Victoriano Huerta were to learn that Pancho Villa was free?

He had considered escape once, before meeting Gildardo Magaña. But then his motives had been petulance and self-pity. It had been no great sacrifice to transform his prison into a schoolroom and remain. Now he felt the spur of fear against his ribs. Fear for Madero and the revolution. He couldn't go to Madero, but by escaping he could still be a threat to the president's enemies.

"*Demonio!* It's too complicated for me," he said to Magaña as they sat that evening in Villa's cell. "All this belly-crawling from plot to plot. I'm too stupid to understand it all."

"So are all the rest of these gentlemen plotters," said Magaña scornfully. "But they won't admit it."

"Just tell me one thing out straight. Is Huerta really a danger to Madero?"

"For an answer ask yourself why he tried to have you shot. Was it whim—or plan?"

"All right, you tell me. You're the smart one."

"Where was Urbina? Herrera? Those who might have helped you? And that beautiful division of your brigade. Didn't you tell me it was a perfect plan? *Plan* was your own word."

Villa sat kneading his strong, brown hands, nodding without being aware of it. "Yes," he said. "I see . . . But *why?*"

"Because you were a threat to him!" Magaña almost shouted. "Your growing popularity. Your growing sense of strength. He wouldn't be next to Madero today if that had continued. You would have been. You, Pancho. So you had to be eliminated."

"All that for power?" asked Villa, seething.

"Yes, *mi general.* All that—and more. Because lies, treachery and murder, my dear Pancho, are often only the beginning. And there is no end. Not for the really sick ones. Not for such as Huerta." He stood up trembling with rage, the one and only time Villa saw his patient little teacher out of control, and staring down into the *guerrillero's* face he said: "You and Zapata. You're in their way. You are stupid Indians. Stubborn, incorruptible, unpredictable. You frighten and puzzle them. You can't be toppled, and you won't be sidestepped. So, shall I tell you what the end will be? Treachery. Out of the darkness will come the silent knife, the sudden bullet. Yes, you laugh now, *amigo.* Zapata laughs, too, because he's strong. And you are strong. And neither of you can begin to imagine the filth,

and hate, and desperation in those vulture-minds. But you will
learn. And you will remember my words . . . you don't even
understand what I've said, do you, Pancho Villa? No. You're just
like Zapata."

5

He sat alone, clutching a clerk's pen between unaccustomed
fingers, forming each syllable with silent lips before the pen had
finished it. He was tired of childish words: colored pictures of
ducks, of dogs, cats and flowers. He wanted to write something.
To communicate the thoughts which had been burning in his
brain for weeks now. Ever since he had begun to painfully
block his first *A*.

This volatile man, found himself longing to express another
facet of himself; to communicate long-buried thoughts which
only his innermost voice had ever articulated. Could he say them
to someone? Could he put even one of them on this ruled paper,
in the big, crooked letters of a six year old, so that they would
not laugh?

After a long moment he sighed deeply and began:

When man was born

But he couldn't go on. He was too nervous, too self-conscious
of his pitiful inadequacies, and he gave up. Magaña had talked
lately about military men and their campaigns. About a soldier
named Napoleon Bonaparte—a foreigner Rubio Navarrete had
once mentioned and Villa made a fool of himself by thinking
him a Zapatista. Much could be learned from the words of such
men in books. More than he had ever suspected. He could read
most words in a newspaper, too. He had read, just this morning,
about someone named Álvaro Obregón, a new friend of Carranza
and Huerta, who had formed a battalion of Sonorans to help
defeat Orozco. Now that Orozco was gone, everybody had
helped defeat him. But wasn't that always the way?

It was very late. Within the cell block the heavy sounds of
sleep could be heard: echoing snores, grunts and bedsprings,

men's throats clearing and occasionally someone lighting a cigarette.

Pancho Villa blew out the candle stub which was allowed him as a privileged night-owl, and lay, hands behind his head, staring up into the darkness. He had to escape. No doubt about it. And soon. He'd done a lot of thinking. Days might count. Even hours. He could go to *don* Abraham González. He'd read, just recently, that *don* Abraham had returned from hiding, and been restored to his governorship.

He had read. The thought of it was stunning. Imagine. He, Pancho Villa, reading . . . and even writing! Well, almost writing. No good, though. Chihuahua was the first place they'd look for him, and that might compromise *don* Abraham somehow.

His flight would have to be meaningful. He wasn't an ignorant peasant anymore, and he didn't want himself caught. He understood things now. Reviewing his previous efforts, like an eagle looking down on the scurryings of a field-mouse, he could see why he'd been worth nothing to *don* Francisco. A stupid *peón*, that's all. Ignorant, dirty and poor. And such fantastic airs that he'd put on as a captain of men. It was a miracle Madero hadn't laughed right in his face.

Now education added to his practical experience gave him a new potential, and he, himself, was the first to feel it. Gildardo Magaña had turned a light on in his mind, and never again would he stumble in ignorance through a world he could not see. No. The doors to truth lay open now.

He straightened up, struck a match, and sat over his tiny table staring at the paper and the pen beside it. Finally he picked it up, dipped it, and added to the first line:

When man was born he was not born alone,

Again he could not finish, so he blew out the light and lay back. How long had he been locked up? It was nearly December. June to December, without hope, without friends, without a part in the world. Without . . .

It was funny to think of saying: without Luz. *Luz* meant

Light, and he'd just been thinking happily about that Light in his mind. *Women,* he thought. They're so strange. Such funny, little things. Just a pretty face, and a warm body. *Pero demonio!* The trouble we go through for them. And he thought: *Cabrón,* I wish I had one right now. What I wouldn't do to her!

How many women had he had in his life? God knew, but not enough of them. There could never be enough for a man who felt about them as he did.

For a long, delicious moment he lay there, imagining that his hand was roving over those warm, delightful mounds and heated valleys, feeling again the wonderful sensation of a full erection. He wasn't an institution or a symbol now. He was a man. A creature filled with yearning and longing to act as his desires dictated.

Damn them! Damn their rotten plots and machinations. Damn the Orozcos and Díaz's and Huertas, and all of their stinking ambitions that corrupted and killed and enslaved! He was a man, and he would show them. They had driven him into the hills, like an animal. And caged him, like an animal. And ignored him, like an animal. Yes, well, even the animal could feel love and loneliness, and scorn, and desperation, and cruel needs. But he wasn't an animal now. He knew it. He swore it. Goddamn them all! He was a man, not a beast. A man!

XIV. "WELL, THERE GOES VILLA'S MOUSTACHE!"

HE'D BEEN WATCHING THE YOUNG MAN for a while now and had managed to learn something about him. He was slender, pale and earnest. His name was Carlos Jáuregui, and he was employed by the Third Military Judicial Tribunal as a copying clerk. A job which paid him 40 *pesos* a month. It was scarcely a fortune, and the boy looked it. He was haggard, his clothes were frayed and he seemed in need of a good meal.

To make extra money the young clerk came back late each evening and hired himself out to lawyers and prisoners. He would write letters and typewrite appeals. In this way he could perhaps double his income.

Pancho's cell was on the main floor at the end of a corridor formed by a blank wall on one side and four cells on the other. The other three cells had been unoccupied for some time. At the end of the cellblock, and facing directly into a dark hallway stood a tall iron grille. This divided the cells from the administrative section of the penitentiary. Beyond these offices numerous halls led directly to the street along which Carlos Jáuregui arrived each night.

Carlos was sitting preparing for some work one day, when he chanced to glance up and saw a prisoner staring at him from behind the grille. It was the *guerrillero* of whom he'd heard so much, Francisco Villa.

"Good afternoon, friend," said Villa. "I wonder if you could do me the kindness of copying a letter for me?"

His voice, Jáuregui would remember later, was pleasant and folksy to the Mexico City ear. His manner, for a man of his reputation, had been almost self-effacing. Carlos was flattered to hear himself addressed as an equal and easily entered into conversation with the famous prisoner.

Next afternoon, when Jáuregui returned, the friendly chat was continued: "Say, *muchacho,* what's the matter? *Porqué te ves tan triste?* Why do you look so sad?"

"Nothing, General. I'm always like this."

"Well, if you're always like this, it means there's always something the matter. Come on. What is it. Maybe I can help you out."

His tone, half rough, half affectionate, gave the boy a feeling that Villa really cared what happened to him. That day, as Carlos left, the *guerrillero* pressed a bill into his palm.

"For that work you did, *amigo*. And a little something so you can cheer yourself up."

Outside Carlos opened the bill, and gasped. "A hundred *peso* note! God!" He'd never had so much money, at once, in his life. And just for copying a letter.

By the following evening Pancho Villa could see by the young clerk's face that he'd made a new friend, and when the boy tried to give back the money, Villa laughed and slipped another 100 *pesos* into his hand.

"But, it's too much money, General," the boy complained.

"Listen, Carlitos. I've got plenty, so why shouldn't you enjoy some of it? Anyway, you could do me a great favor—if you like."

"Anything, *mi general*. You just name it."

"*Whoa, amigo*. One little moment there. This favor might require plenty of guts. If you're not a brave man, it's better not to talk about it."

"Well, I know you're a good man, General," said Carlos. "And you wouldn't ask me to do anything wrong. That's the most important thing. As for courage—I've got as much as any man."

Villa smiled appreciatively. "I believe you, Carlitos. As for rights and wrongs, well, you've been writing up my trial. Do you think it's right for the government to keep me here?"

"No, General. I don't."

"Don't you think it's a frame-up?"

"Yes, I do."

"Then, don't you think I should take things into my own hands, since the judges won't release me?"

Carlos Jáuregui thought for a moment, then said: "Yes, I do."

"Then it wouldn't be wrong for my friends to help me out of this hole, would it Carlitos?"

"I think it would be right," said Jáuregui.

Villa grinned. "Well, sir. Then you're going to help me, because you're my friend. You and me alone, Carlitos. Yes?"

Carlos swallowed and appeared stunned, but he nodded.

"Good," said Villa taking a small package from under his

coat and passing it through the bars to the young clerk. "Now, pay attention, *muchacho*. This is how it's going to work . . ."

Villa's plan, as outlined to Carlos, was so obvious as to be ingenious. Each evening when Jáuregui arrived now, he was to saw through two bars in the front grille, using the iron saw in the package, and filling the cuts with black wax (also in the package) to make them invisible. There was oil to keep the sawing quiet in case of wandering prison guards, and a whisk-broom to sweep up the filings. There would be eight bars to saw in four visits.

The clerk was nervous, but loyal. Each evening now he arrived, checked the halls, and set to work quietly and methodically. Villa, who had rented a typewriter, sat in his cell, working away at his typewriting lessons. The guards paid scant attention to the busy clerk.

"Well, friend Carlos," said Villa cheerfully on the fifth afternoon. "I'm getting pretty clever at this machine-writing business. How are things with you?"

"Fine, *general*," said the boy. "In fact, I've just finished a very important job, and I'm ready for other things."

"You're a brave boy, *amigo*," said Villa guardedly. "Tomorrow then. When you come in, check the hallway fast, then get in here. I'll be waiting. And not a sign to anyone, eh?"

Villa stood like a shadow, next evening, when Carlos arrived and gave him a nod. Quickly, the *guerrillero* tossed off the *sarape* he'd worn over his shoulders and unrolled a large, Spanish cape —such as many judges and attorneys wore. Inside the cape was a bowler hat. Villa put both on rapidly, before removing the eight bars and slipping through. Then he deftly replaced the bars, which hung in place because of the wax. "*Bueno, muchacho.* Let's walk. And don't stop for anything."

"*Sí, señor,*" said Jauregui nervously.

Villa walked down the first corridor, with Carlos just behind him. But turning a corner, toward the street entrance, a lone guard appeared, and Carlos froze. "Come on, my friend, we'll be late," said Villa calmly lighting a cigar he'd thoughtfully added to his disguise. The guard, scarcely noticing the two "lawyers," continued his walk.

"Some friend," said Pancho outside. "I thought I told you not to stop for anything?"

"I got scared," said the boy meekly.

"Well, you nearly scared me out of this silly outfit, and back into the *calabozo.*"

Hurrying through the semi-darkness of the lamplighted city streets, they saw a motor-cab, and Villa hailed it. "Take us to Tacubaya," he said urgently. "And fast. It won't be too expensive, will it?"

"Naw, chief. Not at all."

At Tacubaya, Villa told the driver to wait while he dashed through the gates of a large house, then out again, with the puzzled Carlos following.

"Well," said Villa to the driver. "We just missed the fellow. He's on his way to Toluca, and I've got to see him. Is the trip expensive? If it's too much, maybe I'd better—"

"No, no, *jefe,*" said the driver eagerly. "It's cheap."

"Really cheap?"

"Sure. For you gentlemen—I'll make it very special."

At Toluca Villa paid the driver, then gave him an extra 10 peso note. "Look, *amigo.* Tomorrow my friend and me are returning to the city. You pick us up, right here at four sharp, and there'll be a bigger tip yet. *Bien?*"

"*Muy bien, señor.* You can count on me."

"But you won't raise your price on me, will you?"

"Me? Never, *señor.* You are safe with me always. *Adiós!*"

That night, on a train for Manzanillo, Carlos Jáuregui sat limp in the compartment, staring at the *guerrillero.* "My God, *mi general.* In the midst of all that—I just can't get over it—in the midst of disaster, and you bargaining with that driver for a few *centavos.*"

"You've got something to learn, *muchacho.* Particularly about escaping prisoners. Tell me, how many of them stop to bargain with cabdrivers, eh?"

"But, why did you tell him to come back for us?"

Villa laughed. *"Pero, muchachito.* What am I going to do with you, my innocent baby? Do prisoners usually drive back, next day, to the place they started from? And while the *gendarmes* are puzzling that one, we'll be on a boat, on the way to Mazatlán."

"And then, *mi gene—*"

"Demonio, muchacho. Start getting used to it. My name is Doroteo Arango . . . And then—well, to Nogales. And over the *gringo* border on a cattle-buying trip . . . if you know what I mean."

"Dios mío, I didn't bargain for so much!"

Pancho Villa rose and took a small box from his cape pocket.

"Come, Carlitos," he said, setting his shaving gear by the tiny washbowl and mirror. "Isn't any freedom better than bars—or copying cockeyed court orders forever at 40 *pesos* a month?"

"Anything's better. Yes," replied Jáuregui bitterly.

"Amigo," said the *guerrillero* turning to the boy. "I'll never forget what you did for me. For starters, you have my word that when I take Juárez, you'll get the gambling concession, free and clear. Everything but poker and roulette. They'd corrupt you— and, besides, I promised those to my brother, Hipólito. But you'll be rich enough, don't worry."

"Pay or no pay, *general,"* said Carlos. "I don't regret it. And I'd do it again."

Pancho Villa's grim face softened. "Goddammit, Carlitos. You're a *man,"* he said proudly. And turning to the mirror he began soaping, then stropping the straight razor.

"Well, there goes Villa's moustache!" he said, leaving his long, straight lip bare. "It's a shave, my friend, that somebody's going to find very expensive."

2

Pancho Villa's sensational escape had taken place the evening of December 26th, and the authorities had promised an "early apprehension of the fugitive."

On the morning of December 29th, a cold, squally day, a clean-shaven, professional-looking gentleman in his mid-thirties, very elegantly dressed, left the passenger steamer *Ramón Corral,* at the port of Mazatlán. With him was a young gentleman, apparently his secretary, for they were overheard discussing the current listings on cattle and grain.

That night they passed Guaymas, and by next morning they were leaving Hermosillo—halfway across Sonora, the Mexican state which bordered Arizona.

Everywhere in Mexico, for the past three days, the big excitement had been the mysterious "disappearance" of Pancho Villa. He was rumored everywhere in Mexico City, and the vicinity, where the police and army promised now "the earliest possible apprehension of the fugitive."

The tall, curly-haired man in the bowler and Spanish cape sat munching from a bag of sugar-candy, while daydreaming of peanut-brittle and seeing an American Western film. He'd eaten brittle many times in Juárez, and seen several movies starring William S. Hart, and now he was addicted to both, as he could never be to liquor or gambling.

Beside him sat a worried young man, and across from them an obese and aging gentleman who had all the earmarks of a wealthy merchant.

"Look here," said the fat man, putting his paper down with horror in his face. "That wretched bandit's still loose."

"Incredible," said Villa.

"Yes, quite incredible, with the whole world hunting for him. You know, the superstitious Indians say he's got the devil's mark tattooed on his back, and he can't be killed. Not till his fiendish master's ready to take him below. *Por Dios,* I'm almost ready to believe it."

"Absolutely true," said Villa, his eyes twinkling with what the stranger took for a touch of mystery. "I once saw it."

"Saw what?" asked the stranger intently.

"Well, that mark."

"You knew this murderer?"

"He's nearly gotten me killed. Several times."

"Jesus protect us. What luck. And each time you managed to escape."

"Exactly."

"Mother of God!" said the man crossing himself hurriedly. "Well, here is my stop, gentlemen. What a frightening story. I shall have nightmares. Well, *adiós, señores.* Be very careful."

"*Gracias, amigo.* Will you take some candy?"

"Alas, no," said the merchant staring tragically down at his girth. "But I thank you. You are a true and gracious gentleman. Remember, *señores.* Suspect everyone. That maniac, Villa, would think nothing of leveling you right on the spot!"

3

After facing a firing squad, seven months of prison and the loss of everything he owned, Pancho Villa was across the border and safe. Yet, despite his obvious abandonment by the man he'd valued most, Pancho's first concern was for Madero.

From El Paso, Texas, where he'd registered in a small hotel under the name of Arango, Villa composed and sent messages to Governors Abraham Gonzáles and Maytorena, urging them to warn President Madero of impending treachery. He was convinced, by now, that old Bernardo Reyes had known what he was talking about—and was the key to the next revolt.

"They're preparing it right under his nose," Villa warned. "They're hatching it right in the barracks, and in the prisons. Tell him to move, right now, and smash them!"

But it did no good. Either his warnings never got to Madero, or else Madero was too involved to pay attention.

XV. DAWN OF THE 10 DAYS

PRESIDENT FRANCISCO INDALECIO MADERO had scant time to ponder
what incorrigibly rebellious twist of mind had prompted Pancho
Villa's astonishing escape before the usual monument dedications
and state dinners which tended to fill the holiday season fell on
him.

Some sinister—possibly dangerous—indications of internal
plots to overthrow the government had crossed his desk, but
neither Madero's agents, the army, nor the police had been able
to penetrate, or even find the source of these rumors. The
complex machinations remained, for the time being, at least, in
the realm of supposition.

The holidays were pleasant enough, and spent with *señora*
Madero. The gentle General Felipe Angeles had left his post
as head of the Federal Military Academy to take command of the
tedious campaign against the Zapatistas in the south. A splendid
banquet was arranged to honor Gustavo, the president's older
brother who was soon to depart for Japan as ambassador, and
Félix Díaz, the insurgent general, had been transferred from a
prison in Veracruz to the Federal Penitentiary in Mexico City.

The President, ever kind, ever thoughtful of his people, tried
to improve their lot, but opposition from the "Conservatives"
(the Porfiristas, under their new guise) was stiffening. On February 5, 1913, the smiling chief executive and his cabinet
attended ceremonies to honor the Mexican Constitution before
the statue of Benito Juárez. As Francisco Madero left the crowd,
waving his top hat, an official photographer snapped his picture,
thus recording the last public act Madero would ever perform.

What became known in Mexican history as *The 10 Tragic
Days* commenced at dawn on February 9, 1913, with the
seizure of the National Palace by the cadets of the Federal
Military Academy. Simultaneously, a regiment of cavalry, and

one of artillery, departed Tacubaya. One column proceeded to Tlaltelolco, and released General Bernardo Reyes, the other went to the Federal Penitentiary, where Félix Díaz and his cohorts were liberated. These mutinous government forces, under Generals Manuel Mondragón, Gregorio Ruiz, Manuel Velázquez, and others marched back toward the Palace, not realizing that the cadets had already repented and surrendered to loyal government contingents.

Old and plump General Ruiz was the first to be surprised. Riding in advance of his regiment he saw the troops spread along the ground and on top of the National Palace, but mistook their significance. Minutes later he was a prisoner and on his way to a firing squad by order of the Minister of War, General Angel García Peña.

General Reyes, thinking Ruiz in possession, now placed himself at the head of the rebels for a triumphant entrance, only to be met, instead, by Commandant of the Plaza, General Lauro Villar, who called on him to surrender. In the resulting skirmish General Villar fell gravely wounded, and General Bernardo Reyes fell dead—an old man's hunger for power finally stopped by bullets.

When he heard the news, General Mondragón, head of the rebellious forces, ordered a withdrawal, and took possession of *Ciudadela*—the ancient fort converted into a government arsenal —with all his men, their cannon, and machineguns.

At this point, in the early morning, President Madero left his home, in Chapultepec Castle, accompanied by General Huerta and a cadet escort, and rode toward his offices in the *Palacio Nacional*. At the city's edge the party heard firing and realized, for the first time, that there was fighting in the streets of the capital. Within the hour, *don* Francisco was meeting with members of his cabinet, and his military staff, to formulate a defense.

"With General Mondragón in firm command of 1500 soldiers, and a stout fortress," worried Madero, "we're not in a good position. How many troops can we count on, *mi general?*" he asked the aged Minister of War, Angel García Peña.

"About 2,000, your excellency. Certainly not sufficient for an adequate defense."

Madero agreed. "And with General Villar all but dead, our prospects are bad."

"I know one man who could take your troops and stop this damned rebellion," said Huerta.

Everyone present turned to the pugnacious little Indian.

"You do?" asked Madero. "And who is that, sir?"

"Myself, sir!" snapped Huerta. "Given the proper authority, I could squelch this simpleton's uprising faster than I smashed Orozco. I know Mondragón, Velázquez and Díaz. I've never seen the day I couldn't out-think or out-fight the lot of them."

"And just what is this 'proper authority' you allude to?" asked the War Minister.

"Command of the Plaza, sir. General Villar is dying and incapable of doing anything more. You need a man here who can move aggressively and decisively. Give me a few days—two days —and I'll drag those filthy traitors, Mondragón and Díaz, out of the *Ciudadela* and into a prison cell with my own hands!"

As Huerta spoke a light of hope was appearing in the eyes of Madero. Of course. How could he have overlooked this small, fierce man whose experience and determination had brought the tough Orozco to heel?

"Sir," replied Madero, extending his hand to Huerta. "As of this moment you have both the authority—and my undying gratitude—for your actions on behalf of our country!"

Huerta took the hand and smiled from behind those dark glasses.

2

Mexico City was paralyzed. Except for troops and occasional ambulances searching the residential sections for the wounded, the streets were deserted. The situation was desperate when *presidente* Madero decided to visit Cuernavaca and then to return with General Angeles and the 2,000 troops previously committed to combat Zapata.

"But you can't," argued Gustavo. "The danger is too great. What if Angeles is pledged to the rebels?"

"The very reason I must go myself," replied Madero. "I know Angeles. He's an honest man, and I must convince him, no matter what, that General Huerta and I need him desperately."

3

With his customary—if somewhat alcoholic—vigor, General Victoriano Huerta waited for no man's help. At 10 A.M., February 11, he stood beside the last of the field artillery batteries he had inspected since dawn, and watched the vanguard of the rebel Felicistas (it was now: "Félix Díaz for President!") coming up the deserted streets toward his barricades. As he'd surmised, Díaz and Mondragón had heard of Madero's ride for help and had decided to act before reinforcements could arrive.

"*Capitán,*" he ordered the battery commander. "Open fire on those troops."

With this, the bombardment of the *Ciudadela,* of the rebels and of Mexico City's innocent population began. Huerta had placed batteries near San Diego Street, Ferrocarril Nacional, the national railroad, the Hotel Imperial, the Cafe Colón, the National Theatre, San Juan de Letrán, Niño Perdido, and Calle de Lucerna, among other key locations, and these joined the bombardment. Before the first day of shelling and fighting was over, more than 500 men, women and children would be dead.

4

Presidente Madero returned on the 14th to find the city in shambles. The breakdown of Public Services resulted in garbage piled along the curbs. Gutted buildings stood like skeletons suspended against the sky. Dead soldiers, drenched with gasoline and set afire on the spot to prevent disease, formed little heaps of charred matter, marking the progress of the fighting. Huerta's bombardment and Mondragón's reply had been relentless and insane. But no man could prove either had been unnecessary.

Immediately upon his arrival with the Cuernavaca contingent, General Felipe Angeles was designated Deputy Commandant by Madero and assigned to the siege of the *Ciudadela*. It was General Huerta's war now and he was literally calling the shots.

What Angeles saw there disturbed him deeply. A sensitive and educated man, he was everything Navarrete had once described to Villa, and more. A career officer, without politics, Angeles had no admiration for those generals who felt compelled to interfere with government functions. That Huerta was one of these, Angeles had long suspected. Yet he'd never felt it his place to correct his fellows or to gossip. Now, however, he was so repelled by Huerta's savage measures without regard for the helpless civilians that he quietly said so—an attitude which scarcely endeared him to the bombastic martinet.

Huerta: short, cocky, blasphemous; a fiery personality in khaki uniform, snap-cap and puttees. Angeles: tall, slender, refined; a thoughtful man, a troubled man in the white uniform and pith-helmet of the southern regions. On these two, the future of Madero's government now rested.

5

"I'm almost certain of it," said Gustavo Madero to his brother. "Haven't you noticed the order in which he has committed the troops? Those foremost, in the most bloody assaults against the Felicistas, are invariably the regiments filled and captained by our original people; the revolutionaries from the 1910 fighting. What one might call your hard core Maderistas."

"But they are the best troops," said Madero trying to think logically. "General Huerta warned me these attacks on the *Ciudadela* would be bloody."

"Suicidal is a better word!" snapped Gustavo. "I tell you he's purposely, and systematically, destroying your most loyal men. Throwing them away. Wave after wave of them. Letting them

One of Pancho Villa's "fruit-trees." These are Federal
soldiers executed by the Centaur after the capture of a town.
Pancho wasted neither rope nor bullets on his enemies.

Dead rebels after a battle.

The magnificent *División del Norte* in the field. Photo shows only a portion of one brigade. Note artillery in foreground, plus cavalry (rallied around flags near horizon).

Villista officers in the field. As Villa's armies expanded, huge Mexican sombreros were replaced by smaller Stetsons, as shown above. Notice excellent quality of mounts.

Rebels traveling "first class" to war. Developing transportation techniques later used in Europe (men on top, horses inside). Mexican rebel armies acquired great mobility.

One of Pancho Villa's famed cannon trains. Note small openings for rifle defense of artillery piece all around the armored walls. Piece could be serviced under small-arms fire.

Unidentified Rebel officer.
Clearly a *vaquero* (cowboy),
as seen from his clothes and
accouterments. These field-
hardened types gave Villa his
finest, most dedicated
combat leaders.

Unidentified Durango fighter,
obviously of good breeding and
family, judging from his clothes
and weapons. Such dedicated
young men made up the bulk
of Villa's staffs.

Pancho Villa shown here on his horse, Seven Leagues.
This was the rebel's favorite photograph of himself.

Some "Brothers of the Cucaracha" gather to sing their unhappiness
away en route to another bloody campaign. These cowboys,
farmers and other hard-working Mexican classes made up the armies
of Pancho Villa.

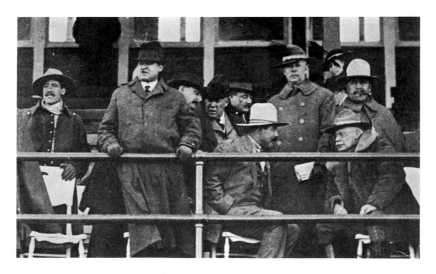

Generals Francisco (Pancho) Villa and Hugh L. Scott seen as they
conferred in Juárez, Mexico. As a representative of President
Wilson, General Scott's mission was to bring about peace between the
Villistas and the Carranzistas; but the breach was, by then, too great.
Between them is seen Scott's aide, a Major Mickie. Immediately behind
General Scott stands Rudolfo Fierro. He was never far from his "jefe."

Pershing's Punitive Expedition searching Chihuahua for
Pancho Villa. Such rugged terrain, plus Villa's knowledge of it doomed
the Yanqui effort from the start.

Pancho Villa in retirement, at Canutillo. Taken in 1920, this photo shows some
of the *guerrillero's* personal staff. Seated (left to right) General Ricardo Michel,
Colonel Miguel Trillo, Villa, Generals Nicolas Fernández, Sostenes Garza, Porfilio
Ornelas. Standing (left to right) José Nieto, Colonel Ramón Contreras, Daniel
Tamayo, Colonel José Juáriette, Alfonso Gómez M., General Lorenzo Avalos,
General José García, Colonel Ernesto Rios, Colonel Silvero Tavares, Ramón
Cordova, Daniel Delgado.

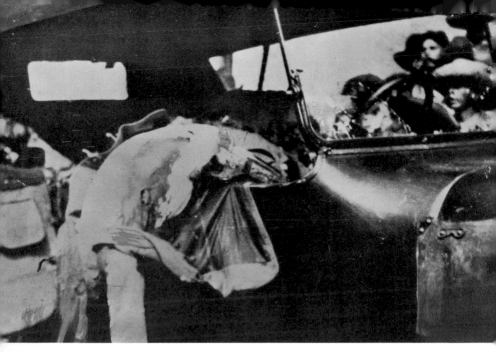

Eight a.m., July 20, 1923. Trillo has fallen backwards, over the door, his pistol still in its holster. Villa slumps against Trillo's lower body. A bodyguard lies crumpled in the rear seat. The eternal spectator is already there. Within half an hour of the ambush an enterprising photog was on the spot selling souvenir photos like this one.

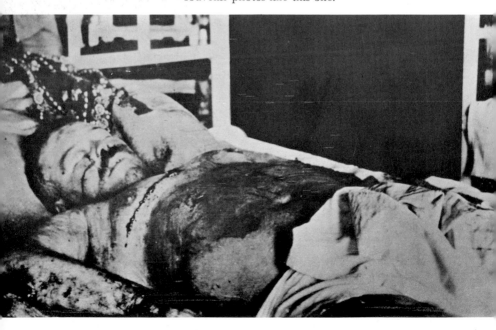

The end of the *guerrillero*. The body lies in the Hotel Hidalgo, which Villa owned, in Parral, Chihuahua.

and the Felicistas slaughter each other, while the men under his personal command remain intact. Look how he's changed the Presidential guard. General Blanquet, that fat conniver, guarding you. And with Huerta troops."

"What of General Angeles? He's loyal."

"What can he do? Huerta has virtually assimilated Angeles' command into his own. General Angeles is as blind as you are."

"Then we must do something, and fast!" said Madero, finally alarmed.

"I fully intend to," said Gustavo, straightening his pince-nez decisively. "General Huerta has invited me to dinner this evening at the Restaurant Gambrinus. I intend to be there and to discover what sort of business he's really up to."

"But . . . would it be wise, under the circumstances?"

"What could happen?" asked Gustavo scornfully. "After all, this is a civilized city, and we will be in public . . ."

6

Gustavo Madero, tall and reserved, watched his host, General Victoriano Huerta sipping onion soup and port. But beyond the old soldier's repeated assurances of his absolute determination to "vanquish the damned traitors!" he learned little else.

Dining with them was *señor* Adolfo Basso, caretaker of the *Palacio Nacional,* and a loyal Maderista who had personally manned a machinegun during Bernardo Reyes' march on the capital.

The late afternoon ground by in boredom. They attempted to leave, but Huerta, with many pleas, detained them. Finally he agreed it was growing late. Everyone made polite excuses. They shook hands. But as Gustavo and Basso called for their hats, General Huerta spotted a party of other friends and joined them.

Shortly after 4 o'clock of February 17th, Gustavo Madero and Adolfo Basso left the fashionable restaurant and were promptly intercepted outside by a detachment of plainclothesmen and driven to rebel headquarters at the *Ciudadela.* There

Gustavo learned what he'd been unable to discover at dinner: that *señor general don* Victoriano Huerta and *generales* Manuel Mondragón and Félix Díaz had—sometime in the previous days —"reached an understanding." The fighting now was only for show. The revolt had ended that very afternoon, at 3 o'clock. General Huerta had "accepted" the Presidency of Mexico in return for a full pardon to the beseiged Felicista generals. It only remained now to make the "acceptance" a concrete fact by removing the existing President. And then to make it public.

XVI. THE PEANUT-BRITTLE EATER

MR. ARANGO, his landlady concluded, was a "nice gentleman." He never drank, smoked, consorted with questionable females or kept late hours. Yet, he certainly had his own share of "mild" peculiarities. For example, he'd told her his stomach was in "terrible condition," and that his doctor had prescribed tender, young pigeons. But the cage of birds sat there, still full, while each morning his waste basket was filled with empty tins of sardines, baked beans, asparagus and boxes of peanut brittle.

Then, too, Mr. Arango was always writing letters and haunting the mailbox. He'd even procured one of those typewriting machines and seemed determined to beat it half to death.

Mr. Arango didn't strike her as "educated," but he sure was refined. He dressed wonderfully, in Norfolk tweeds, silk cravats, high, shiny shoes and was always barbered and spiffy to within an inch of his life. And so friendly. Unless you counted those days when his young friend, Mr. Jáuregui, visited him, which were followed by afternoons and nights of pacing and muttering over the *El Paso Herald*. And then that awful look in his eyes, fit to freeze a person's blood right in her veins!

He was, after all, a Mexican. Not one of those ordinary greasers, but still a Mex fellow. And Lord! when those half-civilized people got their Injun up, heaven only knew who might end up with their throat slit!

The afternoon of January 10, one week after Mr. Arango's arrival, the landlady noticed two suspicious-eyed Americans across the street by a lamp-post. When Mr. Arango left, they followed him. The lady noted these strangers carefully. One was tall and spare, wore a homburg and round frame glasses. The other was younger and bigger, with red hair, a brown bowler and a suit which seemed too small. She worried because it was no secret that Mr. Arango went around well supplied with money.

Through the following week she saw the men loitering about. Poor Mr. Arango. They even followed him into the movie. She knew, because she often followed *them*.

El Paso, Texas, in early 1913, might have been described as a "little-big city." Possessing all the modern conveniences, such as streetcars, electricity, automobiles, hotels and motion picture houses, it was still no more than a ten minute stroll from the center of the Plaza to the edge of town. Understandably, it wasn't difficult for Mr. Arango's landlady to know much of her boarder's activities. Any afternoon he might be seen in the Elite Confectionary enjoying a banana split—and right outside, across the corner of Mesa and Oregon, one of those gimlet-eyed shadows would be waiting.

She was positive that the bulges in her lodger's pockets were caused by two enormous Colt pistols. Perhaps he was really a secret Mexican agent hunting down some American desperadoes who had robbed a bank in his country. And those two criminals were on to him, just waiting their chance to do him in. During their long vigils she observed their close-set eyes and unusually long earlobes, from behind her curtains. Definitely ruthless types. Mr. Arango, although a Mexican, had the warmest, most twinkly eyes. It was clear where her loyalties lay.

It was all quite disappointing. When she finally told her chilling story to Mr. Arango, he smiled, thanked her in his broken English, and offered her a piece of peanut brittle.

2

"It's getting worse every day, Carlitos. They're so close I have to watch every move I make. I'm scared to go to the toilet for fear I'll find one in my pants."

"But are you sure they're *gringo* Secret Service agents?"

"Certainly I'm sure, boy. That big redhead puts me to bed, and *señor* Homburg wakes me up. If I slipped on a banana peel I'd squash one of the bastards. *Óyeme, muchacho.* Listen boy, we've got to be very careful but work faster. I can't afford to be deported. If those two *gringos* catch me at it, *reata!* Internment at Fort Bliss and back to Tlaltelolco—or worse."

"What do you want me do to, Pancho?"

"I want you to contact Governor Maytorena from the Juárez side and press him for an answer. Also press Governor González. Tell them there's no time to waste, or there won't be a President Madero anymore. He'll be up here, with us, and we'll have Díaz —or somebody like him—back again."

"I'll cross tonight, Pancho," said Jáuregui.

"We'll leave together," said Villa. "You make sparks for the border, while I take my redheaded *gringito* for a walk. I'll be at the Mexican Club, at the southern end of town, in case anything comes up. Tell the boys. And tell them to be patient."

3

Villa sat in the Mexican Club, in the sector of El Paso known as "Little Chihuahua." He had been staring at the tiny bubbles in a glass of strawberry pop, almost hypnotized into serenity by the frantic climb of thousands of those little bubbles to the top, when he sensed the presence of the man.

"Good evening, *mi general*," said the man with a slight bow and an accent, neither of which went with Spanish. "Might I intrude, my General?"

"You might. Except that I'm not a general, and I'm waiting for a friend—who is also not a general. Some other time."

The man laughed, a deep-bellied laugh, his blondish, up-turned moustache fluttering with fun. "Ah, one cannot take too many precautions. And quite rightly. The Chinese have some sort of saying about it . . ."

"I don't like Chinamen," said Villa, "and I don't care what they have to say. I'm waiting for a friend."

"And what if *I* turned out to be that friend?" said the man confidentially. "What if I, a warmhearted man, with his heart on the right cause, and his fingers on several million *pesos,* told you I am that man you have been waiting for?"

"My friend is darker than you. She is also prettier and has a hell of a lot of things you don't have."

"Ahhh," said the man sitting unbidden. "I have heard some little things about a certain personage's amorous adventures. It's good to have time for those little things."

"Just tell me what you want," said Villa. "As long as you're already sitting down, let's have what you want. I'm not as clever or well informed as you seem to be. Let me ask you who you are, who you think you're talking to, and why."

"I have arranged that we won't be disturbed. The orchestra will play loud music, and . . ."

"Look friend, don't be more clever. Just answer."

The man looked indignant, then hurt, then philosophical. "Suffice it to say that I am the representative for a most important power. A certain European power which has—shall we say —the deepest and most sincere interest in the affairs of your nation."

"What would your power like to steal: the oil? the minerals? the cattle interests?"

"Ah, General. You're a born joker. A sense of humor keeps a man fresh for the awesome responsibilities of state. Actually, my country wants to see your country prosper for herself. See her fight her way up from the mud of domination and tyranny. We admire you, General. We feel that—"

"What do you want?"

"We are prepared to back your struggle for the Presidency of Mexico with troops, money, armament and propaganda."

"What do you want? Oil?"

"We would crush your most stubborn opposition. Drive them out for you or give you—mind you, give you—the means of driving them out yourself."

"Minerals? Land?"

"An insignificant concession . . ."

"What?"

"Simply sign a treaty with my nation, assuring her of—of a few submarine bases. A few refueling stations for our battle-cruisers . . ."

"You're not a Spaniard because you don't lisp. And you're not an Englishman because you don't talk through your nose . . ." said Villa, staring at his visitor.

"I, sir, am a German. It is Germany who shall save you, my General. Our glorious Kaiser's understanding and . . ."

"What will you do with those bases. Attack the *gringos?*" asked Villa, grinning horribly.

"Certainly not!" said the man outraged. "Our aims are simply peaceful aims of commerce."

"Don't feed me that crap, *amigo*. I've been reading about your Kaiser. First a war in Europe. Then you hit the *gringos*. Then we all learn German. All with Pancho's help."

"Preposterous!" said the man half standing.

"What if I let you in, and the *gringos* hit me? Then what?"

"We protect you, of course."

"How?"

"We'll have ships in your harbors."

"But they just walk across the Rio Grande, *amigo*."

"We'd have troops. Many divisions. Overwhelming power!"

"Ah," said Villa grinning. "Machineguns and cannon all along the border—the way President Taft set them on us when we took Juárez, eh?"

"Certainly, do you think the German Imperial Staff is a pack of fools?" said the man, aroused.

"The peaceful aims of commerce don't sound so peaceful anymore. Those same guns that keep the *gringos* out, might keep the Mexicans in, *señor Alemán. No es verdad?*"

The German sat stiffly in the booth, staring at Villa as a fascinated rabbit might stare at a snake.

"Since I am a reasonable man, *señor,*" said Villa slowly, "I'm going to give you three reasons for my answer: *Primero,* I'm a guest of the *gringitos* here, and good guests do not pay with treachery. *Segundo,* Mexico has kicked out the French, the Austrians and the Spaniards. And that's three too many. *Tercero . . .*"

Pancho Villa rose slowly, took the man by the lapels and dragged him out of the booth. Firmly, moving faster as he went, he propelled the man to the edge of the stairway, then planted a foot squarely on the seat of his pants.

"*Tercero,* I told you, in the first place, that you were talking to the wrong man."

It might have seemed a vulgar and undiplomatic gesture to *Herr* General Maximilian Kloss, but it was immensely satisfying to Villa. The German suppressed a cry and went headfirst down the stairs. Pancho Villa returned to his booth to finish his soda—the world little noting that the Monroe Doctrine had just received a helping foot from a peasant of Durango.

XVII. NIGHT OF THE 10 DAYS

PRESIDENT FRANCISCO MADERO was concerned about many things. The bombardment pained him, the suffering of the people haunted him, the conduct of his chief defender worried him. Deep in his mind lay the disturbing realization that he'd done many things quite badly. But he was confident in his heart that he'd been honest and had done his best.

Shortly after 3 P.M., while Madero conferred with his advisors in his *Palacio* conference room, Lieutenant Colonel Jiménez Riverol, aide to General Blanquet, rushed in with news that a newly arrived officer from Oaxaca, General Rivera, was ready to defect.

"Your Excellency, only you can prevent it!" Colonel Riverol assured Madero practically in tears. "General Huerta begs your help."

"You are right," said Madero. "Please take me to Rivera immediately."

They were leaving the chamber when word arrived by a trusted messenger that Gustavo Madero had been arrested. In that instant Francisco Madero saw the full plot—the removal of everyone closely concerned with the presidency.

In that instant, too, Jiménez Riverol yelled for a platoon of the 29th Battalion—members of Madero's own guard—which had waited outside the chamber doors. There was no question as to his intentions. As the soldiers broke in he was already calling as to a firing squad: *"Soldados! Apunten! Fue—"*

He never finished the final syllable. As he started to shout *"Fuego!"*—"Fire!" Captain Gustavo Garmandia, a member of Madero's staff, shot him dead. Instantly, Major Izquierdo, the platoon's commander, leaped forward attempting to continue the assassination, but Captain Federico Montez, another officer on Madero's staff, emptied his pistol into him.

In the ensuing confusion the mutinous soldiers fired at Madero, but *señor* Marcos Hernández, a friend of the President, leaped before him, taking the full discharge. He, too, died instantly. But it was enough to demoralize the murderous platoon which retreated as the president's adherents locked the chamber doors.

It was but a temporary damming of an inevitable torrent.

"So much blood's been spilt to make me president," wept the distraught Madero over his friend's body. "So much blood to keep me here. I can't face the thought of any further violence on my account."

Minutes later Madero went to the ground floor in the desperate hope of winning the loyalty of his Palace Guard. He was met by General Aureliano Blanquet, gun in hand, and placed under arrest. Vice President José María Pino Suárez was also apprehended and both were charged with "Treason to the Republic."

General Felipe Angeles returned from dinner to find a detachment of soldiers waiting to arrest him. The charge: insubordination. His own troops had been carefully diverted into other units, and there was little to do but submit.

Four months earlier Victoriano Huerta had smashed the tail of the Revolutionary snake. Now he had the head. His vision had been wrong in only one sense: he was not an "eagle," triumphant in combat. No. Far less than that. He was a vulture, feeding on a dying thing.

Shortly after dawn of February 18th, the bodies of Gustavo Madero and Adolfo Basso were discovered near the outskirts of the city. Both had been shot to death.

2

"My dear Suárez," said Francisco Madero. "In going over my life I can truly find little I'd change, had I the power. Is that the sign of vanity? I certainly hope not."

The aesthetic, young, half-Indian Vice President listened attentively, eyes fixed on the face of Madero. He shook his head sadly. "What did we do wrong?" he asked. "What was our crime? Why has God deserted us this way?"

"I still feel God with me," said Madero quietly. "As for our mistakes—I don't . . . see . . . what we did that was cruel, ungentlemanly, or dishonest. I've asked my conscience."

José María Pino Suárez sighed deeply.

"There was a man once," said Madero. "Someone, somewhere . . ." He shook his head, as if puzzled. "I wonder what will become of General Angeles? He's such a splendid person, really. Huerta . . . well, I don't know, Suárez. I can't believe this is what all our work comes to. Can you?"

"I don't know," said Suárez.

"Well, I do," said Madero suddenly cheering. "We'll be all right. We'll go to Cuba or England, or even Japan. Their ministers are with Huerta right now. It's just a matter of where— and when. We've been exiled before." His mood settled down and he added pensively: "Do you remember Juárez? You and I were going to save Mexico and do such glorious things. Victory seemed so bright then. Ten whole months ago. Please don't worry, my friend. I only hope they'll let our families go with us, Pino."

But Pino Suárez sighed and said nothing.

3

To The Congress:
In view of the events which have developed since yesterday, and in order to solve the grave problems which beset our nation, we hereby submit to the honorable Chamber of Deputies this formal resignation of our charges as Constitutional President and Vice President of the United States of Mexico. Submitted for legal process.—Mexico, February 19, 1913

—Francisco I. Madero
—J. M. Pino Suárez

4

It had been arranged with *señor* Manuel Marquez Sterling, Minister of Cuba, that Madero and Suárez would receive asylum in that country. But at the last minute General Huerta changed his mind and ordered the prisoners taken from their confinement in the *Palacio Nacional* to the penitentiary. They never arrived.

According to army Lieutenant Rafael Pimienta and Corporal Francisco Cárdenas of the *rurales*, joint commanders of the escort troops, an angry mob suddenly surrounded the car in which the prisoners rode—near the outskirts of the city—and in the melee numerous shots were fired into the vehicle, killing both the President and Vice President instantly. The killings were listed as "accidental." No arrests could be made.

Remarkably good fortune seemed to attend the careers of Lieutenant Pimienta and Corporal Cárdenas after this. In the following year, for example, both received repeated promotions until each had attained the rank of general. Victoriano Huerta, it would appear, valued faithful service.

XVIII. LITTLE WHITE BULLETS

"DESGRACIADOS ANIMALES!" he raged between clenched teeth. "Disgraced animals! Sons-of-their-tarnished-mothers! Oh, but they'll pay for this. Oh, God, how they'll pay for it!"

"It was an interesting campaign," said Manuel Ochoa. "The first I've ever seen in which both sides won. The only one who lost was Madero."

Pancho Villa crumpled the newspaper and hurled it at the floor. His eyes were bloodshot, his face swollen.

"Goddamn them," he moaned at the wall. "That man never did anything but good."

"He forgave too many people, Pancho. It's easy to plot against a man who won't kill a fly. Félix Díaz found it out. So did Reyes, and our friend, Huerta. One advantage to being born a bastard, there's no father to teach him ethics, no mother to teach him love, no God to teach him fear. He can start where his conscience lets him, and go while he has the strength. Look at Huerta. He broke the sugar-pot and whistled up the flies. And there they are."

"Pedro Lascuráin, Minister of Relations, was provisional president for 45 minutes after Madero's resignation," said Carlos Jáuregui to Villa, who was hearing the whole, sordid story for the first time. "Then General Huerta assumed the presidency by 'popular acclaim' of the Chamber of Deputies."

"Popular acclaim at bayonet point," said Ochoa. He was a hard, blunt, mud-colored man from Juárez who was no stranger to armed persuasion, and whom Villa considered a friend. "My God, Pancho," he said, grimacing, "it doesn't seem possible that men could be so shameless. Brother, I was raised in a hut, like you. My mother cooked *frijoles* in a tincan. But I was taught the value of human decency, of respect for other people. But these miserable—!"

"Madero, Suárez, Gustavo, Basso—and God knows how many faceless, voiceless poor people, lying in the streets," said Villa. "And for what? Where's the work we did, Manuel? Where's the liberty we bought with all that blood?"

"The flies have eaten it up, Pancho," said Ochoa.

"How did they do it to him, Manuel?"

"*Don* Francisco?" Ochoa shrugged. "The story I believe is that Huerta had Madero and Suárez driven to the army firing range. They woke them just before dawn, and told them they were going to the penitentiary. When they got to the range, that butcher, Cárdenas, ordered them out of the car. Neither of them knew what was happening until they saw their own escort raise their guns. And that was it."

"I tried to tell him," said Villa slumping on his bed and crying softly. "I tried to save him in every way I could. But he wouldn't let me."

"Well," said Ochoa. "Huerta won't have it all his way. There's a storm rising out of Coahuila, and from Sonora. Carranza's already denounced Huerta as an usurper, and Maytorena has joined him. They're calling on their anti-Orozco volunteers to lead the fight. Colonel Álvaro Obregón has already responded with his Fourth Sonora Battalion."

Villa roused himself angrily. "I'll go to Chihuahua City, see *don* Abraham and raise my own army. I can use his garrisons for a start. I'll be in the field within a week."

"That isn't possible," said Ochoa.

"And what's to stop me?"

"Governor González was arrested for attempted treason, and all Chihuahua is now under the military governorship of your old friend, General Antonio Rábago."

"A Huertista to the teeth!" said Villa.

"Exactly. So you see, it would be wiser to wait."

"Wait how long, *amigo?*"

"*Pues, amigo.* As long . . . as necessary."

"What you're saying is that there's no room for me," said Villa reading his friend's saddened eyes. "That there are younger roosters in the game, is that it?"

"Not younger, Pancho. But . . ."

"This Obregón. I've seen pictures of him. Sleek, like a well-fed cat. Curly moustaches and a fancy uniform. An irregular who affects all the regularities possible. Swords, medals, gold buttons and the fattest slender waist in Mexico. Is that what we're talking about?"

"He's a very good officer," said Ochoa. "In all fairness."

"And Carranza and Maytorena are educated men."

"The ways of war are changing, Pancho," said Manuel Ochoa. "Men like Obregón have studied the military styles of the French and Germans, their maneuvers in Europe. They understand . . ."

"What do I care about Germans and Frenchmen, and their

military pigstys?" said Villa. "What the hell does Obregoń or
Carranza, or that whole pack of perfumed *pendejos* know about
what's inside me? I fought to give Mexico a chance. I fought for
Madero because he believed in me. Yes, me. Villa! Do you think
he really forgot me? Don't you know he had to choose between
the country and me? Yes. And I thank God he chose the
country, because that showed me what sort of man he was."

Ochoa and Jáuregui stood back, seeing that the *guerrillero*
wasn't talking to them anymore, but to himself. And as he
talked he flailed the air with his powerful arms in a fury.

"The rest of those *paparruchos*. What did they ever know of
Madero's real feelings for Pancho Villa? They talk of war. They
talk of vengeance? They say there's no room in their Mexico for
a peasant. Do they think they've seen fighting? Do those Judases
in the Capital think they've seen blood? Well, not yet, they
haven't. Not if their French and German friends were to invent
a soldier that eats horses whole, and spits out cannons through
his teeth. No. Not if they've been in battle all their miserable
lives have they seen one drop of what they'll see when Pancho
Villa calls for revenge!"

He sat back down on the bed, slowly, still glaring directly into
the eyes of both men. "You think I'm crazy? *Loco?* Go ahead.
Say it. I sing, I cry, I talk, I dream with passion. And my soul is
all Mexican.

"Please, *por favor,* believe me," said Ochoa. "I know how you
feel."

"No," said Villa bitterly, "you don't. Or you would want to
kill someone right now."

2

A man sits alone in his room through a long, bitter day,
recalling other days, far away days of happiness and of hope. The
child of uncertainty, the youth in flight, the man embattled
have become the angry soldier.

But if he is a soldier without an army, he's not a soldier without hope. Throughout the width and length of Mexico are millions of peasants. Mixed with their red and humble blood flow the juices of rebellion. Alone, each rebel may be meaningless. Together they combine into a mighty, surging, irresistible torrent which can wash away the enemies of Mexico as filth is swept off by the rivers to the seas.

Pancho Villa knows the sources of this power. Now, once more, he will summon it up from the mountains of Durango, from the deserts of Chihuahua, from the villages of Zacatecas and the farms of San Luis Potosí. If he is denied an army by the *políticos,* he will go to the people. He will sound the Cry of War once more, and this time he will trust no man, forgive no crime and leave no enemy unscathed. His bitter heart will be a stranger to the cry for mercy.

Once decided on his course, the *guerrillero* frames a simple message, and through the night he sits copying it 20 times. There are that many pigeons in his cage, each brought from a different part of northern Mexico. Twenty little white bullets: soft and swift and deadly, and aimed at Huerta's heart.

Near the *Pueblo* of Carrizal, southward along the railline leading from Juárez and Samalayuca, a plowing man looks up to see a white speck high in the northern sky. Silently the slender dove approaches the field, fluttering low behind the crowning trees. The man observes the bird, able now to distinguish the soft, sharp beating of the wings against its body. He waits patiently as the traveler circles once more, finds its bearings, then glides gracefully onto the open perch of a wooden cage beside the adobe house.

The man whistles through his teeth and a woman emerges, followed by a small boy. *"Chole,"* he calls. *"La paloma ha vuelto.* The dove is back."

She lifts it from the roost and examines its legs, holding up something tiny for the man to see as he rushes up.

"Call Cayetano," he tells the boy. "Tell him I've got something he must read right away."

When Cayetano hurries up from a neighbor's house (he is

the man's younger brother, and the only one who has been to a
school) he studies the note carefully, his tongue between his
teeth, then reads aloud, pointing a finger at each word:

Arm yourselves and be ready when I come. Mexico needs us.
—Francisco Villa

"Chole," says the man. "Start jerking meat and grinding extra
maize for me and Cayetano. Tiburcio, dig up the rifles. You,
Cayetano, saddle the mare and go fetch the other men. Tell
them Pancho Villa is coming. Tell them we've got to do it all
over again."

3

On the night of March sixth, another blow was struck at
Villa's emotions, stoking the swift flames of vengeance which
were consuming him. *Don* Abraham González, who had dwelt
next to Madero in the *guerrillero's* heart, was ordered taken to
Mexico City from Chihuahua, by President Huerta, to be con-
fined in the penitentiary. Like so many others who had embarked on this now fateful journey, he never arrived.

As the prison detail reached the Mapula Station, *don* Abraham
was taken off, shot, and his body thrown under the wheels of
the train to make his death appear an accident. His severed
corpse was then buried along the railroad bed by orders of
Colonel Benjamín Camarena, Major Hernán Limón and Captain Federico Revilla, the "escort" commanders.

XIX. MONKEYS AND CATS

SHORTLY AFTER MIDNIGHT of March 23, 1913, the first horseman
broke cover and plunged across the chest high Rio Grande,
toward the shore of Los Partidos. On the Mexican side, he
spurred his mount into the trees, and past them, onto the open

field beyond. Still reconnoitering, he galloped the full width of the field, past the trees again, and along the riverbank, describing roughly an elliptical course which brought him to his starting point. From there he hooted softly, stood on his stirrups, and waved his hat.

Moments later seven other riders left the protection of the *Yanqui* shoreline, splashed across and joined the lone rider. They were Manuel Ochoa, Miguel Saavedra, Dario Silva, Carlos Jáuregui, Juan Dosal, Pedro Sapien and a man known only as Tomás N.

"*Bueno muchachos*. If my father was rich, I'd buy you all kisses. As things are, you have my undying gratitude. Let's go."

With 8 men, 8 horses, 8 Winchesters, 9 pistols, 36 *pesos* and a silver watch, General Francisco Villa had begun his personal invasion of Mexico.

Galloping through the farm country of northern Chihuahua the war party grew by ones and twos, and by morning they were nearly 20. Villa led them down the rail line. They commandeered new horses where they found them. By midday they'd dragged up volunteers from a dozen tiny settlements and were raising dust and excitement all down the line. The Cry of Revolution had penetrated the remote mountain *pueblos*, and mounted men stood ready by the roadside, waving weapons and shouting: "*Viva* Pancho Villa!" as the growing troop cantered up. Then they, too, joined in and turned southward.

At Samalayuca the troop picked up 50 men and went on to San Andrés. It was the first time Villa had seen Luz since her departure from Chihuahua City, and that night's brief reunion was beautiful for the *guerrillero*.

At San Andrés, too, Pancho learned that many of his old comrades had deserted the Federal army following his arrest, and were ready to rejoin him. Fidel Avila, a friend of his Juárez days, was now a colonel commanding the *federales* in Santa Isabel. Here Villa saw an opportunity to gain a real army, as he had in Parral, when Maclovio Herrera had left Orozco to join him.

"For the sleeping man the cock always crows too soon," said Villa. "Let's go to Santa Isabel and see how it's going to be with Ávila."

"And what if he's uncooperative?" said Ochoa.

"Let's go see," said Villa.

The *guerrillero's* luck held. As in Parral, he was suddenly in possession of a Federal garrison, 80 well-trained soldiers, machine-guns, and desperately needed supplies. Almost as important was Fidel Ávila, himself.

"*Hombre,* Fidel," said Villa as they exchanged backslapping hugs. "So they made you a *coronel, eh muchacho?*"

"Well," said Ávila sheepishly. "What can I tell you, Pancho? *Don* Francisco was kind to me, and Huerta hasn't found me out."

"Compared to that *piojo,* you should be a minister, at least," said Villa laughing. "Listen, *amigo.* Did you learn to march and salute, and all that cowdung?"

"*Pues,* you know the Federal army."

"How would you like to do me a favor, Fidel. One that will help the Revolution?"

"Name it, Pancho."

"Well then, I want you to make a camp for my troops. You give me your 80 men, I give you 100 of mine, and you teach my *pelados* how to act like real soldiers, eh?"

"You mean march, and bayonet drill, and all that?"

"I mean everything, *amigo.* Real soldiers. Good as any in the government. I want a military school started near Sotevo, because I'll have plenty of people coming in to join, and I want them to be the best. But the best, *amigo.* And you're going to teach them everything they taught you."

Ávila stared at the *guerrillero* in astonishment.

"Pancho, am I hearing things? Are you serious?"

"I haven't wasted my time, *amigo,*" said Villa pointedly. "Not in the *calabozo,* and not around Huerta. He was an ass with glasses, but he ran that outfit like a bull runs the pasture. And that's what I want for my boys. I've taught them all I know about *guerrillas*. Now you take over, and we'll have them kicking with either leg. I want my infantry to look good. No half-disciplined farmers this time. Teach them to make clean camps and keep themselves free of *piojos*. Only, for crissakes, no shaved heads. Nothing makes a man feel more like a prisoner or a fool than a bald head."

"What about uniforms?" asked Ávila. "I haven't nearly enough."

"Then let them wear what they have. They don't have to be pretty—just dangerous. And now, where's your telegraph? I've got a few things to say to an old friend."

That same afternoon Pancho Villa sent the following message to the military governor in Chihuahua City:

> *Señor general* Antonio Rabago: Knowing the government you represent will seek my extradition, I have saved you the trouble. You have me here in Mexico ready to combat the tyranny you defend. That of Huerta, Mondragón and their henchmen.
> —Francisco Villa

After leaving his trainees in Satevo, Villa rode on to Pilar de Conchas, through Valle del Rosario, and on to Chavarria, still picking up people. There Villa—balancing now between the instincts of an old *guerrillero* and an embryonic full field commander—made what would prove a brilliant decision. He elected to send all new men to Ávila, in Satevo, keeping with him only a superbly armed band of 25 men for guerrilla operations. No one who had known Villa's past history would ever imagine that the "illiterate *peón*" was training and arming a formal army at Satevo while he was conducting raids somewhere else. Yet Villa understood well the dangers he ran by splitting his forces.

"From now on, *compadre*," he told Ochoa who had remained with him. "We are like monkeys and cats. Silent and tricky—otherwise we're dead. Here you make noise, there you creep. *Como changuitos y gatitos, amigo*. To look, but not be seen. To catch, but not be caught. To kill, but not be killed."

News had reached Villa by telegraph that a train was due into

Chavarria within the hour, and that it carried a sealed military car. To the *guerrillero's* mind, it was worth investigating, and before the train had pulled to a stop, he and his men were already swarming aboard.

"I swear to God, Pancho!" said Ochoa returning from the mail-car, gun still in hand. "You must play games with the devil. Do you know what we found up there?"

"Your mother-in-law," said Villa grinning.

"One hundred twenty-two bars of pure silver, and a brave *federale* hiding in the toilet. That's what."

The two hurried forward where the men were already unloading the silver, and the Federal captain sat mutely staring at them out of fear-glazed eyes.

"Commandeer me some wagons," said Pancho to Ohoa. "I want that stuff sent to San Andrés. Have an escort sent by Colonel Ávila to meet it. And I want it to get there. Make that clear. No sticky pockets, or I'll know how to deal with them. This is going to buy us ammunition and supplies, not *tequila*."

"*Mi general*," said the *federal* nervously. "What about me? *mi general* I can be of great assistance to you."

"I hear you hide in toilets," said Villa.

"I am a paymaster, sir. I can do much for the Revolution."

"You already have," said Villa smiling at him.

The *federal's* eyes lighted with relief. "*Ay, señor.* I'm so glad you feel this way. I have a dear, old mother, and a wife and three children who will thank you, sir. I, myself—"

"Shoot him," said Villa to Ochoa. "And don't waste bullets."

The man's eyes bulged, his mouth quivered. He began trembling visibly. "*Señor* general. You must have misunderstood," he stammered. "I'm only a poor paymaster. I—I never killed anyone. I ask you to have mercy, in the name of my—"

"Are you in Huerta's army?"

"*Sí, señor.* But I—"

"Then I'm going to give you the same mercy your boss gave mine." Pancho Villa's hand flashed to his side, and the big Colt's six-gun roared directly in the man's face, toppling him over. For only an instant longer the *guerrillero* stood glaring down at the corpse, then he slowly holstered the gun. "Manuel," he said, "get that silver going and turn the train loose."

"What about the *federal, jefe?*"

"Toss a *reata* over his neck and put him up that post, where his friends can see him."

"You mean hang him, Pancho?"

"I think that's what they call it," said Villa, walking away.

2

BY TELEGRAPH
TO: Secretary of War,
    Palacio Nacional,
    Mexico City
    Sir: In reply to your wire asking the whereabouts of Francisco Villa. I have the honor to inform you that according to all information which is true and verified, Villa at this moment is in all parts and none in particular.
                              SIGNED: General Antonio Rábago
                                      Commandant,
                                      Chihuahua City

3

Moving with incredible swiftness, the man who was "in all parts and none in particular" suddenly appeared before Casas Grandes, with a force which made the garrison commander realize the futility of resistance. Shortly before sundown the awesome army of conical hats and Winchesters appeared from every rock and bush, and as daylight faded the guerrillas launched a savage flanking movement to the cries of "*Viva* Villa! Long live the Revolution!"

Taking advantage of Villa's one apparent error—attacking in the dark—the garrison commander withdrew, sacrificing only 60 men of his 400, but leaving the town in Villa's hands.

It was these 60 prisoners (discounting 30 dead besides) who were to learn the painful truth. That Villa's army of hats had nothing under it. That its guns were sticks. That 400 regulars had been routed by a few dozen *guerrilleros* using darkness as their major weapon.

In the flickering, yellowish light of the campfires, Pancho Villa walked slowly, staring at each prisoner as they stood aligned before the wall of the garrison compound.

"All right," he said. "Shoot them."

"*Mi general,*" said Ochoa. "There are too many and we're bad off for ammo."

"Let me show you something," said Villa without raising his voice. "You—the first three men. Get one behind the other."

An Indian-faced sergeant and two young privates moved stoically to obey.

"All right," said Villa. "Let's see what kind of soldiers you are. *Attention!*" As they stiffened to his command, Pancho Villa's gun came out slowly and rose, as slowly, to the level of the sergeant's chest. The men's faces tensed, but none of them moved. The hammer of the Colt cocked back with a metallic *click* that was chilling. For an instant Villa stared into the Indian's eyes to find a trace of fear. But there was none.

"*Bueno,*" said Villa. "Have you anything to say?"

"Only," said the sergeant quietly, "that you are a miserable son-of-a-whore."

"It always pains me to waste a man with guts," said Villa. "You want to join me? I'll make one exception."

"Stick you," said the sergeant.

"Don't be stupid. I'll make you a lieutenant."

"Stick you twice."

Pancho Villa pulled the trigger and saw the bullet hit the noncom and plow through the others. "What a pity," he said looking down at the sergeant's dead face. "But can you imagine that boy? Balls like a bull. All right, line the rest of them up and finish it fast. Goddamn, but I liked that boy. Listen, find out who he was. I'll write a letter to his father and tell him what a man he made."

XX. BROTHERS TO THE CUCARACHA

"MAYBE WHAT YOU CAME HERE to tell me is that the revolution hasn't gone too good for your boss, Carranza, eh?"

"*Pero cómo no, mi señor general?* How can that be?" asked the first young man plainly scandalized by the suggestion. "He is, after all, the First Chief of the Revolution."

Pancho Villa shifted his behind on the rock, put down his plate of fried *frijoles* and eggs, wiping the excess food off his thick mustache on his shirt sleeve.

"What Revolution is that, *señores?*" he asked smiling.

"Surely," said the second of Carranzas's emissaries, "you've followed the events in Coahuila since Madero's death?"

"Sure I have. Do you think I'm asleep? And I know the real ones, not that 'rallying symbol' cowdung you people put out."

Colonels Ochoa, Ávila and other Villista officers around Pancho's fire laughed aloud, to the visible annoyance of *señores* Juan Sánchez Azcona and Alfredo Baraceda, who had traveled to Villa's encampment in Ascensión to propose an alliance.

"For example," continued the *guerrillero*, "your *primer jefe* was beaten in Saltillo, Monclova, Piedras Negras . . . well, *señores*, I could run out of fingers counting. Then, *generales* Mass and Rubio Navarrete ran him out of Coahuila and into Sonora, where Maytorena and that rooster, Obregón, took the *pelones* off his back. Well, is that true or not true?"

Carranza's emissaries glanced at each other unhappily. They'd expected to find a stupid, eager peasant, readily flattered by *don* Venustiano's offer. They'd found, instead, a man who knew as much about the situation as themselves. A well-heeled, well-organized army, flushed with victory.

"You must understand, sir," said Baraceda. "Our idea is to

unite all loyal revolutionary forces under one supreme command. One flag. A protector of the Presidential power."

"Your chief?"

"Well, sir," said Baraceda uncomfortably, "that depends entirely on leaders like yourself. *Señor* Carranza, of course, is willing to serve, if called upon."

"That old warthog's so sure of himself, he's already appointed his cabinet," said Ochoa. "And that's no hearsay, but plain fact. He thinks he's Madero's natural successor."

"Let him think he's the reincarnation of Saint Joseph, if he likes," said Villa rolling a hot tortilla between his fingers and wiping up cold beans. "Listen, *amigos,* the moon doesn't come out because the coyote wants to howl. Ninety days ago I crossed the Rio Grande with my tongue hanging out, but Carranza didn't know me. Now it's the other way around. You see, that's life."

"But we have an understanding with Chihuahua," said Azcona desperately. "She's included in *don* Venustiano's plan."

"Maybe with Chihuahua, but not with me," said Villa. "And these days I'm Chihuahua. And Durango, too. If you don't believe me, ask the *federales.*"

The emissaries got up, seeing their mission in shambles, but Villa swallowed a mouthful of *frijoles* and motioned them down. "Do you have any cannon? Any field-pieces?"

Baraceda answered eagerly: "*Don* Venustiano has four French 75's he can't use for lack of crews, *mi general.*"

"Well," said Pancho matter-of-factly. "I have crews already trained, but no cannon. How would you like to make me a little trade? The day I get those pieces from Sonora, I recognize Carranza in Chihuahua."

Captain Baraceda jumped to his feet smiling. "I'll have them here by special convoy, *mi general.* Within one week."

"And that includes a supply of shells," Villa added artfully. "I can't throw *mierda* at the baldheads, although I'd like to."

One week later, to the day, Villa had his cannon. He also

had diminutive and cheerful Colonel Juan N. Medina, a career artillery officer who had found Pancho Villa's aims worthier then Huerta's.

Colonel Medina, like Ávila, was assigned to staff duties, the field-pieces were unlimbered, and artillery-infantry tactics were adapted. The transformation of Villa's force from guerrilla to a standing army was now complete. His hit-and-run days were over. From this point on the Durango *peón's* strategy called for the capture of terrain.

2

With the solidarity and weight of a growing army, and with the broad scope of his projected operations, Villa's chief means of mobility, the horse, was no longer adequate. The horse, itself, had to ride and for such increasing demands only one mode of transport would suffice. Pancho Villa needed rails.

He met the need in typical fashion. On August 26th Villa confronted General Félix Terrazas (*don* Luis Terrazas' warlike nephew, and Orozco's one-time friend), at San Andrés where he and his *federales* had gone to "trap" Villa. Terrazas, expecting light guerrillas, massed and attacked frontally, only to be swamped by Villa's shell fire, then counterattacked by solid infantry. Terrazas' defeat was overwhelming, and his losses oppressive. Villa took more prisoners, supplies and weapons than he'd taken in all previous campaigns. But the grand prize of his victory was Terrazas' three trains.

It illustrated a simple, but essential lesson which Villa forever tried to impress in the minds of his sub-chiefs: "When you need eggs," he'd said, "walk to the henhouse."

3

Meanwhile General Pascual Orozco, a man whose profession had become the reversing of his coat, was re-establishing his red battleflag throughout Mexico—but this time under the benevolent eye of Victoriano Huerta.

On March 14, 1913, following Huerta's dramatic *coup* and his own exile in the United States, Pascual Orozco had returned to the Capital to surrender himself and to offer his allegiance to the new dictator. With him had come all his staff.

"I am satisfied and honored to offer my respects to the *señor presidente*," Orozco's public declaration had read, "and to manifest to him my desire to work for peace, offering my services to help combat banditry, or any who may try to take advantage of the situation to subvert themselves . . ."

Villa's eyes blazed hatred whenever he thought of Orozco, for to him the gaunt, dour wagonmaster was "that sonofawhore who first betrayed Madero." The man without whose revolt the scheming Huerta could never have come to power.

Now they worked together; the liars, the traitors, those two cold, ambition-driven hypocrites whose lives and plans Villa had sworn to crush.

Villa, a man who deep within his soul believed in the sanctity of life and human dignity, had often killed in battle. Never, until recently, had he killed in cold blood. A new-born cynicism spurred him on to show contempt and loathing for his enemies, to match them grave for grave, to pay for each atrocity with more atrocity—one hundred-fold. There was but one policy cruel enough and durable enough to match the treachery of those twin Judases: Extinction. Eradication of their aims, their lives, their supporters' lives. Physical slaughter of these traitors by the most efficient, public and degrading means. Had he his way, the bodies of Pascual Orozco and Victoriano Huerta would have been smeared with human excrement and staked out in the desert sun to feed the ants and buzzards. But this was a dream, and he knew it, even as he relished it.

In the meantime, reality was almost as good. By the express orders of Francisco Villa none of Huerta's officers, not one Red-flagger of any rank, would be given mercy. To fall into Villa's hands was to die—and not always quickly.

4

In Mexico City, former corporal of *rurales*, Cárdenas, and his stablemate, former Lieutenant Pimienta, of the Federal Army, were kept busy earning their promotions. Fearing "internal enemies" within his own Chamber of Deputies, *señor presidente y general don* Victoriano Huerta was "forced to make them disappear." Deputy Serapio Rendón was assassinated at Tlalnepantla. Nestor Monroy and a group of 18 "enemy workers" were arrested and met strange deaths. Deputy Adolfo C. Gurrión was murdered in Juchitan, Oaxaca. Solon Arguello, poet-newsman, and a loud opponent of Huertaism was assassinated in Lecheria. Generals Félix Diaz and Manuel Mondragón—aspirants to the presidency—had seen the folly of their ways, and accepted foreign posts: Mondragón to Belgium, Diaz to Japan . . . after renouncing, publicly, all rights to candidacy. General Felipe Angeles, considered too gentle and ineffectual politically to worry about, had been shipped off to Paris to "study military technique."

In Huerta's bright skies only two clouds hovered around that warm and happy sun called *el Palacio Nacional*. That damned, obstinate farmer, Emiliano Zapata, could not be bribed or corraled. And Villa, that impertinent *peón*, whom he should have shot long before, was making fools of Rábago and those other idiots in Chihuahua.

But no real worry. Zapata and Villa were only *guerrilleros*, free-flying scavengers, and no danger to real garrisons. Their native talents lay in reconnaissance and harassment. They were threadbare, vulgar nuisances. Big-hatted clowns. Perfect foils to keep his regular troops in trim shape.

5

Around the desert plains and foothills between Bermejillo and Torreón, one of the most dramatic events of the Mexican Revolution was unfolding during the final week of September,

1913. Like one long and savagely splendid pageant out of the Middle Ages, all the chiefs and sub-chiefs, with their noisy, teeming, milling masses of men, boys, horses, transport, cannon, trains, campfollowers, flags, tents—all that made up the Irregular Armies of embattled Chihuahua—were coming together into one enormous force, drawn there by the magic of one man's name. By the name of Francisco Villa.

Pancho was first to arrive with his 1,000. Next came Tiburcio Ortega with only 120 men. Then Urbina with 600. Maclovio Herrera gathered with 400 first class riders, Calexito Contreras with 200. In the following days, like barons drawing up to pay homage to their lord, Aguirre Benavídez, Benjamín Yuriar and Juan García brought in their groups. Then came Manuel Chao, Rueda Quijano, Orestes Pereyra, Rosalío Hernández, José Isabel Robles, Trinidad Rodríguez, and many, many lesser known *cabecillas*—guerrilla heads—of local reputations. Among these was one Rodolfo Fierro, soon to share headlines with his new leader, Villa.

It was Pancho's suggestion, at this first conference of chiefs, that the combined bands advance on the important city of Torreón (from which Huerta had once sallied to crush Orozco), attack and occupy it.

"*Camaradas*," he called loudly to the council. "Together we're invincible. Together we are the most powerful single army in all Mexico. This is a time for deeds, and we are the men for the times. I vote to attack Torreón!"

Amid *vaquero yiiipes*, the cracking of weapons in the air, and cries of "*Viva* Villa!" the new, impressive army faced southward again, followed the rails toward the Federal stronghold. A new song, composed for their army, began filling the clear Mexican air, sweeping against the hills and towns along the route, over the rattle of wheels and clatter of horses. It was a song of the people, sung by the bighatted, ammo-belted soldier and their *soldaderas* (those hordes of campfollowers, married or not), sung from their perches atop the trains, from cantering horses, from caissons and on foot. It was chanted by the white-clad *Yaqui* infantry to the beat of Indian drums, or chirped to the strings of Guadalajaran guitars by tipsy *vaqueros*. It was a song which poked fun at the common soldier and his *vieja*—his "old lady"— a song which encompassed all their hopes, failings, fears and plights in a few, simple stanzas and melodic bars. It likened them to the little cockroach: humble, ugly and indestructible. Part of it went like this:

> *La cucaracha, la cucaracha*
> *Ya no puede caminar;*
> *Porque no tiene, porque le falta,*
> *Marihuana que fumar.*
> *Una vieja y un viejito, se cayeron en un pozo;*
> *Y la vieja dijo al viejo:*
> *Viejito tan asqueroso!*

> The *cucaracha*, the *cucaracha*
> He won't travel anymore;
> Because he hasn't, because he's lacking
> Marihuana left to smoke.
> Once a *viejo* and a *vieja*, fell into an empty well;
> Said the *vieja* to the *viejo:*
> Dirty old man go to hell!
> *La cucaracha, la cucaracha . . .*

6

Shortly after dawn of September 29th, General Francisco Villa awoke to the most exciting sight of his life. There, around him, as far as his eyes could see, waited a mass of armed humanity, a surging, whirling sea of infantry, cavalry and artillery prepared to throw itself at Torreón and wash the *federales* away.

"*Buenos días, Panchito!*" called Tomás Urbina galloping up, already dressed for war. "Just look at that. Over 3,000 first class fighting men, and every one is yours!"

"No," said Villa. "Not mine, Tomás. The Revolution's."

"*Qué va, hombre?*" laughed the small rebel dismounting to take a cup of steaming, black coffee. "And who is the Revolution?"

"Their *jefes* brought them, and their *jefes* must decide," said Villa checking his pistols out of habit. "In an hour we meet up there, on *La Loma*. Then we'll know."

"Pancho, you're as pigheaded as ever," said Urbina shaking his head. "You think I wouldn't make myself the commander of all this if I could? You're *loco* as hell! Just look at them, *amigo*. There, the *Brigada Juárez*. Over there, *Brigada Victoria*, and to the left, the *Durango, Zapata, Guerrero . . .*"

Pancho Villa had begun shaving, but looked as Urbina pointed proudly. "The *Cazadores de la Sierra*, the *Cuerpo de Guias*. Christ! but they're beautiful! And look at the *Brilliant Thirteen* —suicidal, every one of those bastards. Sworn, to a man, to strike like a bolt of human lightning on horseback, and if they don't win, to go back till they're all dead. Pancho, I'd give my soul to hell for this!"

"And you deserve it," Villa replied. "You're one of the three I'm nominating, *amigo*. And I hope you get it."

Urbina looked up at the man who had always been his natural leader and again shook his head. "You crazy bastard," he said, infinitely touched. "You crazy, wonderful bastard!"

Some obstacles cropped up at the council, particularly the fact that General Manuel Chao, one of the *cabecillas*, had been named Provisional Governor of Chihuahua by Carranza, weeks before. Moreover, many of those present considered themselves fit by their deeds to be supreme commander. Yet, when the memorable meeting ended, that September day in 1913 on "The Hill," there was but one man whom all the leaders would accept as their General-in-Chief, and this was Francisco Villa, henceforth called "Chief of the Northern Division"—their own Northern Division—the most powerful military force in all Mexico.

7

"We'll hit them where it will stun them," Pancho Villa had told his new brigade and regimental commanders. "*Un golpe terrifico*. One terrific blow—then grind them under our horses' hooves."

And that was how it went. Pancho directed his army with the deadly intuition he'd once shown in minor skirmishes. He flung General Urbina's brigade down the course of the Nazares River to hit General Felipe Alvilez' defenses. Then Maclovio Herrera's splendid Juárez Brigade went against the neighboring defenses of Gómez Palacio and Lerdo. An old enemy was there: General Emilio P. Campa, entrenched with sappers, artillery and *rurales,* putting up a battle both fierce and aggressive.

Had their enemies heeded the signs, they might have stood a chance. But to their narrow minds, Villa was a peasant leading brave, but stupid rebels who could never master the intricacies of war. Even when Medina's artillery hit them, tearing their massive defenses apart with shrapnel and explosives; even when Villa's cavalry smashed their flanks, and his infantry broke through the breaches in perfect order, they still couldn't—or wouldn't—believe the incredible fact that Francisco Villa had drawn a fullfledged army up before them, that they were being defeated by superior strategy and soldiering.

On October second, the end came. Pancho Villa entered Torreón behind the fleeing *federales.* The booty was immense: arms, supplies, trains and prisoners. Among these prisoners were many Orozquistas. These were executed.

Aided by Ávila, Medina, Urbina and other former regular officers in his staff, Villa now launched into his first attempt to govern a city. He established a garrison, headed by Calexito Contreras. He borrowed 300,000 *pesos* (always from the complaining commercialists and industrialists) to pay off his war debts, and finance future campaigns. He bought clothes and food for the destitute families of Torreón, and ordered daily band concerts to cheer the people. But his consuming passion was for the welfare of his wounded. Visions of the dying and maimed lying in the streets alone, or bleeding white, or putrid with gangrene, or crying in pain for lack of care and medicines, had haunted him since 1910. And he'd sworn many times that one day he would change all that. Now he had the chance, and his instructions were simple and direct:

"We've got trains. We've got money. I want a hospital on rails. Every car scrubbed and repainted. Put in cots, tables, ice-boxes, stoves. Everything covered with clean, white sheets. Get me the best doctors for a Medical Corps. Hire them, enlist them, drag them in by their tongues—I don't care. But be sure they're good, not butchers. Goddamn them, they'd better be good! Get me the best medical stuff there is. Plenty of morphine. And the first surgeon who mistreats a man . . . Well, just tell those doctors Pancho Villa's very good at amputating balls."

XXI. "YOU ATE THEM – HORNS AND ALL..."

"YOU SAY HE KNOWS TRAINS?"

"Like I know *putas*, Panchito. Inside and out."

"And he probably treats them like you treat *putas*, too. He screws them up good. I know these amateurs."

"Panchito," said Urbina. "He's first class, I tell you. When I met him, he was brakeman on the military run from Chihuahua to Torreón. I talked him into my brigade and made him a captain so he'd supervise my troop runs, and he did damn good. You were in Huerta's *calabozo* then, remember?"

"Well, and then?

"He wanted to fight, so I finally turned him loose. Listen, Pancho, you've been yelling for a railroad officer, and I'm telling you he's your man. Do you think I want to lose him? He's the best combat leader I've got."

"But that's all *mierda* about the Redflaggers, isn't it?"

"No, sir, Pancho. That man's a terror and a half. Damn near as *loco* as you."

"*Pero hombre, Tomás,* a hundred artillerymen? Without exaggeration?"

"Without exaggeration. I swear it by the milk of my mother. You can ask Maclovio here if I'm lying."

"You can believe him this time," said Herrera. "I saw it with these two eyes. *Chispas!* How that man loves blood!"

Urbina nodded re-excited by the memory. " 'Get off that train, you Redflag sons-of-tainted mothers,' he yelled at them. 'And line up there along those tracks. I'm going to kill you stinking turncoats, right now,' he said."

"He talks like that?"

"Like a muleskinner and a half, Pancho. He walked down the line with a .45 in each hand and shot them all."

"Every one?"

"Every last mother's son. *Tras! Tras! Tras!* Stopping only to reload and cuss them out again."

"By God," said Villa. "I want to meet the *cabrón* who's got the balls to do his own killing like that. What's his name again?"

"Fierro," said Urbina. "*coronel* Rodolfo Fierro."

"Good," said Pancho. "You bring him to dinner tonight, and we'll discuss his taking over my transportation."

That was how Pancho Villa and Rodolfo Fierro met. Each sized the other up, and from that moment, Fierro was Villa's man and Villa was Fierro's admirer.

"They were two of a kind," one intimate later recalled. "Brave, fierce, bloody and irresistible. Both destined to live boldly and violently. In this year of 1913 their twin stars were on the ascent. And their—*cómo se dice?*—their roles dove-tailed perfectly, without friction, for Pancho was just that much more than Fierro and Fierro knew it and accepted it. *Pero* Pancho was that much more than any man in Mexico, more even than the great Francisco I. Madero, who had fathered the first revolution, who had dreamed the great dream of a Mexican utopia, and whom Villa had idolized. So as Villa had looked on Madero, Fierro, the terrible, the unmanageable, the butcher, looked on Villa. He was ready to die for him—as eventually he did."

"Then it's settled," said Villa glancing at Urbina. "Colonel Fierro is released to my headquarters."

"Funny, I'd swear nobody asked me," said Fierro to the ceiling.

"Well, any objections?" said Villa, staring at him.

"Who, me?" asked Fierro innocently. "No. As you say, *mi general,* it's all settled."

"Well, settle this, too. The first time you screw up—"

"The first time I screw up, you'll know it, because I'll tell you myself, *mi general,*" said Fierro, staring right back.

"And then," Villa continued, "we're going to miss you, colonel, because when people screw up—I have them shot."

"Man, this is fine booze, general," said Fierro sipping a cognac and relaxing. "I think I'll like it around here."

2

Leaving the garrison under General Contreras, a wily and dedicated rebel, Pancho put the best of his fighting force on trains and headed for Chihuahua City in a move calculated to capture and control the Capital of that state. If he could succeed, he'd then control southern Chihuahua, eastern Durango, and southwestern Coahuila—Carranza's own home state. More important, strategically, he would also hold the railway from Juárez to Saltillo and down to Zacatecas. This was nearly half of Mexico's length.

On November 2, 1913, the Villistas opened a sharp volley and rushed Chihuahua City. They were bloodily repulsed, and Villa set up a siege, determined to take the city.

Chihuahua's defenders were equally determined he would not. They were old and ardent enemies, among them Salvador Mercado, Marceo Caraveo, Antonio Reyes, José Inéz Salazar (who'd once retaken Parral, but missed Villa) and Pascual Orozco. These Generals had additional incentive: they were all men Villa had sworn to hang.

Twice more Pancho Villa tried his favorite attack: that *"golpe terrifico"*—the terrific blow—which had overwhelmed Torreón.

It didn't work. And then Villa did something inexplicable. To the amazement of both enemy and friend, he suddenly ordered a total withdrawal.

Federal cavalry pursuing his rear-guard reported a southward flight, convincing General Mercado of his triumph over the audacious rebel. By nightfall there wasn't even sight of a small band. The desert was clear. Villa was gone.

But not quite. Twenty hours later the advance elements of Villa's "retreating" army appeared at a small railroad station north of Chihuahua, headed by the General, himself. Mercado could not know that since the attack Villa had kept Rodolfo Fierro and the Northern Division's telegraphers busy tapping wires, listening in on the Juárez-Chihuahua City communications. And he could not know that Villa was alerted to the arrival of an ammunition train, enroute from Juárez. Nor could he know that Generals Tomás Urbina and Maclovio Herrera had just intercepted that train, a few miles above this station, and were now replenishing their empty ammunition belts and loading the empty freight cars with their men and mounts.

Colonel Rodolfo Fierro, looking like a sleepy tiger, gently poked a pistol barrel against the startled telegrapher's ribs, saying: "Move over, sonny." Then he motioned Major Carlos Moreno, Villa's chief telegrapher, into the empty seat. "All right, *jefe*," he said to Villa. "What do we send?"

Pancho thought for an instant. "This is for General Castro, commandante de Plaza, Juárez. Say: 'Villa in full retreat to south. Am sending you reinforcements of 800 men with ammunition and supplies by returning train. Signed, Mercado.' "

"They've acknowledged," said Fierro before Moreno had finished deciphering the return clicks.

"Any fuss?"

"No fuss," said Moreno. "Their code is K. That'll identify the returning train to all stations, and highball us through."

"*Muy bien,*" said Villa. "Cut the wires both ways, and let's join Urbina."

"All right, jefe," said Fierro drawing his pistol. "Just let me take care of this boy, first."

Villa glanced at the terrified telegrapher in the corner. "Leave him alone," he said. "He looks like a nice kid. We'll take him with us and turn him loose when it's over."

"It's easier to shoot him," complained Fierro.

"And it's easier to shoot you, than argue with you," said Villa flatly. "So make up your mind fast."

Fierro grinned slowly and holstered his gun.

3

On the morning of November 15th, a few minutes after 1 o'clock, a freight train returning from Chihuahua City entered the yards in Juárez and was sided while the "Federal reinforcements" aboard unloaded—in full combat gear—and were formed and marched toward the barracks in the heart of town.

Scant attention was paid to them, or to their commanders, for troop movements were nothing extraordinary in that frontier city. Moments later Fierro, pistol in hand, entered the stationmaster's office. "All right, you sons-of-disgraced-mothers—This place is in Pancho Villa's hands. Get over there!"

The gaudy nightclubs and casinos of the city were going strong. Indifferent Mexicans, stray *federales* and hundreds of curious *gringos* milled through the streets, restaurants, saloons and whorehouses which flourished from 16th of September Avenue to the American border. A ceaseless hubbub of music, shouts and laughter filled the air, and in select cabarets, Federal staff officers, their women and guest *norteamericanos* chattered about anything but war.

Suddenly the cry of "*Viva* Villa! *Arriba la revolución!*" stopped the merriment. The outbreak of firing electrified Mexicans and tourists alike. The sleeping barracks was taken by storm. Villistas in broad hats and jingling spurs, their chests crisscrossed with ammunition belts, broke into the clubs, rounding up the terrified

enemy officers, while machineguns outside swept away any resistance by their troops.

The attack had been a complete surprise. Within three hours
the city was secured, and Villa in absolute command. In one bold
stroke, with just 800 men, a *peón* who'd never heard of a Trojan
Horse, had employed his wheeled version of it to trick a garrison
of 3000 men, and capture the most important city in northern
Mexico—without suffering a single casualty.

The customhouse where Pancho Villa had set up headquarters
was a mass of consternation that day. Outside, hordes of anxious
businessmen, favor-seekers, admirers (some of these quite suddenly converted) and well-wishers crowded about, hoping to get
a glance of "the bandit-general." News of his amazing victory
had been reported by American newspapers, flashing for the first
time the name of General Francisco Villa around the world. The
peasant from Durango was the man of the hour; Juárez the biggest story since the recent election of Woodrow Wilson.

Villa, meanwhile, with the tenacity that characterized him,
hadn't forgotten Chihuahua City.

"Fierro, what about that rail line?"

"They couldn't run a baby-buggy up here, *jefe*. My rear-guard
chopped hell out of the tracks and blew out a dozen small
bridges. They'll have to come fixing road all the way."

"Will it buy me five more days?"

"Easily."

"Urbina, what's the report from our people below?"

"The main body's in position, awaiting your orders. They can
jump Chihuahua or move up here."

"Keep them put. I'll need them there when Mercado comes
after us."

"Our spies in Chihuahua report he's mobilizing 5000 *pelones*,"
laughed Urbina. "He's mad at you, Pancho."

"Imagine that. *Too-roon-toon-toon.*"

Toribio Ortega came in wearing an ankle-length Federal
officer's overcoat of European design. He'd been cold all night,

even during the fighting, and he had the big collar up and his fingers nearly hidden.

"*Eiy,* anybody here seen General Ortega?" asked Urbina.

"Ask that coat that just walked in," said Herrera.

"Gentlemen, I'm going to give you another chuckle," said the funereal Ortega. "General Mercado has assigned 11 trains for his counterattack on Juárez. Suck on that a while."

"Is that straight?" asked Villa.

"Straight as hell, *mi general.* Medina just wired us."

"*Chispas!*" said Herrera. "He wants blood. Eleven trains!"

"That reminds me," said Villa. "If you're going to execute the rest of those baldheads today, Rodolfo, don't shoot any clarinet players."

"Why not, *jefe?*" asked Fierro annoyed.

"Goddammit, why do you think? How can we have a military band without clarinets?"

"Now it's a military band, eh?"

"Goddammit, Fierro, I like bands, and we left ours in Torreón to entertain the people."

"So?"

"So, the people of Juárez and Chihuahua like music, too. Come to think of it—don't shoot any musicians. We'll make two bands."

"*Demonio!*" muttered Fierro. "Well, that does it."

"You know," said Villa to the others after Fierro had left. "Some day I'm going to shoot that bastard—if I can ever find a reason. Or maybe even without it."

4

On November 19th word came from the southern scouts that Mercado's entire force had departed Chihuahua City for Juárez. Pancho immediately marched out to meet the *federales.*

His plan, as always, was simple and clever. Proceeding southward with most of his 800 men, he planned to rendezvous with his *División del Norte* and fight where Mercado's generals least expected. He was so confident of success that he dispatched Rodolfo Fierro with a picked detachment of railroaders and dynamiters to circle behind Mercado's trains and cut the tracks, delaying his retreat.

Within 24 hours all elements of the Northern Division had joined, resupplied from Villa's vast Juárez stores, and were formed for battle.

Surprised by the entire rebel army waiting across their tracks, the *federales* were forced to attack half-ready. Villa promptly counterattacked, and for three days the battle of Tierra Blanca raged. Mercado's 5000 regulars, reinforced by a column of 2000 Juárez survivors proved unequal to Villa's 5000, and by November 25th the *federales* were attempting to withdraw toward Chihuahua City. Then Rodolfo Fierro struck.

In a moment of inspiration, Fierro had decided to ignore the laborious and temporary destruction of track. Concentrating instead on the last of Mercado's trains, Fierro's detachment blocked the rails, charged the train, surprised its troop escort and disarmed them. He then shot the officers. Finally he uncoupled the engine, loaded its cowcatcher with a tremendous load of dynamite and studded this with explosive caps.

Grinning happily, the man the world's headlines would soon dub "Pancho Villa's Butcher" got into the cab, opened the throttle and leaped out. "Boys," he announced. "We're going to have some fun!"

The "crazy engine" raced northward, around a broad bend. Ahead lay Tierra Blanca and Mercado's 10 other trains, stalled end to end by Villa's attack. As the cowcatcher met the last caboose, an earthshaking explosion ended Mercado's hopes. When the enormous black ball of fire and smoke had lifted, the rear troop train lay scattered over half a mile, a broad stretch of track had been twisted into blackened junk, and the *federales* were in wild retreat. Unable to move up or back 10 valuable engines and their cars loaded with war materials were just sitting there, waiting for Villa. Meanwhile Urbina's cavalry was in savage pursuit of the panic-stricken *federales,* cutting them to pieces.

Back in Chihuahua City, General Mercado gathered the pathetic remnants of his once powerful army and retreated toward Ojinaga, leaving the Capital to the Villistas.

For Villa this wasn't enough. Splitting his Northern Division again, Pancho personally led the attack on Ojinaga against Mercado's remaining troops. By January 11, 1914 the last government force north of Chihuahua had ceased to exist. Those Huertistas who could escaped over the American border and were interned. Those who didn't were executed by Villista firing squads. General Mercado had been one of the luckier ones.

5

"I really feel terrible about screwing you up so badly," said Rodolfo Fierro, lighting up a huge, dark cigar, and tilting his Stetson nearly over his eyes.

Pancho Villa sat at his desk, picking cold asparagus and sardines right out of the can with his penknife, his booted feet up on the Mexican saddle somebody had tossed on the floor. He wasn't looking at Fierro and didn't seem aware of his voice, yet the man's way of speaking always fascinated him. Fierro—according to the little anyone knew of him—had once been the Chief of Police in Guaymas. He had railroaded with many *gringos,* and spoke English fluently and Spanish like an educated man. He also wrote like a schoolteacher. But he killed like a demented devil . . . and thank God for the sonofabitch.

"Yes sir," said Fierro puffing away. "I knew when I blew up all those Goddamn Huertistas that I should have followed your orders and just ripped up a little track—."

"Shut up," said Villa.

"Look at this, Pancho!" said Urbina breaking into the room, waving two handsful of newspapers. "You're famous. Everyone of these papers says so! By God! You ate them—horns and all!"

"My, my," said Fierro studying his cigar.

"Get the hell out of here, before I lose my temper," said Villa drawing his gun and laying it on the desk.

Fierro got up grinning cynically. He started out.

"Fierro," said Villa. "You're a general now."

"My, my," said Fierro flicking his cigar.

XXII. THE ANGEL AND THE DEVIL

THE PRESIDENT OF THE UNITED STATES, the aesthetic and professorial Woodrow Wilson, regarded with revulsion and undisguised horror the mess his Republican predecessor had helped create in Mexico City.

Graft had been rampant and Wall Street speculation incredibly callous. Deals had been made. Moreover, President Taft, with the aid of Ambassador Henry Lane Wilson (no relation), had managed to confuse every effort at internal reform.

What to do?

Daily that maniac in Mexico's National Palace became increasingly impossible. Crazed with alcoholism and delusions of grandeur, his penchant for political assassination grew more obscene, his policies toward the United States more hostile. At a time when the crisis in Europe looked its worse, the miserable tyrant made no secret of his pro-German inclinations. To Wilson, new in office and an incurable busybody in foreign affairs, Mexican domestic politics required a solution. Quite naturally, as he searched for an answer to Europe's difficulties, it came to him that both State and War Department representatives should be dispatched to study the Mexican problem. In the meantime, he would make it his business to keep an eye on that scene with the object of discovering a proper successor to the unreliable Huerta.

A quick evaluation already told him that only two men were realistic possibilities.

One was Mr. Venustiano Carranza, one-time governor of Coahuila State, a former member of the late President Madero's first cabinet, and an active political and revolutionary figure dating back to 1895. Mr. Carranza was stately, well-bred and politically persuasive.

The second possibility was General Francisco Villa, a soldier whose recent victories throughout northern Mexico had been pronounced "brilliant military achievements" by such American professionals as Generals Hugh L. Scott and John J. Pershing, both of whom had met the man and seemed to admire him. Unfortunately, Villa's personal history left something to be desired. He was reputedly illiterate. He was also said to possess a maniacal temper which often terminated in bloodshed. Finally, he was a barely reformed bandit who had only been pardoned by enlisting to fight against Díaz. Now he seemed to represent no cause but his own, while displaying no political inclinations or talents.

There seemed little doubt as to the more suitable candidate to rule Mexico. Unfortunately, General Villa held all the meaningful territory, including the vital border crossings.

Yet, even as Mr. Wilson deliberated the future of his country's southern neighbor, something was happening which dramatically caught his attention, causing him to reconsider. Huerta grew more obnoxious. Mr. Carranza floundered about Sonora, sending grandly worded directives which his Chief of the Northwest Army, General Obregón, could not carry out. Other leaders rose and fell. Villa was showing an astonishing display of native good sense, and administrative ability, which no one could have foreseen. Villa, the bandit-soldier, was emerging brilliantly as Villa, the benevolent dictator.

Once the firing squads were still, Francisco Villa's immediate concern seemed centered upon the welfare of his long-oppressed people.

Political prisoners were freed and restored to full rights. New

schools were established, and Villa passed a truancy law which
he enforced vigorously. (Villa's legislative processes were simple:
When he wanted a law, he had one drawn up and signed it into
being.) Youngsters were encouraged to learn new trades. Railroad rates were lowered and poor families given passes if they
wished to migrate elsewhere for work or personal reasons. Mexicans returning from the United States were permitted duty free
entry for their furniture and automobiles. He employed capable
help to supervise his school, hospitals and other institutions.
Large industries were taxed, and price-ceilings set to protect the
poor from profiteers. Better engines, passenger and freight cars
were bought from the United States. Heavier rails were installed
to take increased loads while making travel safer. Liquor laws
were rigidly enforced. United States Custom authorities were
given powerful aid to stop the smuggling of drugs across the
border, and to further help relations between the two countries
Villa ordered that English be taught in all public schools under
his jurisdiction. Finally, a tax was placed on all gold or silver
transported across the border. This, plus the revenue from
gambling and other sources, was directed into public works and
a strengthening of the *División del Norte,* without which all of
Villa's efforts would have meant nothing.

Progress was astonishingly smooth, and Mr. Wilson was halfway through a sigh of presidential relief, when it happened . . .

Much as sea, winds and temperature combine to make a storm,
so did a proud man's temper, Villa's contempt for Europeans and
Rodolfo Fierro's quick hand tragically combine to create The
Benton Affair.

2

"*Señor* William H. Benton would like to see you, *mi general,*"
said Benavídez, Pancho Villa's personal secretary.

"*De qué?* What about?" asked Villa glancing up from a paper
he was examining at his desk.

"It's about that tax you put on the unconfiscated *haciendas.*"

"*Bueno,* Luis. Tell him there's nothing to talk about. He just pays 1000 head of cattle, and that's all. I'm busy."

Pancho had heard of Benton before. Benton was a British subject, a hotheaded, tough, desk-pounding, pistol-packing man with large cattle interests in Mexico gathered over the past 20 years. He wasn't a man one dismissed in a summary fashion. Still, Villa wasn't prepared for what happened next.

"Who the hell does he think he's putting off?" roared a voice from the ante-room, and a massive, sharp faced man shouldered the door open and marched up to Villa's desk. "Listen, Villa," he said. "Do you know who I am?"

"I know who you are. What do you want?"

"You know bloody well what I want, Villa. If you think I'm going to pay your Goddamn, thieving tax, you're a raving maniac. What's more, I'm sick and tired of seeing your Goddamn peons riding all over my land, do you understand that?"

"Listen, *Inglés,*" said Villa staring up at him through narrowing eyes. "First, the Mexican *hacendados* are paying my tax. Second, I could have confiscated your *hacienda,* but didn't do it out of respect for your consul, who is my friend. Third, I don't like your words, thieves and *peónes.* And last, where the hell do you get your nerve, busting into my house? Just be glad I don't stand you up against a wall!"

Carlos Jáuregui, sitting beside Pancho Villa's desk, glanced nervously around the room. Villa was in his shirtsleeves, his nearest pistol in the closed desk drawer before him. Benton was obviously carrying a large gun underneath his coat. By now he was out of his mind with rage, leaning over the desk, hurling a barrage of threats and insults at Villa, whose face grew redder as he struggled to control himself.

To Benton's right, completely ignored, stood a huge, dark figure. He wore a trim, white campaign hat, like his chief's, a long, black military cape (under which one could see a massive gunbelt), and his watchful eyes, looked directly at the Englishman.

". . . So just don't think you can scare me, you cow-thieving, Mexican sonofbitch!" yelled Benton, "because I—"

"You're under arrest!" shouted Villa, jumping to his feet. "I'll teach you how to talk to me, *cabrón Inglés!*"

"You'll teach me nothing!" yelled Benton going for his gun. In that instant Fierro's hand moved, his .45 roared and William Benton fell dead with a bullet through his head.

That shot, although fired defensively, was to echo down the halls of Washington, D.C. and through the chambers of the British Parliament. On February 20th a mass meeting protesting Benton's death was held in El Paso. The British government began an investigation. The world's headlines once more blazed with Villa's name—and beside it, the name of Fierro, known now as "Villa's Man of Blood," and "Pancho Villa's Butcher."

As for President Woodrow Wilson, in his highly moral, cool and logical, Virginian mind, the machinery of selection was once more clicking. The fearful suspicion grew that General Villa was, after all, only a volatile savage. A remarkable one, perhaps, but not one fit to rule a country. He, Wilson, would wait for the recommendations of General Scott and Mr. George Carothers, his representatives in Chihuahua. And he would weigh these factors fairly. But it seemed to him that Mr. Carranza's prospects were much improved. After all, a man who enjoyed fine European wines and the opera was infinitely preferable to a man who still engaged in the murder of British subjects. And then, too, Mr. Carranza's latest wire, assuring Wilson of protection over all American and English interests, had struck the man in Washington as just the appropriate touch.

3

"You know where you are? In the lair of a crazy bandit, a killer. I can't really recommend myself to you, *mi general.*"

The tall, aristocratic man shook his head sorrowfully. His brown eyes shone compassionately. "Most unfair," he said. "I've read the periodicals. Grossly unjust."

"I wonder," said Pancho Villa, "what the Americans would have done if some half-drunken Mexican had broken into the El Paso city hall and tried to shoot their mayor? But here, in Mexico, we're supposed to be fair game for the insults and whims of any foreigner, eh?"

"Ridiculous," said the man.

"Well, *señor* Carranza made political hay at my expense, general, with his so-called Carranza Commission. I suppose it's part of being a politician—which I am not. But it stinks. And I won't lie to you. He was my guest in Chihuahua; running his 'government' in territory I took. All of a sudden I find myself being 'investigated' by him. Well, maybe he sent you to me to make up for it. I don't want to think badly of a man if I'm going to share a cause with him."

"I think your attitude is a very generous one, *señor*."

"What the hell!" said Villa, rubbing his face. "I'm angry one minute, and trying to be sensible the next. I—Ah, here comes the 'Butcher,' the man whose crime was to save my life."

As Rodolfo Fierro entered, the smartly-uniformed General Felipe Angeles drew up, snapped his heels and saluted. Fierro looked confused, pulled the cigar from between his teeth, and touched his hat in a half-hearted show of military courtesy.

They were exchanging pleasantries when Urbina and Herrera entered, then Medina and Ávila. "*Señores*," said Villa. "Let me present to you *el señor general* Felipe Angeles, the new chief of artillery for the *División del Norte*."

Villa's staff all saluted smartly and shook hands with acceptable grace, displaying their Federal training.

"We've arranged a little parade for you, General Angeles," said Urbina. "Nothing much, because we're not too fancy here. But, well, you'll see. We'll have the Brigada Fierro, Brigada Juárez, Brigada González-Ortega, Colonel Medina's artillerists, our machineguns, and General Villa's Dorados. Everything humble, but pretty. *Muy bonito*."

"It was not necessary, really," protested Angeles, although his face showed he was enormously pleased by their tribute. "But I do extend my gratitude, gentlemen."

"That's what they would do in Mexico City," said Villa, "so we'll do it here. We're trying to become an army, eh?"

"You know, *mi general*," said Angeles. "Your *Dorados* have become famous. In fact, many of us in Sonora have found the exploits of your Northern Division exciting."

"Would that include General Álvaro Obregón?" asked Villa as the officers burst into laughter, Angeles joining them.

The joviality continued through the parade, and into the evening. Felipe Angeles, whose expressions Pancho Villa carefully watched, had appeared greatly impressed by the long display of Villista power. The Villistas, in turn, were equally impressed by his charm, manners and professional reputation. The Chapultepec graduate's vast experience would clearly be an asset to the Northern Division, yet, it seemed to Pancho, there was something manifestly odd in Carranza's eagerness to part with such a man.

All the cunning on earth might simply bounce off General Angeles' polished exterior, Villa knew. But there was one way which wouldn't fail and this was to wait for Felipe Angeles to find the time, the place and subject, himself.

"I've been preparing to attack Zacatecas," Villa said. "Now, *don* Venustiano wants me to take Saltillo instead. If I should, I'd be sacrificing my campaign for his benefit, since Saltillo is the Capital of Coahuila."

General Angeles sat back listening attentively while rolling a snifter of brandy between his long, white hands.

"Now, the question is this," continued Villa, "if I do take Saltillo for Carranza, am I giving prestige to a good man? Or am I sacrificing good blood to glorify a louse? You see, I must be sure that these campaigns all mean good for Mexico, because I'm paying for them with good men."

"Are you asking me about *señor* Carranza?" asked Angeles.

"*Si, mi general*. I think maybe I am."

"It isn't my habit or desire to malign another man," said Angeles. "Especially if he is not present to offer a defense."

"Nor is it mine," said Villa pointedly. "But I'm going to throw 10,000 men into a fight, and one out of every 10 is probably going to die. Their *soldaderas* are going to walk around the camp in a daze. Their babies are going to suffer. The few *pesos* I give them aren't going to erase the fact, *mi general,* that *I, me,* Pancho Villa, ordered those men to their deaths. Do you understand, *señor?*" He tapped his chest hard with his finger. "I have to justify it to me, as well as to those women."

"I never dreamt you felt their loss that much," said Angeles visibly moved. "Never. You always seem so . . . well, self-assured."

"Some call me an animal, *señor.* I'm not supposed to see, or hear, or notice. Well, animals cry too. People say I love blood. That I throw myself into these fights. Well, yes, I do. I throw myself into them because I want my men to see me and to know that I can die for Mexico, too. All of us, together. You see?"

"Yes," replied Angeles. "I do see."

"Now, what about Carranza? The one you know?"

"*Señor* Carranza pretends a liberality of view and a patriarchal concern for the nation which are non-existent," said Angeles. "He is, in fact, not only a conservative stuffed-shirt, but an opportunist whose real desire is to re-establish the old Díaz order with himself as its new strong man. Madero's assassination has given him a double-edged sword with which to carve out his ambitions. First, he has a perfect scape-goat in the villainous Huerta. Second, he has the perfect excuse for violence. He cannot fight, so his true masterpiece must be the title he has conferred upon himself: He is *el primer jefe.* The First Chief of the Revolutionary Army. But which—whose—Revolutionary Army? Yours? Maytorena's? Obregón's? *Señor* Carranza, my dear General Villa, is the Old Badger of the revolution. He will find a way."

Villa had listened, astonished by the sudden flood of bitterness which had poured from that gentle and compassionate man.

"As to what *señor* Carranza might say of me," added Angeles, "I've no doubt. When I first joined him, following my return

from Paris, he created me Minister of War. I could not get on
with the man. He affected the manner of Caesar. At dinner one
was silent while he expounded on a variety of subjects. If one attempted to comment, he was cut off with a glare. I was reduced
to Assistant Minister of War . . ."

"I'm not interested in all that," said Villa.

"With your permission, general. I think you should hear it,
in all fairness to *señor* Carranza."

"All right, so he sent you to me to get rid of you. Is that
what you're going to say?"

"Precisely."

"*Muy bien.* So we're both misfits. I hear you're the best
artillerist since Napoleon—"

"Ah," said Angeles, his unhappy mood vanishing. "You're a
student of Bonaparte, *mi general?* Marvelous, we'll have some
fine chats together."

"All I really know is that he's not with Zapata."

Angeles looked puzzled, then broke into laughter. "*Mi general,*
you're an amazing man. Truly amazing. Your facets seem endless
and equally fascinating."

"*Y usted es un hombre muy bueno,*" said Villa. "I think you
are a fine gentleman. Maybe the kind of gentleman I would like
to have been. But . . . we are what we are. And what I am—"

"What you are," said Angeles, "is good for Mexico. I came here
wondering, looking, hoping. And now I am happy."

When General Angeles had left, Pancho Villa sat alone, thinking, trying to find a path through the maze of complications.
Freedom for Mexico, nothing else, was Francisco Villa's eternal
vision, his guidepost, his reason for existence. Without it he
would be lost; driven back into the ignorance and slavery which
degraded, twisted and eventually destroyed a man's soul. The
eagle on the hill was his standard, sacred and unalterable. No
obstacle must ever obliterate it.

That vision had come to him from Madero, through the
instruction of *don* Abraham. Now both were dead. Orozco was a
Judas. Zapata, loyal to his own oaths, was a man unto himself.

And in these early days of March, 1914 only he, Pancho Villa, still carried forward the standard first lifted by Francisco Madero. But what if he should fall in battle one day? What if he, too, should become a casualty of the dream? Or, what if he were to become confused by matters beyond his simple understanding? True, he read much now. Being no drinker or carouser he devoted his evenings to long discussions with his best-educated officers, denying himself even the company of lovely ladies.

But:

Why was he fighting still? When the moment of victory came, who was there to harvest the fruits of it? Who would rule their liberated Mexico if he, Pancho Villa, could not—or would not?

He had thought about that through countless sleepless nights. In the midst of battles as his men went forward from conquest to conquest he had paused to wonder about the ultimate goal. There was no Madero now. No Abraham González. Perhaps Maytorena? Carranza, of course, displayed the aggressiveness necessary. But the bitter words of General Angeles had merely echoed his own dark suspicions. Yes, if this was a time of opportunity, it was also a time for opportunists. Self-seeking and self-sacrifice walked hand in hand. If he killed traitors forever, he could never kill them all, because some of the lowest of their breed were unknown and walked around him wrapped in disguises of smiles and syrupy words and false sentiments.

He wished sometimes that he could drink. Then he would get stupid drunk and stop his thinking and his worrying. There was a time when he had just fought, and laughed, and sang—and loved, exactly like any other man. Now he even kept Luz in a different house, while he slept on a canvas cot like a penniless bachelor, or in that silly, little red caboose he'd made into his living quarters and office for campaigns.

He was a General now, Goddammit! And he had less than he'd had as an outlaw. And responsibilities, fears, worries he'd never dreamt of in those days! Did Urbina sleep alone? Did Fierro?

Alone.

He knew the meaning of loneliness so well. In his strange, male fashion he loved Luz, because she had displaced his sadness for a little while, giving him her body and soul. But he'd responded by driving her away, thus imposing upon himself the awful sentence of loneliness once more.

Tonight he didn't want to think or to worry. Tonight . . . Goddammit! He was a commander of a whole army. He stood an absolute king of more than 20,000 soldiers; with a camp full of women; with all the booze in the world, and the music, and the—whatever the hell he wanted—all his for only a whistle! Why in hell did he have to worry? Why was he alone? By God, if he wanted it he could order Tomás, Rodolfo, Herrera—the whole pack of them in with their *viejas*—and have himself one hell of a brawl. And why not? Why?

If Villa was a crusader, he hadn't stopped being a man. If some of the idealism of Angeles (whom the men were already calling "Villa's Angel") was in him, so were the lusts of that bloody devil, Fierro. He was both good and evil, because the times had made him so.

Pancho rose, going to his roll-top desk. There, among the piles of orders, paper-stacked spindles, and drawers filled with the paraphenalia of running an army and a government he found a tiny, battered, metal box crammed full of such foolish and unimportant little things as a ten year old boy might accumulate and treasure. There was a pencil stub with which he had once learned to form the letter "A." There was a piece of candle and a single paragraph torn from the back pages of a newspaper in which he had first found the name of Pancho Villa. It said that he was going to prison. There were some coins from Juárez and a few creased and fading photographs. But most important of all was a piece of ordinary, schoolboy's writing paper on which appeared the first thought he'd ever tried to set in letters. It read:

When man was born, he was not born alone,

Why, of all things, had he written that? He wondered now, and tried to reconstruct his thoughts of those bitter, hopeless days.

Slowly, almost involuntarily, he picked up the pen at his side.

That childish, wriggly scrawl had given way to a firmer, surer hand, so that it seemed now to Pancho that it should have been written by a child—himself as a child—many, many years before. Before the death of his father, before the killing of that first man, the *hacendado,* long before the name Madero, or the words "liberty" and "revolution" had ever entered his life.

He held that pen over the sentence, because there was something more he wanted to say; something bursting within him struggling to be out, to be expressed, to be read, to be cried out. He held the pen there, then slowly put it down.

Oh, God . . . he thought. Then putting his head down Pancho Villa began to cry, because there was nothing else he could do.

XXIII. THE FIRST CHIEF

THE RUIN of his hopes flustered and infuriated *don* Venustiano Carranza. Treachery from underlings, disrespect from that ambitious clown, Álvaro Obregón, and the unsettling fear that some day that damned peasant, Villa, might fight his way to an unshakable position; all this preyed unceasingly on Carranza's mind as his train pulled into Saltillo, the capital he had been driven from by the *federales* nearly a year before.

Villa was not at the station to greet him, and this angered and humiliated Carranza. In fact, it angered and humiliated him to reflect that he was back in his own capital only by virtue of that—*peón.* Obregón might have taken it, had he not been bogged down in his own campaigning down the western coast. Pudgy, fatuous fool. The ignominy of having to tolerate Obregón every day, to listen to his bragging and his hypocritical humility. At least Villa wasn't around all the time. Less evil!

Yet he needed them both. No use deceiving himself about that. Obregón's western campaigns were simpler than Villa's horrible bloodbaths. But Obregón was craftier than the bandit. Where Villa was hitting the big extremely-fortified Federal citadels, Obregón was employing guile, conserving his forces, and still winning both territory and a reputation. Moreover, he was pacing Villa's southward drive, victory for victory—and who knew the difference? Who understood that each time Villa attacked he drew the Huertistas from the coast, giving Obregón a chance to take the weakened garrisons, and look good?

Unquestionably, beneath Obregón's fat face lay a vicious brain. A petty man with large ambitions. But, never mind. The time would come. Obregón was no *politico* yet, so he needed Carranza, as Carranza neded Obregón. And both needed that *pelado*, Villa, to grind the *federales* to bits. Insolent, common dog!

It was incredible how Villa prospered. Battle after battle: buckets of blood and bone strewn about those bleak hills and deserts. Yet he continued to grow, as though he thrived on pure gore. My God. It was absolutely frightening.

Well, at least he'd had the satisfaction of having ordered Villa to take Saltillo, and made him submit, when it was Zacatecas Villa had wanted to take. There was a deep satisfaction in bending such Neanderthals, and greedy, little *peso*-pinching merchants like Obregón, to his will.

Carajo! But he still worried. What if Villa should beat Obregón to Mexico City? Little danger there. Hadn't he been diverted to Saltillo with a few speeches about "patriotism," and "the motherland," and such nonsense? And that had given Obregón plenty of edge.

What would happen when he informed Villa that he'd sent General Natera to attack Zacatecas independently? *Carajo!* That would require a bit of diplomacy. But then, reports had it that Villa had stopped to get married in Torreón to celebrate his victory. Some celebration. Those *peones* had the sensibilities of rabbits and cats. Some shopgirl, no doubt. No bother about silly matters like bigamy. Villa with his damned, self-built morality. He'd take them to bed, then to the preacher because he felt women liked to get married!

Well, there were compensations for everything in life. Ever since Villa had publicly labeled Obregón a "chocolate-drinking lounge-lizard," the obese little pea-merchant seemed half out of his mind with the need to beat Villa to the Capital. And that was just splendid for *don* Venustiano, for the Capital of Mexico; or more precisely, the *Palacio Nacional,* was where his ultimate goal lay.

Bueno. Todo al provecho! It was a good philosophy. Health, happiness and confusion to one's enemies. He had to remember to propose that as a toast at dinner, and Villa would probably drink to it, considering his mentality.

Ah, demonio! Curse it! Villa was a damned teetotaler.

2

"It isn't possible!" growled Villa. *"No señor.* It isn't possible that you can walk right into my office, stick your whiskers in my face and admit that you betrayed me the minute my back was turned!"

"Your office, *mi general?"* replied Carranza ironically. *"Betrayed* you? I was under the impression that Saltillo was the Capital of my state. And that I was the leader."

"But I took it for you. Yes, and Camargo, Conejos, Mapimí and Bermejillo. I took them, to support your leadership. Because I was stupid enough to believe you might be sincere with me!"

"You snarl as though you would like to kill me," said Carranza. "When you accepted me as First Chief, was it your plan to win victories for yourself? To act only for Villa?"

"Damn you, Carranza, you're trying to confuse me."

"And now insults and insubordination?"

"You knew I wanted Zacatecas. You deliberately sent Natera to attack knowing that."

"I only consider what is good for the Revolution, not for any individual," said Carranza seeing that his forced calm had worked on Villa's sense of inferiority and shame.

"And now Natera's bogged down, calling for help, eh? And you have the audacity to ask me to send him 5000 of my men."

"Of the *Revolución, mi general.* Or so I thought."

Pancho Villa paced the room, head down, hands fidgeting behind his back. He was striving to control himself, knowing Carranza delighted in rocking his composure, and that each time it
constituted another victory for the tricky, old bastard. What a
fool he'd been to trust him, after Angeles' warning. But no. It
wouldn't go that way. When Villa lost his temper, he sacrificed
all traces of logic. There were other ways for civilized men.
And he meant to be as civilized as any man, by God! Suddenly
he had it. He saw Carranza's defeat. He would reason him right
into a corner.

"*Muy bein, jefe,*" said Villa. "Natera needs help. So I'll give
him help."

Carranza's eyes grew suspicious. He didn't like the way Villa
was grinning. "What sort of help?"

"Everything. *Todo.* All of it. Zacatecas guaranteed."

"I don't understand. What do you mean—guaranteed?"

"I'm sending him the whole Northern Division."

"Preposterous!"

"And me with it."

It was Carranza who flushed now, spilling his glass of port
as he rose. "Absurd. I will not permit it."

"You forbid me to move my own army?"

"Emphatically. I absolutely forbid it. Do you think I can't see
your game? You are to send 5000 men as I've directed, not one
more. Or I'll brand you as insubordinate and a traitor to this
Revolution. I, Venustiano Carranza, its First Chief."

Villa stood for a long moment as if reflecting. "In that case,
don Venustiano, I have to ask you to accept my resignation."

"You must be joking," said Carranza stupefied.

"*No señor.* Before I leave Saltillo you'll have my resignation.
And Mexico will wonder why. They'll ask why I lost my army,
the army I made. And they'll wonder what you intend to do with
it. And they'll wonder other things."

"Very clever," said Carranza. "Very well put. But, in view of
this turn of events, I can only think of rewarding the hero of

Torreón and Saltillo with a post befitting any General no longer
fit to fight. Chihuahua needs a governor."

"Me—a governor?"

"Ah, but you underestimate yourself, just as you've under-
estimated me, *mi general*. You've done a splendid job of govern-
ing the state already. Of course, I can't guarantee I can let the
peasants keep the land you gave them."

"You touch that . . ." said Villa moving toward the old man.
"You touch that—and I'll kill you!"

"You will do what I want," said Carranza coolly, "or suffer the
consequences."

"Yes. I was a fool," said Villa. "Those whiskers, I know why
you wear them now: they hide the face of a shameless liar!"

"There is no need for us to quarrel," said Carranza. "There
is enough here for all of us. You need but learn to obey."

"You have my resignation," Villa shouted. "And with it my
promise that I'll die before I knuckle under to you. I swear it
on my sacred mother's grave."

Carranza stood smiling. Out of long habit his carefully mani-
cured fingers combed his full, white beard toward the third
brown button of his khaki uniform.

"When you step through that door, General Villa," he said
"I shall immediately summon the leaders of the Northern Di-
vision and instruct them to select a new General-in-Chief. Then
I shall order 5000 men to Zacatecas. Is that clear?"

"Then order them. Take the army, my rank, the whole damned
state of Coahuila, and stick them up your aristocratic *fundillo*.
Is *that* clear?"

Pancho Villa glared at the suave, towering figure of the First
Chief, then stalked out, motioning Angeles and Medina in the
outer office to follow.

"We heard it all," said Angeles shaking his head. "It was incredible. Even for Carranza."

"Well," said Villa. "You work for him again. And you, Juan.
And all of you."

"Impossible," said Angeles. "Unthinkable. I go only where you go, General Villa."

"And I go, too," said Juan Medina.

Villa stopped suddenly and as he did a smile spread over his face. *"Señores,"* he said. "I don't know about you, or about the Northern Division. But Pancho Villa is going to Zacatecas. And he is going to take Zacatecas."

"Is anyone else invited?" asked Medina.

"Cómo no? Any of Pancho Villa's friends are welcome. All who want to come."

"When do we leave, *mi general?"* asked Medina.

Villa shrugged. *"Quién sabe?* It would depend on what baggage we take, wouldn't you say, *mi general Angeles?"*

The artilleryman shook his head. "Incredible. At my age to find the world upside down. Felipe Angeles, once the Director of Chapultepec, participating in a mutiny—without remorse."

"Mutiny?" asked Medina innocently. "What mutiny, sir? We are going to a ball, sir. To dance our way through Zacatecas."

Don Venustiano Carranza was in his elaborate governor's palace, preparing to depart for the north, when the astounding news arrived. Villa had left Saltillo during the night, but he had not gone alone. Every man, cannon, car, horse, cartridge and train belonging to the *División del Norte* had pulled out for Zacatecas. Villa had not ordered them out. He had merely loaded his 300 Dorados, and his new woman, on his personal train and left. And the entire division had followed.

As to *don* Venustiano's suggestion that they meet to elect a new chief: they had left him a counter-suggestion. It was all quite vulgar, and just the thing to send the "First Chief" off to Sonora in a very ugly mood.

XXIV. THE CENTAUR OF THE NORTH

EVEN THE WIND stood still. As day broke that June 23rd, of 1914, the clatter of caisson wheels, the blowing of horses, the sharp click of bolts and hoarse whispers of the men. It was that magic pause between preparation and execution of a battle.

On a hillside overlooking the capital city of Zacatecas, only 500 kilometers removed from Mexico City, General of Division Francisco Villa galloped up to his staff and leaped gracefully from Seven Leagues' back, and stood patting the animal fondly.

Generals Angeles, Medina, Avila and other staff members, greeted him with formal salutes which he acknowledged with a nod. The pants under his right legging bothered him, so he sat on a rock, unbuckled the thigh-length, leather legging and redid it. He glanced at his silver watch, rose and took a pair of binoculars from a case on his saddlehorn. He blew on the eyepieces to clear them. "Everybody ready?"

"*A sus órdenes, mi general,*" replied Angeles.

Villa hung the glasses about his neck, untied the black bandana from his throat and wiped his dusty face. "*Chihuahua!*" he said, spitting. "All the dust in the world's in Zacatecas. Doesn't it bother you, Angelito?"

"I ignore it, sir."

"So do I," said Villa. "But it makes my nose tickle. After all these years, I hate dirt. Except for farming, of course. But I'd like to be buried in cement."

"In cement?" asked Medina. "Why?"

"*Hombre,* it's clean . . . Well, *señores.* Now to business."

Turning slowly, still with one hand holding the bandana and binoculars, Villa raised the glasses and studied row upon row of artillery pieces far behind—their muzzles elevated, their khaki-clad crews braced stiffly beside them in the fashion prescribed by the military Angeles.

Further up, but still behind the long, brown lines of his infantry, stood the mounted brigades of Fierro, Urbina, Herrera, Ortega, and many other line commanders. And near the hill crests lay the machinegun position and his snipers.

Twenty-two thousand men brought in by 20 trains from Torreón and Saltillo, faced the 15,000 Huertistas under General Luis Medina Barrón, and his subordinate Generals, Antonio Olea, Soberanes Vásquez, Caraveo, Argumedo, Rojas—and that old and hated enemy, Pascual Orozco, leader of the Red Flag Irregulars.

Pancho Villa, a man on the crest of the most spectacular Mexican military career since the fabled Porfirio Díaz; Villa who had parleyed eight men into an army; the unconquerable horseman whom the newspapers had dubbed "The Centaur of the North," raised the black bandana above his head, twirled it, and brought it down.

Behind him a bugler sounded a call which was echoed by the buglers along the lines of brigades. From the artillery positions came the reply, and this resounded from the infantry buglers on the slopes of La Bufa, Tierra Negra, Loreto, La Sierpe, El Grillo.

Again Villa's bandana fluttered. The artillerists broke formation. Eight thousand horses snorted, pranced impatiently and pawed the earth. Even the wind caught their excitement, sending the red, white and green flags of Mexico flapping brilliantly over the heads of the mounted bearers.

"*Bri-ga-daaa Juárez . . . A-van-ce!*"

"*Bri-ga-daaa Fierro . . . A-van-ce!*"

"*Bri-ga-da—*"

"Sound commence firing," said Angeles to his music.

Wave after wave of horsemen surged forward at a gallop as the roar of cannon shrouded the morning with smoke. The Federal perimeter around Zacatecas seemed to sigh with a releasing tension as its own artillery replied. The earth exploded in flames, and the mighty *División del Norte* moved on like a sweating, clattering, flame-belching beast, to grind still another enemy force into broken flesh and running blood under its pounding feet.

Pancho Villa's first charge never paused, nor did it reach for tactics. *Un golpe terrible*—one terrible blow—was what the fierce Villa hurled at his enemies, and it was enough. Within three hours the Federal positions were in shreds, their trenches broken, their cannon overrun. Caught in that awesome and merciless grinder called the Northern Division, General Barrón's officers and men went under. By nightfall Villa was master of Zacatecas.

During the fighting, two days before, General Rodolfo Fierro had received a painful leg wound. He was still suffering from it next morning as he finished his breakfast. Perhaps more dangerous was the fact that he was also bored.

An hour later, as was his custom, he visited the stockade to look over the prisoners. There were several hundreds, of which 300 unlucky men were Redflaggers. The enlisted non-Reds were offered the usual choice: Villa's cause or a firing squad. To the Reds who asked to join Villa, Fierro smiled and replied: "I have something more interesting for you boys. It's a little game I've just invented."

He pointed to an adobe wall which stood only about 100 yards away. "You see that little wall? Well, I'm going to stand right outside this stockade gate, and you are going to run out, one by one. If you clear the wall before I pick you off, you're a free man. If not . . . But don't worry too much. I'm a very bad shot."

Understandably the prisoners weren't overly anxious to play human trap-shots. Fierro then instructed the guards to bayonet anyone who refused his turn. With that he told his orderly to spread a blanket on the ground for him to sit on, bring 300 rounds of pistol ammunition—one shot for each prisoner—and to keep his guns loaded.

With his particular genius for such matters, Fierro waited until the first prisoner was almost to the wall before he killed him. So for the second, the third, and on and on. Firing with either hand he tracked each man's desperate run deliberately then dropped him whenever he was ready. By noon he was still fresh, and rather than waste time, he had his lunch brought and ate it standing, without interrupting his game. He hadn't missed a man yet. His orderly busily loaded one gun as Fierro fired the other. The last 100 were a bit tougher. His hands were beginning to swell, the guns becoming heavier, and it was difficult tracking as the men leaped over and around the bodies of their comrades. But none had made it, yet.

It was growing dark as the last man broke from the gate. He raced, frantically, weaving and dodging, while Fierro, his hands throbbing now, his eyes blurred, found his lead. Suddenly the man was on the wall. Incredibly, as though in fiction, the last man seemed just about to make it when Fierro's pistol roared. The prisoner stiffened and fell.

"Shall I see if he's dead?" asked the orderly.

"When I shoot a man—he's dead," said Fierro unsmiling. Then with a yawn he let the heavy gun drop, and lay down beside it. By the time the orderly had thrown another blanket over him, he was fast asleep. What he dreamed about no one can know. But if the deaths of those 300 men moved him one way or the other, he never mentioned it to anyone.

3

On July eighth, General Álvaro Obregón, taking advantage of the Federal confusion in central Mexico, threw his Army of the Northwest—18,000 strong—against Guadalajara and won his greatest victory to date. Caught by surprise the Federal garrison lost 2000 dead and 5000 prisoners. Obregón's booty was 16 cannon, 30 locomotives and a tremendous store of small arms and ammunition.

On July 15th, seeing his western ports cut off, his main railway and cities in central Mexico blocked by Villa, and the indomitable Zapata again approaching from the south, *señor presidente* Victoriano Huerta gave some sober reflection to his grim future. With undiminished hypocrisy he composed a maudlin farewell to "The Mexican Public," pilfered two million pesos from the national treasury and took what Pancho Villa ironically termed "the road to Veracruz." There he boarded the German cruiser "*Dresden*," bound for Cuba. His rule of terror, drunkenness and disgrace had lasted 17 months, and the man most responsible for his downfall had been the *peón* he had once placed before a firing squad.

It was no time for indecision. Learning of Huerta's resignation, Pascual Orozco fled for the American border and asked asylum. Neither Huerta nor Orozco would ever see Mexico again. The *peón's* triumph was complete. Madero was avenged.

XXV. "VIVA VILLA! VIVA ZAPATA!"

IN THE UNEASY PEACE which followed Huerta's escape, the four leading revolutionary figures of Mexico displayed their natural bent. General Emiliano Zapata's peasant army, swollen to 20,000, reached Cuernavaca and waited. Pancho Villa left the major strength of his 30,000 Villistas along the garrisons north of the Capital and returned to Chihuahua to further his civil agrarian reforms. *Don* Venustiano Carranza waited in Tlalnepantla while his army chief, General Álvaro Obregón, entered Mexico City on August 15, 1914, and claimed the city for the "Constitutionalist Government," as the Carranzistas called themselves.

Finally, on August 20th, the "First Chief of the Constitutionalist Army" and "Keeper of the Power" (*don* Venustiano Carranza's own splendid titles) made his triumphant entry into the Capital of Mexico. His reception was as tremendous as would be the public relief to see him departing six years later. But at this moment the only thorn in Carranza's perfect *político* garden was Villa, the Centaur, who had broken with him over Zacatecas. Villa, whose ideals were not too far removed from that other *peón,* Zapata's. Villa who commanded the most powerful, most battle-hardened army in Mexico.

Carranza's needs were clear: One, he must again woo Villa's support. Two, he must convince the combined Revolutionary generals and Governors of his total indifference to personal power. Three, he must somehow separate Villa from his best supporters.

If *don* Venustiano Carranza had sought to increase his personal popularity through political theatrics, he was in for a rude surprise.

At the first conclave of the new revolutionary Chamber of Deputies, Carranza appeared, read a long report of his "government's" accomplishments, then offered his resignation as "Keeper of the (Presidential) Power" and retired. But, like Richard III, he had left behind his clackers. Instantly, Luis Cabrera, a deputy, leaped to his feet and delivered an impassioned speech which ended in: ". . . Let us not accept *señor* Carranza's resignation!" The applause was polite. The best achievement was that the convention agreed not to name a successor for the moment.

A second convention was held at Aguascalientes, 400 kilometers north of Mexico City, on "neutral" ground. Already the initial meeting had demonstrated that three distinct camps were forming. There were the pro-Carranza, the pro-Villa and the pro-Conventionists who felt the Deputies should rule Mexico through a neutral President. Confident of making gains Carranza sought to win these factions to himself by delivering a character assassination speech on Villa which concluded: ". . . *There is an ambition greater than that of becoming president of the Republic, and this is the ambition to become omnipotent militarily, that a man may so be able to dominate all powers in the Union. The insistence of General Villa on maintaining an army . . .*

indicates clearly his dream of naming presidents, appointing deputies, designating the supreme court, dominating governors of states and, in general, overwhelming the power of the Republic. I shall not now dwell on the ambitions of General Zapata, but I'll venture they aren't much different from those of General Villa . . ."

Carranza's remarks were calculated to frighten the members of the convention, to panic them into electing him President. But he had misjudged Francisco Villa's growing political sophistication. Villa's immediate reply, read to the Deputies by his representative, was brief, characteristic—and crushing.

"If, as señor Carranza contends, I constitute a danger to Mexico, and if, as I contend, he constitutes the real threat, there is but one honest and meaningful solution: I therefore propose that for the common good of our country, we both meet, at some appointed place, before this delegation, and that we both commit suicide—which act should erase all threats to our nation."

The *guerrillero's* proposal—whether entirely serious, or simply meant to expose Carranza's hypocrisy—was greeted with thunderous cheers and applause by the Convention, and by that single *"golpe terrifico"* smashed Carranza's hopes of dominating the vote and branding Pancho Villa a traitor.

Instead, the Conventionalists chose General Eulalio Gutiérrez, one of their own, to serve as interim-President, and Gutiérrez' first act was to confirm Villa as General-in-Chief of the Northern Division and to select that Division as protector of the Convention's rights. Furious at this flagrant disregard of his virtues, *don* Venustiano Carranza disavowed the Convention he, himself, had called together and immediately left Mexico City for Veracruz where he established his "Government" in exile.

The talking was over. The hordes of belted, gun-heavy men who had fought together to defeat Huerta, now stood looking at each other through the eyes of friendship for the last time. Then they turned and parted as enemies. Pancho Villa and *don* Venustiano Carranza were openly at war.

2

Even politically the once humble *guerrillero* had proven the better tactician. Yet a deep hurt lay in the discovery that Maclovio Herrera, a friend whom Villa had loved as a brother, had defected to Carranza, seduced by lies and promises.

Determined to seat the new Conventionalist President, Gutiérrez, Pancho Villa now turned his powerful force southward and occupied Tabuca, in the outskirts of the Capital. Zapata's Mongol-like hordes had already entered Mexico City, and the moment of confrontation between these two peasant generals was finally at hand.

3

"I'll begin by not lying to anyone or wasting your time," said Pancho Villa as he dismounted. "I've come here to seat President Gutíerrez, *mi general* Zapata, and that's what I'm going to do."

Surrounded by that ocean of enormous *sombreros* and white-clad southern peasants, Pancho Villa and his companions seemed positively cosmopolitan in their northern woolens and Stetsons. Villa looked like a tiger-hunter in the white pith helmet and silk scarf he'd added to his Oxford tweeds. He scarcely looked the hillsman anymore, but the big hatted, charro costumed Emiliano was too polite to comment.

"That's why I'm here, too," said Zapata after a moment.

"And you must know I stand against Carranza," said Villa.

"That's why I'm here, too," said Zapata again.

"My armies belong to Mexico," said Villa.

"That's why I'm here, too," said Zapata.

"Then, *don* Emiliano, there's no more need for words," said Villa opening his powerful arms wide.

Emiliano Zapata's dark eyes smiled and he pulled grandly at his huge moustache. Amid the cries of *"Viva Villa! Viva Zapata!"* the two *peón* leaders dove into each other's arms, laughing and pounding each other loudly, happy in their meeting, secure in their aims, and welded as one in their mutual respect.

All that day and all that night the two *campesino* leaders walked amid the surrounding and serene beauty of Xochimilco discussing their views, comparing programs for the poor and laying plans for the future.

"Is it true that you've given the *peones* land?" asked Zapata.

"*Sí, cómo no?* Sixty-two and a half acres for every man who wants it, and with enough money to work it and buy seed. Otherwise, what good is it? They need food for their families while they await the first crop. They need tools, animals, houses. Otherwise they have to sell part of their land, or give their crops away to landsharks to stay alive."

"*Muy verdad,*" said Zapata. "That's what I'm trying to do, too, in Morelos, my own state. But first we need decency in the *Palacio Nacional,* don't we? Why is that so hard to find?"

"I don't know," said Pancho.

On the morning of December sixth, 1914, a year to the month since he had fled Mexico City as an escaped Federal prisoner, General Francisco Villa, resplendent in a field commander's uniform, mounted *Siete-Leguas* and placed himself at the head of the combined Northern-Southern armies. Beside him rode Zapata, in a splendid charro uniform, and on either side of them rode Generals Urbina, Fierro, and Zapata's Rafael Buelna. Behind Villa came his magnificent *Dorados,* then General Felipe Angeles before his artillerists. Then what the newspapers termed "the terrifying horsemen of the Northern Division," followed by more brigades and regiments of the two forces. Zapata's peasant bandsmen, in straw hats and sandals, provided music from the south, Villa's khaki-uniformed bands played music from the north, and the satisfaction and wild cheers were shared by all. It was typical of Villa to reflect that parading with Carranza he would have ridden in the rear . . . "and carrying a shovel."

The largest army modern Mexico had ever seen: 50,000 first class fighting men, marched down *Paseo de la Reforma, Juárez* and *Plateros* Avenues, and into the *Plaza* where Reyes had died and the loyal troops had fought for Madero less than a year before.

It didn't seem possible to Pancho Villa that so much had changed. So very much. So many deaths, so many faces gone, so much suffering, defeat—and finally triumph. He had been an obscure colonel then. He had not known Felipe Angeles or Zapata. Madero still lived and dreamed. Mexico had been another nation, really. Less mature, less blooded, despite its long history of war and its struggle for maturity. The *científico* and the *hacendado* had ruled. But who ruled now? They had killed Madero, a moderate. Now their punishment was before them: the *peón* was marching, flushed with victory and power, toward the doors of the *Palacio Nacional*. Villa and Zapata, side-by-side, not fighting over spoils like two dogs, but content with giving their victory to the people. For what could a sane man do with victory, with freedom, but give it to the people?

A little after 3 P.M., Generals Villa and Zapata reached the National Palace, dismounted, and walked in, accompanied by their staffs. They stood in the balcony, acknowledging cheers, then walked through the *Palacio* accompanied by President Gutiérrez, and into the main reception chamber, where the enormous, gilded presidential chair sat.

Surrounded by photographers and chattering people Pancho Villa stood staring at the magnificent object. He'd been fighting his way toward this chair for years; never intending to sit in it, but certainly intending to see somebody sit in it. Somebody like . . . who?

Half embarrassed, half joking, he let himself be maneuvered toward the chair. Gutiérrez looked distressed. The photographers and newsmen went wild. "General Villa, how about a picture? Please. Just one picture. Come on everybody. Just sit down for a second." No one ever thought to ask Gutiérrez.

Villa grinned. "All right. For just a second. Let's go. Emiliano, you take the big one, I'll sit next to you and Urbina."

"No, Pancho. The gold one's more your style."

"Not mine, dammit!"

"You sit in the big chair, general," said Johnny Roberts, an American newsman. "General Zapata, take the chair beside General Villa. And General Urbina, right over here, on General

Villa's right. That's swell. Come on, *amigos*. Let's shoot it while everybody's grinning."

Puff!

"Great shot! Everybody get it? One more now."

"No, that's plenty," said Villa rising, blushing. "That damned chair's too big for me. I'd get lost in it. *Vámonos*, Emiliano. Let's get away from this gang of crazy *gringos* and politicians."

They returned to Xochimilco, listening to the sweet singing of Zapatista soldiers with their *viejas* around their fires. It seemed to Pancho that National Palaces didn't really exist, that the crowds and cheers were only phantoms.

"You know something, Emiliano? I'm going to confess this between us. I found myself thinking: 'It's a big chair, and I'm in it. I could stay here forever, if I felt like it, and nobody could move me, if I didn't want to move! That's a hell of a thing to think, isn't it? That's why I couldn't wait to get out of it."

"I'll confess something, too," said Emiliano Zapata smiling. "You know, when me and my brother first got here? Well, Eufemio guarded the door, and I sat in that Goddamn gold saddle. And man, I felt like God! It really scared me. I thought: '*Hombre*, that's all Mexico would need—another imbecile."

"Well, this is goodbye, Emiliano. I'm going home as soon as I can get loose. This place is not for me."

"I been thinking about Morelos, too. There's nothing like a man's own land, *amigo*. Anyway, I think we scare these chocolate-drinkers, you and me. And . . . we got what we came for."

4

"*Bueno, compadre*. I'm waiting for you to say something."

"Ah, *pues*. You see, Panchito—*mi general*—it's this way: With all the goings and comings, and all the turns and returns, I got a little mixed up, you see?"

"So damned mixed up that you fleeced half of Mexico City, and now you're starting on the other half, *eh, mi general?*"

"Well, you see, *mi general*. It was all pure strategy, really, if you want to know the sacred truth."

"It would be nice to hear the truth from you, *mi general* Urbina. It would make the devil tremble."

"Well, I . . . thought . . . if I took their money away from those rich bastards . . . Well, then they couldn't give it to Carranza."

"Ah, so you were really thinking of the Revolution."

"Panchito," said Urbina, his tiny eyes growing moist. "May a bolt of lightning strike me if I ever had any other thought!"

"Well, sir, I'll tell you what's going to strike you—right through that come-crazy crooked brain—six bullets, *mi general*. That's what. Six pieces of .30 caliber lead right out of a firing squad's rifles. A squad commanded by me. Is that clear? Now, you bring me that money. All of it. And you'd better not be missing *one centavo*, because the owners will know."

"*Ah,* Panchito, *mi compadrito.* You're so good to me," said Urbina tearfully. "I'll never do it again. Never. I promise!"

"All right, get out. I'm still mad at you," said Villa.

Fierro and Villa watched the sobbing general go, then Fierro threw down his cigar. "Well, you fell for it, as usual."

"Aw, he didn't mean any harm," said Villa shuffling papers.

"Yeah," said Fierro. "A quarter of a million *pesos*. Just a kid's prank. Who cares?"

"Don't make a big noise, Rodolfo."

"Big noise? Anyone else would have been against a wall. But not Urbina. He cries a little, wheedles a little, and you act like a fond mother. When are you going to wise up to him? He's a thief, a diddler and a Goddamned liar. Everybody knows it, except you."

"He's also my *compadre*. We starved together, shared the same horseblanket, and felt the same cold winds. We were two men, alone, who would have bled white for each other. And there were days when only the sound of his voice—only that—kept me from going crazy! You think I don't see his faults? I see yours, too!"

For the first time since they had met, Rodolfo Fierro's face registered pain. A deep, unmistakable hurt.

"Go on," said Villa. "Get out of here. Leave me alone."

5

"I like good food, and I love music," said Pancho Villa, explaining to his dozen or so distinguished guests why he'd sent his cook into the kitchen of the elegant *Hotel Palacio,* and brought the headquarters military band to play during their dinner. This was the sort of peasant eccentricity which both charmed—and worried—the Mexico City sophisticates.

"*Carajo*," whispered Raoul Madero after a moment. "Just look at what eyes that *guerrita's* making at you, Pancho."

"Who?"

"That little blonde behind the cashier's box."

Pancho glanced over and caught the girl's coquettish, sidelong glance. Her interest was unmistakable.

"She's French, you know," said Raoul. "Delicious."

"*Demonio,* you don't say. *Francesa? Ay, Chihuahua, amigo!*"

"From Paris. And what a body."

"By God!" said Villa, pounding the table. "Fierro, get me a preacher. That settles it. I'm going to marry her right now!"

"But she might already be married," said Fierro.

"Then I'll give the Goddamn Frenchman one minute to run, before I make her a widow. Get the preacher. I'll call her over." Motioning: "You, *señorita.* Come here, please!"

She walked up, smiling seductively at him.

"*Señorita,* my name is—"

"The famous General Francisco Villa," she finished for him. "The whole world knows you by now, *monsieur.*"

"And your name, *señorita—?*"

"Yvette," she said. "*Mademoiselle* Yvette."

"Well, *Señorita* Yvette, we're going to get married. What do you think of that?"

"Married? Who is getting married, *monsieur?*"

"Me and you, who else?"

"Married? But *c'est impossible.* I don't even know you!"

"What do you mean you don't know me," asked Villa puzzled. "You just told me my name."

"But I don't want to marry you," she said nervously.

"Listen, when a woman looks at a man the way you looked at me—they'd *better* get married. Because she's going to get—"

You're crazy, *monsieur!*" she cried in a panic.

"Sure, I'm crazy about you. Raoul, talk to the desk clerk. Tell him I'll need a bigger room."

At that point, with the whole dining room staring, and the men at Villa's table scandalized, the girl cried, "Help! Someone call the French Embassy!" and fainted.

"Good," said the philosophical Villa. "Now she'll be easier to carry upstairs. Everybody come up to my suite. After the wedding we'll have a big party!"

But there was no wedding and no party. With half of Mexico City talking about "that bandit's" antics, the French *Chargé D'Affaires* arrived, taking a most provincial attitude, and demanding the girl's release. Villa was puzzled and angry. To him a woman's invitation meant action—not fainting spells and pimpy diplomats threatening to wire complaints home.

For the world's newspapers it was a great story: *French girl kidnapped by Mexican bandit!* For French, English and American readers it was shocking. Villa was a menace. For Pancho Villa it was the final straw. For the man in the White House, it was another moment of crisis. How could he recognize, as Chief Executive of a major nation, a man who had so little regard for protocol and propriety? *And that repulsive photo in the presidential chair!*

Drop by drop, day by day, Pancho Villa had tasted the bitterness of ridicule, and a growing distrust among the stuffed shirts of Mexico City. Confused and homesick, he couldn't endure it any longer. "I'm leaving here," he told Gutiérrez, "I'm leaving while there's still something left of me."

On January fifth, 1915, Pancho re-assigned his units, took his *Dorados,* and rolled his trains toward Juárez, where he belonged.

XXVI. CELAYA AND LEÓN

"YOU'VE PERFORMED WONDERS, General Villa. Absolute wonders!" said the American. "I wouldn't hesitate to pronounce your *Dorados* the finest cavalry in this hemisphere. And I'd have to include our own."

Villa understood even before Fierro had finished his translation, and nodded happily. "*Gracias, mi general* Escott." Then, self-consciously, in his labored English: "Tank yoo, my fren, General Escott. *Gracias.*"

Brigadier General Hugh L. Scott, military representative for President Wilson, returned the gracious nod. He had seen this man developing over the past year. He had seen his generosities, and his—well, his genius—as well as his faults. He knew, for example, that Villa had conceived of, and was already building in an El Paso foundry, a prototype of an armored motor vehicle, far in advance of anything owned by the United States army. He also knew that Villa had seen the possibilities of military airplanes, and already owned four of these. And that Villa had also developed a "rolling airdrome," unique in the world, which meant he could carry his aircraft by train, service them, and launch them from any spot along the tracks. Even the Europeans had nothing like that. Villa had even mounted cannon in armored railcars, and had developed the idea of attaching an "explorer" car before his engines to trigger enemy mines along the rails. Furthermore, General Villa had given every spare *centavo*, every spare minute, to the needy people of his land.

Who else had done this? Certainly not Mr. Carranza, or his fat muscle-boy, General Obregón. Hugh L. Scott had small regard for that pair. He'd been around them enough to know.

He came to with a start, realizing that Villa was smiling at him, waiting for him to continue.

"I'm tremendously impressed with everything you've shown me," he said. "And you may be sure I'll say so to the President when I return to Washington. Progress is impressive to Americans."

"*Ah, sí?*"

"Tell me, general. How long has it taken you to build all this? I'd like to point that out to Mr. Wilson."

"*Los Dorados, or todito?*" asked Villa directly.

"Well, I mean your entire military strength and organization," said Scott who caught a little Spanish.

"Tree jeers," said Villa holding up three fingers. "Wan jeer, almost, in prison of Huerta. Habe leetle army afterwart. Not so good before 1913. Bot afterwart take Juárez, and army grow up, yes? I try talk Eenglesh for you, *mi amigo*. For to make frenship weeth United Estates allways and Mexico. Okay?"

"*Mucho bueno*, okay," said Scott smiling. And the two men shook hands. "You're a fine man, general. As far as I'm concerned, there's no question as to your character and qualifications."

"What will your president think?" asked Fierro.

"Mr. Wilson? Well, sir. I think I can tell you that many of us are of a like mind on General Villa. And we're Mr. Wilson's advisors. That's why he sent us. So it's likely he'll listen. I only wish we could convince Mr. Carranza that we Americans want peace in this hemisphere."

"You convince Wilson," said Fierro. "We convince Carranza!"

2

Obregón was back in Mexico City. On January 23rd, following Villa's evacuation, the Carranzists had returned from Veracruz, and General Gutiérrez, the temporary President, had fled after appropriating 10 million *pesos* out of the treasury. Equally painful was the fact that two more of Villa's generals, and close friends, Aguirre Benavídez and José Isabel Robles, had deserted with Gutiérrez. Villa couldn't leave the Capital in Carranza's hands. Once more he wired general mobilization orders to all his garrisons, loaded a long procession of military trains, and turned attention and awesome power on *Ciudad México.*

Carranza, too, was nervous about his opposition. At the beginning of March, General Obregón received orders from his *primer jefe* to vacate Mexico City and proceed to the center of the country to "confront Francisco Villa." To Obregón, cocky and now commanding a "Constitutionalist Army" equal to Villa's, this meant fight. And it was a showdown long overdue.

Villa, moving southward slowly, picking up garrisons and much-needed ammunition as he went, heard of Obregón's plan to intercept him. *"Eso much me quadra,"* he said in his *campesino* slang. "That squares for me, *compañeros.* The sooner we meet, the sooner we tangle tails."

One thing worried his staff, and this was the fact that Generals Angeles and Urbina were on farflung courses with large portions of the Northern Division and at least three days from Villa's estimated point of impact with Obregón. But Villa didn't worry. "They'll get there," he said. "They always get there!"

As Pancho Villa arrived at Irapuato and Alvaro Obregón at Querétaro, their advance forces were just meeting at a town called Celaya. Here was to develop one of the bloodiest battles of any war, anywhere. Celaya would become the "Bloody Shiloh" of Mexico.

3

Pancho Villa approached the long-awaited battle with Obregón as he might have approached a personal gunfight. Excited by the prospects, aroused beyond any possibility of restraint, he wanted only to meet the Sonora pea-merchant, attack and quickly crush him. The telegraphed pleas of Felipe Angeles to wait for his arrival—still three days off—could not deter him. Nor could the supplications of Medina, Avila and others of his staff.

Villa seemed to have lost his reason. He wanted only to fight. "Obregón was the one who got Maclovio to leave me," he raged. "He and that bearded warthog, Carranza drove Robles and Benavídez from me, with their lying talk about my ambitions! Well, I have only one ambition now. I'm attacking."

On April third, with most of his artillery in General Angeles' column, and a minimum supply of ammunition, Pancho Villa opened fire on Obregón.

Álvaro Obregón, adhering to the new European school of warfare, had dug trenches, strung barbed-wire, backed by machine-guns, then placed his artillery behind the high ground —and waited. Villa's tactics were still to be the overpowering blow—which had shattered every army he had ever met. It was the meeting of two vastly different minds: one cool and calculating, willing to wait forever—the other impulsive, reckless, willing to bet all upon its daring originality.

One other man was behind Obregón's defenses: a stiff, proud Prussian who had good cause to remember and hate the *guerrillero*. That man, now in command of Obregón's artillery, was Colonel Maximilian Kloss (better known as Field Marshal Kloss, of the Imperial German Army); a man to whom Villa had once given a brief lesson in Mexican history.

If Villa had refused a pact with the devil—Carranza and Obregón had not. German arms and money were backing this fight.

At Celaya Pancho Villa opened his battle with artillery, then a cavalry charge, supported by more artillery. Obregón's counterbattery fire fell to Villa's rear, while mines, barbed-wire and machineguns tore the *guerrillero's* gallant charges apart.

Villa's face was that of an animal, not a man. It grew red, his eyes almost crossed with rage, his teeth gnashed, his veins stood out. Not even his closest associates dared talk to him.

Again and again he threw in his charges, and again Obregón's well-dug-in infantry, artillery and machinegun nests littered the hillsides with torn bodies and kicking, dying horses. Both Villa and Fierro appeared in the midst of this carnage, just as it seemed that a complete route of the Northern Army was inevitable. They appeared on their foaming horses, waving their murderous pistols, and crying to Villa's famed *Dorados:* "All right, you sonsofwhores! Let's see how good you really are!"

Thundering up the hill at their head, they threw themselves at Obregón's forces, staggering them. After one squadron had been shot out from behind them, they rode back for more *Dorados,* and then a third time for more, each time staggering Obregón with their magnificent and wild charges. Obregón's defenses were solid. He'd been well prepared by Kloss' science and his own cunning. Even so, he was on the verge of crumbling, when he was saved by a fresh column of 1500 men arriving at the peak of the battle.

Bloody, covered with sweat and caked with dirt, Pancho Villa was in a greater fury. Where was Tomás Urbina? He knew already that Felipe Angeles had been intercepted by a Carranzista column up north. But where was that damned Urbina?

By April sixth, Pancho Villa knew that he had lost Celaya. Yet he couldn't admit the bitterness of defeat. Never. Never since that first fight at the train, had he been so defeated by anyone.

He could not be defeated now, not by Obregón.

With that astonishing speed and mystical power of recuperation, Villa disengaged, reorganized, and struck Obregón again.

Toward the end of April General Angeles was finally leaving Nuevo León to join Villa. Rodolfo Fierro, three times wounded at Celaya, was out of action.

Tomás Urbina's disappearance was finally explained. Sick of battle, in one of his moments of weakness, he had detached his private train, and deserted his brigade, taking with him a one million *peso* payroll belonging to his troops.

"Tomás did this to me?" asked Villa unbelieving. "Urbina, of all people? My God! What's happening?"

Villa and Obregón met again, with their lines stretching from Silao to León. Villa advanced with his cavalry on the haciendas of Chichimiquillas and Napoles, and seeing his strongest positions compromised, Álvaro Obregón fell back. Villa charged. Again men fell by the hundreds, then thousands, littering the hills with blood, bodies and equipment. In several places, to the chagrin of Obregón, the marvelous Villa cavalry, covered by artillery, actually broke over barbed-wire, past machinegun nests, and into the trenches, trampling and killing Carranzistas at pistol range.

On June second, 1915, accompanied by members of his staff, Álvaro Obregón rode out on a personal reconnaissance of the lines. At the same time Pancho Villa was learning, to his intense frustration, that most of the reserve rifle ammunition sent to him from Juárez was 25-35 caliber—useless for the 30-30 Winchesters and the Mausers of his troops. At almost that same moment an obscure artillery captain was ordering a harassing fire mission on Obregón's lines. These three events were to determine the balance of the crucial battle of León.

General Obregón had just pointed to a distant Villista stronghold when the air shrieked with incoming artillery. In the resultant burst, Obregón's body was flung from his horse, and when his officers reached him his right arm hung only by a small piece of skin.

General Benjamín Hill, Obregón's closest friend, and fellow Sonoran, was now in command of the Carranzistas—and in that one moment of grief and glory he made the most important decision of his life. It was his decision to throw at Villa the combined forces of Generals Murguía, Castro and Diéguez, and his own, in one last, desperate attack. Had Obregón been conscious, his strategy would have been to wait—and Villa would have found time to replenish his faulty ammunition.

As it was, Villa was caught completely by surprise, and unable to defend himself. Within hours his troops were throwing away their empty rifles, retreating into the hills, scattering before Hill's cavalry and incessant artillery.

Twilight approached, mercifully shielding the remnants of the *División del Norte* which gathered in anxious queues to load onto the waiting trains. Villa's rearguard waited as anxiously for a new attack from the enemy. But Hill didn't seem to realize how completely his advance had demolished Villa's forces, or that

further resistance was impossible for lack of ammunition. And
he hesitated. Hesitated too long.

Down in the valleys sporadic firing could still be heard where
Villa's men made desperate demonstrations to confuse the enemy.
From the edge of a tiny wood, where the *Centaur* had gone to
watch his beaten army gathering, the moments of silence were
awesome, the coming of darkness seemed symbolic of his despair.

He dismounted, walking away from his *Dorados* who escorted
him about the field, and taking off his hat, he wandered to the
far side of the forest. And there he leaned against a tree thinking:
it's over. They've beaten you . . . *Cómo es posible?* How can that
possibly be?

Angeles! Angeles! Why aren't you here? Fierro, you devil!
Urbina! The enormity of it was in his heart—yet it seemed unable to penetrate his brain, and it was killing him.

"I'd rather have been beaten by a Chinaman, than Obregón!"
he said half aloud. "You've all left me. Where are you?"

"You called, *mi general?*" asked a small voice.

It was a boy. A frail, white-clad lad in a big hat, and carrying
a ribbon-decorated bugle.

"I told everybody to stay on the other side," snapped Villa.

"Forgive me, *mi general.*"

"Wait. Don't go. What are you called, *chamaco?*"

"They call me Panchito Segundo, *mi general.*"

"Second Panchito. Why?"

"My father was called First Panchito, *mi general.*"

"Is he dead, your father?"

"*Sí, mi general.* At Torreón."

"Then why aren't you home, looking after your mother,
Panchito?"

"She's dead, too, *mi general,*" said the boy looking at his hands.
"The *soldados,* and the *soldaderas* . . . our camp was hit by the
artillery that day, *mi general.*"

"I remember when I was a little—a young boy like you," said
Villa putting an arm around the boy's shoulders. "I remember

my *mamá,* how much I loved her, and she loved me. How old are you, *niñito?"*

"Fifteen, *mi general."*

"Fifteen . . . Tell me, Panchito. Have you been in the battles?"

"Yes sir. In all of them, since you came back. My *papá* was a sergeant, and we fought all the battles."

"And so did I, Panchito Segundo. We fought them together, you, your *papá,* and me. We dreamed of making ours a happier country. And they can't beat us out of that, can they?"

"No, *mi general."*

"No sir. Not all the Carranzas and Obregóns. Not all the rotten *políticos,* with all their rotten tricks and money, and all the stinking turncoats they can buy. We've got that much left, Panchito. Right up to the wall, and under the rope. Without food for our bellies, or a cartridge for our guns, or a blanket for our backs—we've got that over their kind."

Villa's voice cracked, and he choked up, and finally let the sobs come, the sobs of pain and frustration.

"What's the matter, boy?" he said trying to sound gruff. "Haven't you ever seen anybody cry before?" And then he grabbed the boy, hugging him hard, holding to him, as though that sense of feeling another being close to him was his sole salvation. "They've whipped me, Panchito!" he said. "Goddamn them, they've whipped me!"

"No, *mi general.* They didn't. They couldn't beat us!"

"Panchito. Listen," said Villa composing himself. "I want you to promise me something."

"Anything you want, *mi general."*

"Promise me you'll always feel this way. You and me. That we're not whipped. Never."

"We're not whipped, *mi general.* I know we're not."

"You go along now," said Villa drying his eyes and inhaling deeply the cold night air. "And not a word to anybody. *Conforme?"*

"Conforme, mi general."

"Bueno, Panchito. Tell them I'll be along in a minute."

When Álvaro Obregón regained consciousness, a week later, it was to learn that the terrible and invincible *División del Norte* was in full retreat northward, and that he was minus an arm. Always aggressive in victory, General Obregon ordered a broad advance, occupying Encarnación on June 20th, Aguascalientes on July 10, Zacatecas on July 17th, and San Luis Potosí by July 22, 1915.

Rodolfo Fierro, his arm still in a sling, detached his brigade from Villa's main force, swinging around Obregón's rear. In a maneuver as brilliant as any Villa might have executed, the "Butcher" began surprising outposts, sending false telegraph messages which tangled troops and supplies, destroying rails, communication lines and routes, and sacking Carranzista garrisons.

Even as Pancho Villa retreated into Chihuahua this rear force had retaken León, Celaya, Querétaro, San Juan del Río, Tula and Pachuca. But Fierro's battles were only designed to buy time for his chief. Withdrawing independently through Jalisco and Zacatecas, Rodolfo Fierro rejoined Villa's main column at the end of July.

"What a sweep, *compadre!*" said Villa admiringly. "You've got the balls of an elephant!"

It was the first time Pancho Villa had ever called him *compadre,* and to this strange, dark, murderous man, it meant everything.

XXVII. AGUA PRIETA

"MY OWN BROTHER drunk and making a damned fool of himself, squandering my money on whores, instead of sending me supplies. Urbina bathing in his lousy gold, in Nieves. My old Generals fighting against me. Shameless Judases all. Everywhere, treachery, stupidity and cowardice. And now this!"

Fierro watched through narrowed eyes as his *jefe* stormed around his office kicking over chairs and scattering paper, that same office in *Ciudad* Chihuahua which he'd once occupied so triumphantly.

"Liars!" screamed Villa pounding his fists against the desk. "Lying Chinamen! Those stinking *gringos!* That's all they are—and their promises are made of *mierda!*"

Tears of impotent rage filled his eyes. His jaws clamped so hard they trembled. Even Fierro had never seen Villa in such a wild rage, a rage provoked by the news that President Wilson had just extended recognition to Carranza.

"He'll never ruin this country, not even with Wilson's help. I'll kill him first," said Villa. "Me and you, Rodolfo. We'll go, disguised, to the Capital—and nail him!"

"And then what?" asked Fierro.

Villa looked up, panting like an exhausted animal. "You're right. Not yet. First those turncoats and traitors who helped him. First Urbina, then Herrera, then Benavídez and Robles—. No. Only Urbina now, so they'll know what's coming to them after I've put Carranza and Obregón in their graves. Urbina first!"

"*Qué va!*" said Fierro ironically. "Any day."

"You think I won't, eh? Well, I'll show you. Get a train ready. Order out 50 *Dorados* and horses. Cut the wires south, and get your own gear. Come on, what are you waiting for?"

"Listen, *jefe*, I know you," said Fierro. "This bastard's sitting comfortably in Las Nieves with everything he could steal. But one little sob out of him—and you'll take him back. I won't move one step until you swear to me this time you'll gut him, no matter what!"

"You have my word, *compadre*. If I don't kill him—you can!"

Moving southward, through Chihuahua, past *Ciudad* Delicias and Camargo; right through Obregón's outposts, and into Mapimí; Villa, Fierro and their escort of heavily-armed *Dorados* detrained, proceeding by horseback toward Tomás Urbina's *hacienda*, 20 kilometers beyond the last railspur. By dawn they

were nearing the *rancho,* and Villa's advance party reported a
guard of some 25 soldiers around the estate.

"*Bueno,* you hit the back, Fierro. I hit the front. *Vámonos!*"

With deadly efficiency the *Dorados* moved in, driving Urbina's
guards from their positions. Aroused by the fighting, the half-
dressed Tomás, still groggy from a night of carousing, rushed
to a window, pistol in hand. In an instant he'd taken in the
whole picture. Pancho Villa, the last man he'd expected to see,
was riding into his courtyard; the *hacienda* was surrounded by
Dorados. Resistance within the house lasted only minutes, then
Villa broke in. Tomás Urbina, one arm bleeding profusely, lay
on his bed staring at the door, knowing what was coming.

"*Ola, compadre,*" said Villa. "After coming such a long ways
to visit you, I'm surprised at the reception. One would think
you weren't glad to see me."

"That was an accident, Pancho. I can explain it."

"You mean an accident—like Celaya? You remember Celaya—
that little place where you left me in such a bad way?"

"No, *compadre.* I never—"

"But I know you had other things to do. I understand you've
been pretty busy robbing all the banks in the state, and killing
people who don't like the way you say good morning, and such."

"*Compadrito, por favor,* hear my side of it," said Urbina growing paler. "I was sick in bed when you called me. So sick you
wouldn't believe it. Almost dying. Sure I came here. I had to. But
I was going back. I never deserted you, Pancho. We're like
brothers. Do you remember the mountains? The *rurales*—?"

"Here comes the waterworks," said Fierro.

"Don't plead with me, Tomás," said Villa. "This time it's
not going to do you any good, because I didn't come here to
play games. Where's the money you stole?"

"Money, Pancho? Those were all lies you were told about
me. If I had any money, half of it would be yours. Look, you
know I would have brought it to you!"

"Well?" said Fierro looking at Villa.

"Search the house and grounds."

Within half an hour, over a million *pesos* worth of gold, bills and jewelry had been turned up, and again as much in gold and jewelry dug up outside.

"Well?" asked Fierro again.

Pancho Villa drew his pistol. "Leave us alone."

Rodolfo Fierro and the others waited in the mainroom. They waited like men of stone, listening for a shot. But there was none. Finally Villa emerged, holstering his gun. "I can't do it, Rodolfo," he said in an anguished voice. "We've been too close, too long. I can't get up the nerve to do it."

"Well, I can!" said Fierro.

"No! I won't let you," said Villa. "I'm taking him back to Chihuahua—to a hospital! Try to understand, *amigo* . . ."

"I understand only one thing, *jefe*. Your word. I have your word . . . Yes or no?"

"All right," said Villa at last. "But . . . find a way, so he won't know it. Tell him . . . tell him you're taking him to see a doctor. Don't let him suffer anymore."

"Get a buggy ready," said Fierro to the *Dorado* captain. "You and four men will accompany me. Hop to it."

Fierro then went in, told Urbina he was being taken to a doctor in Chihuahua City, and the crying, grateful little man was loaded into the buggy. "I knew it, Pancho," he said gratefully. "I knew you'd help me. We're *compadres*, aren't we? You're the best friend I ever had."

Pancho Villa turned away crying silently, and could still hear Urbina's happy voice as Fierro and the escort took him away.

Three miles up the dirt road, near a small bridge, Fierro ordered the escort to dismount, then told Urbina to go stand by a tree.

"Why should I do that?" asked Urbina, guessing the truth from Rodolfo Fierro's eyes. "I enlisted you, Rodolfo. Remember? I made you a captain. We were friends . . ."

"I'm not interested in old time's sake," Fierro said. "To me you're just a goddamn traitor, and you cost us Celaya. Because of you, and *piojos* like you, Villa's lost almost everything. Get over here, you sniveling sonofabitch. That walk'll buy you 10 more seconds of life."

It didn't. As the trembling man started walking away, Fierro signalled the squad to fire. Urbina seemed to trip and fall over. He quivered once, then again, and Rodolfo Fierro walked to him and calmly put two bullets in his brain. Then he rode back to tell Pancho Villa that Tomás Urbina's debt had been paid.

2

After Wilson's recognition of Carranza's government, a strict embargo had been placed on all arms and supplies crossing into Mexico. Only Carranza—and Obregón—had access to American war supplies. Yet, so long as Villa held Chihuahua, there was always a hope of receiving smuggled goods from across the border. Praying for the best, Pancho had already sent Felipe Angeles as far as Nueva York, to accompany Hipólito—his brother. Meanwhile, he made plans for a new campaign with what little coal and ammunition he had left to service his *División del Norte*.

"We'll split the *División* into three parts," he told his staff in Juárez. "This way we can hold Durango, Chihuahua, and parts of Sonora. We've got to have this border, *gringos* or not."

For the most part, however, Pancho Villa seemed inconsolable. He fraternized with no one, except the taciturn Fierro. He couldn't get the death of Urbina off his mind. Only his preparations to invade Sonora, and to attack the Carranzista General Plutarco Elías Callas, in the key border town of Agua Prieta, offered any relief.

It would be a difficult campaign, and he knew it. At this time of year he would have to leave the bulk of his army winter-quartering at Casas Grandes and cross the snow-covered Madre Occidental ranges with only a small vanguard to take and hold Agua Prieta until spring reopened the supply routes and let his main body through. But what a surprise those miserable Carranzistas would get! *Demonio!*

But whatever evil star had attached itself to Pancho Villa at Celaya still followed him to Casas Grandes. An unusually early and thick fall of snow in the Sierras, and rain in the foothills, had turned the streams and lakes into swollen obstacles, stalling Villa's artillery and cavalry at every turn. Rodolfo Fierro was in Villa's vanguard, and floods or not, Fierro meant to get through.

On this grey and squally morning of October 24th, Rodolfo Fierro, Sergeant Desedero Espinoza and two other members of Fierro's brigade rode far ahead of the main body. As was his custom in the field, Fierro wore several bands of ammunition wrapped around his body, his pistols on a thick belt and a massive pair of spurs on his heavy boots. In addition to this, he wore a money belt loaded with gold from Urbina's booty. Far to one side men were crossing the Laguna de Guzmán along a narrow bar. Fierro decided he would cross right where he was. His companions refused to follow saying there was a whirlpool near there caused by the entrance of a canal.

"You're just a pack of cowards!" yelled Fierro spurring his horse, which refused to enter. He then called for his remount, a splendid, fearless mare, which he mounted bareback, but still loaded with his own trappings. He dug his spurs into her, and a moment later he was fighting for his life.

"You stupid, sons-of-the-mother-whore," he yelled. "Don't just stand there looking at me. Can't you see I'm drowning? Throw me a rope!"

They could see he was drowning, yet they threw nothing. They sat on their horses watching while the current dragged the greatest killer of the revolution under. Then they rode back and reported proudly that their chief had never cracked; he had never begged for help. He had met death as he had met life— cursing and fighting it.

The version told to Villa was that they'd tried to reach him, but without success. "They've taken my right arm from me!" cried the *guerrillero*. "Goddamn the fates! What else can they take?" That, too, he was soon to learn.

3

The march through the mountain passes of the Sierra was an agony Villa would never forget. With only two batteries of artillery, 30 machineguns and 6500 picked men, he had begun his advance over the brutal, precipitous, blizzard-swept ranges, and down into the flatlands of Sonora. There he reorganized his scarecrow band of survivors, and pushed across a parched, murderous desert.

Up against the *Yanqui* border, with its back to Douglas, Arizona, lay Agua Prieta. Tear General Calles and his Carranzistas from it, and Sonora would belong to Villa, and to Governor Maytorena, an old friend, whose local rebel forces were still fighting for Madero's ideals.

On November first Pancho Villa confronted General Calles. He had every expectation of winning easily, for he outnumbered Calles two to one. Mindful of possible American intervention, Villa aligned his artillery east and west to avoid striking United States territory then launched a frontal assault, firing low into the enemy trenches. To his surprise, his charges were fiercely repulsed. His men fell on the wire and found it electrified. Scores of machineguns cut their withdrawal to pieces.

"Something's wrong," he said. "Calles couldn't have anything like this."

What Villa didn't know was that Calles' troops had been recently reinforced. Woodrow Wilson had actually permitted Carranza to transport new troops by train over American soil while the Villistas had been fighting through the brutal mountain blizzards.

Shortly before dawn of the third day, the sudden cry of *"Viva* Villa!" announced the launching of a night attack. Instantly, the horizon behind Calles' fortifications blinked awake. A dozen giant searchlights turned night into bright noon. Illuminated against the wire, the Villistas became targets for thousands of rifles, scores of machineguns, a barrage of flaming shrapnel which turned Villa's surprise attack into an incredible massacre. It wasn't a battle, but a slaughter.

"The *Yanqui* searchlights," cried Villa in despair. "Those *gringos malditos* are fighting on Carranza's side!"

When the screaming, stumbling retreat was over, 2000 dead or wounded Villistas lay in the field before the trenches of Agua Prieta. Destroyed with American help, caught by the growing power of Obregón's Sonoran armies, Villa had but one way out of that *cul-de-sac* which should have been his victory. Again he began the gruelling trek over the snowbound Sierras and this time in the height of winter. Without adequate clothing or fires, killing their exhausted horses for food, abandoning weapons and frozen comrades where they fell, the wretched survivors made their way back to Chihuahua. 6500 men had left for Sonora three months earlier. Fewer than 600 had come back.

But come back to what?

Believing Pancho Villa dead, and his task force annihilated, by Carranzistas and harsh weather, the bulk of the army he had left behind had scattered. His supplies were gone. His garrisons, once powerful strongholds all over the north, were crumbling. His Generals Natera, Quijano, Banda, Limón, even Fidel Ávila and Joaquín Terrazas had sought out surrender terms. Their brigades and regiments were no more. In one crippling blow Guadalupe, San Ignacio, Villa Ahumada—vital garrisons to Villa—had gone to the enemy without a shot, at the news from Agua Prieta. Then Chihuahua City, Casas Grandes, and Juárez. 4000 men in Juárez, 85 engines and 2000 cars in *Ciudad* Chihuahua, alone.

One year after it had come together as if by a miracle, the magnificent *División del Norte* had again vanished as if by the wave of a scorcerer's wand. It was all gone. Everything Villa had fought for, suffered for, risked his life for. All of it.

The sorcerer's name was Woodrow Wilson. A man who had permitted his personal prejudices to override the recommendations of his own advisors. It was a choice he would live to regret.

XXVIII." IT WAS ALL FOAM..."

PANCHO VILLA opened his eyes and tried to focus on the faces above him. He was feverish, parched and nightmarish. His breathing was feeble and rapid. He knew the signs.

"*Agua,*" he whispered. "Give me a drop of water."

One young man propped him, the other held a canteen to his lips. Drinking exhausted him close to the point of fainting again, but he fought it.

"How . . . how long . . . have I been here?"

"Five days, *mi general.*"

"I wasted your time. I'm going to die, *muchachos.*"

Barnabe Cifuentes and Joaquín Álvarez, the young *soldados* trusted with Villa's life, looked at each other in panic.

"*No, mi general.* You can be all right. We can cut your leg off, if you'll let us. And you might live. Please."

"What good would Pancho Villa be with one leg?" he said. "It was hard enough with two."

2

Defeated, virtually alone, and cut off from all sources of supply, Pancho Villa has been compelled to split the remnants of his once magnificent *División del Norte* into small, determined self-sustaining bands.

Each *cabecilla* (guerrilla leader) will be answerable only to Villa, and no one will know which band Pancho rides with next. His plan is to attack small towns, trains, and minor garrisons. As he did in 1911 and 1913, he will play for time while he grows himself another army.

But in early March, 1916, an event has taken place which changes all this: before dawn, of the ninth, the *cabecillas* Candelario Cervantes, Pablo López, Francisco Beltrán and Martin López have assembled their 400 men, made their way up a dry irrigation canal, past an army sentry, and attacked Columbus, New Mexico; the first foreign invasion of American soil since 1812.

Why? Some people say later that the Villistas have been reduced to this by Wilson's embargo, and Carranza's relentless pursuit. But more people say that it has been a matter of honor. Pancho Villa never forgot those who betrayed him. And that was what the *gringo presidente* has done.

In the battle between the American Army garrison and the Villistas, 18 soldiers die to the cries of *"Viva* Villa!" Some Villistas die, too, and others are captured. But most of them melt back into the hills of Chihuahua.

Carranza's reply to a stern American note is that from 1880 to 1886, during the reigns of Geronimo and Victorio, the United States and Mexico had enjoyed the "reciprocal privileges" of crossing each other's borders in pursuit of marauders. Why not, suggests *señor* Carranza, exercise these privileges now?

To make his suggestion even more palatable, *señor* Carranza declares Pancho Villa an outlaw once more. Washington responds favorably to the "Protector of Mexico's Executive Power," and on March 15, 1916, Brigadier General John J. Pershing crosses the Mexican border at the head of 15,000 men—spreading his cavalry, artillery and infantry into seven columns. Object of this "Punitive Expedition": to capture the outlawed ex-General Francisco Villa.

Having proposed the plan, *señor* Carranza now publicly protests the entry of the Americans, calling on the Mexican people to stand behind him, and ordering Mexican Federal troops out to confront the Americans. For President Wilson, this is but an inkling of what he has bought with Villa's betrayal.

At a little after 4 P.M. of March 27th, Pancho Villa is sitting in the center of the Plaza, in *Ciudad* Guerrero. He is cleaning his Colts, for his men have just taken the city. Nearby sit other *soldados,* also cleaning weapons. One boy has a Colt like Villa's.

As he pulls the hammer back, his hand slips and the pistol discharges. The .45 caliber lead bullet tears through Pancho's right leg, just over the knee. Villa curses. An accidental bullet—the first wound of his life—has ironically altered history. He had hoped to lure the *Americano,* Pershing, here by sending Villistas to hire out as guides to the gringos. He'd expected to isolate and capture the American *jefe.* It is Villa who will have to isolate himself.

Cursing the fates which seem always against him now, Villa proceeded to Cieneguita, where his leg began to swell, and throb painfully. He had himself taken, by buggy to the Sierra del Oso (Mountain of the Bear), where he dismissed his 150-man escort, instructing them to return to their homes—and wait. He kept only two young men to tend him. If at first he hadn't considered his wound dangerous, when he saw it was, the time had passed for regrets.

With the help of his bodyguards he hobbled up to a cave he knows. He made himself as comfortable as he could, and told his two young soldiers to relax.

"All we can do is wait," he said. "If I pass out, keep my leg cool and clean. If I don't make it, bury me right outside and get word to your chief. He'll know what to do."

"Have you got an infection, *mi general?*" asks Joaquín.

"*Sí, chamaco.* I think that's what I've got. Now relax. We're going to be here until this is settled, *gringos* or no *gringos.* Carranza or no Carranza. It's in the hands of God."

3

"*. . . The cords of slavery can only be cut by the sharp edge of anger. Do you grasp what I'm saying? We have to forget sensitivities of the skin, and listen to the cries of our people. They need bread and meat, and some assurance that tomorrow will be there when they wake up . . . Listen. It was all foam. All foam! It went away through my fingers. Into the wind . . . Listen. They leave you so scarred, so broken up, that you're not recognizable*

*as a human being anymore. And yet, all that keeps those little
bits of you together is that you* are *a human being . . . You
listen—I'm telling you God's truth! . . . Oh, what a fool I was.
What a fool . . .* Mamá. Mamacita. *I did something, and I'm
going to have to leave. Don't cry.* Por favor, mamacita, no llore
más *. . . They'll never find me up there, in that sierra.*

*Urbina! Urbina—wake up! They're almost here, wake up!
Rodolfo—you devil. You devil. You devil . . . You're dead.
You're dead . . . Angeles, Maclovio. Don't leave, I need you. You
don't know how I need you . . . Ay, Dios mío. I'm so damned
tired, Tomás. I just want to sleep . . . Listen,* compadrito *. . . It
was all foam.* Pura espuma. *It was never real. It was never
there. . . ."*

4

"I think he's dying," whispered one of them.

"God's truth, Joaquín, I don't know. But I'm scared as hell."

"We're not doctors. *Demonio!* How can they blame us?
Cabrona suerte! A stupid, accidental bullet, and look at this
mess!"

"He's moving a lot. God, just look at that leg, does it look
black to you?"

5

Everything was yellow and black. He could hear voices from
miles away. From a lifetime off. From another world, somewhere. He was in a hole. A huge, yellow cavern, filled with
black dancing shapes and heat, with hissing snakes that made
human sounds. Or maybe they were devils. All the traitors and
assassins coming after him. What were they saying?

"After all the battles he's been in—a Goddamn accident!"

"*Shhh!* He might hear you!"

"I heard him, all right," mumbled Villa.

"Did he say something, Barnabe?"

"No. He just groaned."

6

"The money's never enough to feed the family, so the balance goes on credit. Credit through the great generosity of your generous class, *señor Hacendado* . . ."

"What's that, *mi general?*"

"*Shhh,* you *idiota!* He's out of his head."

". . . So, if a man needs *huaraches,* it's credit; and if his boy needs a shirt, or his old *vieja* a cotton dress, it's more credit. Then a little drop of *tequila* for the wedding, a jug of *aguardiente* for the baby's christening, or a skinny candle for the saint—all on credit. And so each day, each year, each tiny . . . each tiny . . ."

"Help me turn him over. Get the water. My God, he's burning up with fever. I'm going to open that wound if it's the firing squad for me!"

". . . Each tiny . . . One *centavo* after another, driven into the *peón's* back like nails, until he's pinned to the plow and the dirt and the *hacendado's* rule for the rest of his miserable life . . ."

"All right, hold him down, you idiot! Don't panic! This leg is putrid. It's like a black balloon. Hold tight!"

"I know you, *don* Pan Crudo. Yes. *Sí, señor,* I know you well. That's why I'm going to hang you! *Ahhh! Ay, Dios mío!* Let me go. My leg. My leg! I'm . . ."

"It's open. Holy Mother. A ton of pus and—"

". . . *Viva* Huerta! he says. Boy, there's a sentiment . . . Shooting's too good for snakes, *señor* Rural. No. I'm going to have Tomás and the boys hang you from a high tree limb, very slowly, so I can watch you dance while I whistle *Viva* Huerta for your music . . ."

"Lie back, *mi general.* It's all done. Relax. Relax."

". . . Why do you call me *capitán, don* Abraham? You *políticos*—. Never mind nobilities—what does Madero want? In plain words! *Agua . . . Agua . . .* Water . . . Wa . . . *señor,* you are our savior! Look around you. We fought for the people, but where are the people? *Agua! Agua, por favor.* I'm dying, Tomás. *Don* Francisco, I'm dying! I'm—!"

"Dear God Almighty! Joaquín, if he dies, we're screwed. They'll say we killed him. For sure, they'll blame us."

"*Mi general* Angeles, is everybody ready here . . .?"

"He's getting quieter, Barnabe. What do we do?"

". . . Lucita. Listen. You'll hear thunder. Lucita. It was all foam. It was a dream without substance. Without meaning. Without—without—."

"I wonder what he was dreaming?" asked Joaquín after a while.

"I don't know, *hermano*. But as great as he is—I wouldn't be Pancho Villa for all the money in the world, would you?"

"No," said Joaquín. "I'd be afraid, too."

XXIX. THE BLOOD OF MARTYRS

THERE WERE TIMES when it seemed to Francisco Villa that in the blood and pain and anguish of those long weeks in the cave, he had been reborn. He saw the whole course of his life, his dreams and ambitions in a fuller prospective. He could no longer be what he had been; he could only go on pretending that he was.

He still needed to defend himself against his enemies. But the Revolution of 1910 was too remote now. And in this sense, if in no other, Carranza, and Obregón had triumphed. Pancho Villa, at the age of 40, no longer understood the word "freedom." Somehow, through disuse or through abuse, it had gone from him.

Through the remainder of 1916, after the *Yanquis* had left to find more interesting sport in Europe, and during 1917, when the sport had turned to terror; and then into 1918, when terror had become ashes turning into memories, Pancho Villa had continued to ride. But his heart was no longer filled with hope and excitement. He had no dreams for Mexico. He thought idly of summoning Felipe Angeles from his peaceful life in Los Angeles, California, to become his choice for President. But his heart wasn't really in that, either. Nor did he thrill to the cries of *Viva* Villa! for he had heard them too often.

The old hell-bent revolution had changed. Villa, while still brave and dangerous, was outmoded as a plotter. Zapata was dead: treacherously murdered. Euphemio Zapata, the brave Morelian Horseman's brother, killed in a drunken gunfight. Maytorena, that good Sonoran, exiled in the United States, and penniless, having given everything for his beliefs.

In a grave in distant France lay the remains of the old warrior who had started it all: *general de División, don* Porfirio Díaz, suddenly dead at 7 A.M., on the morning of July 2, 1915—and genuinely mourned by that strange, savage, yet forgiving nation he had betrayed.

Pascual Orozco, dead, too. Killed in December of 1915, in a running fight with Texas Rangers. Caught trying to do what Villa had done. Caught with four others, trying to cross the Rio Grande on someone else's horses.

And Huerta, tired of Cuba, disillusioned in France, seeking asylum in the United States, and dying there of booze, dissipation, hopelessness—and God only knows what.

It was a list somehow too long and somehow meaningless, and yet, still painful. A list that tolled like a churchbell over unrealized ambitions and lives tossed about like pieces of cadavers and made to endure pity, disdain, hatred and, finally, indifference.

From ranch to village to city, Pancho Villa had again ridden, sweeping up a compact, well armed and mounted army. If still a bandit to the world, he was forever a patriot and a general to his men. Freshly supplied by the Carranzista garrisons he overthrew, showing moments of the old audacity, Pancho Villa shook the Carranzista government by retaking Chihuahua City and then Torreón. But to what purpose?

Riding on the crest of his power, Venustiano Carranza had finally realized his ambition. He was now President of Mexico. For him, too, a distant bell was tolling. Too arrogant, too unyielding, he had made too many enemies. Even Woodrow Wilson, saw finally the true nature of Carranza's pro-German leanings, had lost all interest in the bearded "Ceasar."

On April 19, 1919, Pancho Villa, joined by General Angeles, took Parral. On June 15th they captured Juárez. But when stray shots struck El Paso, American troops again merged with the Carranzistas, forcing the Villistas to evacuate. It was Villa's decision to split his forces and to rendezvous farther south.

On November 15th, General Felipe Angeles was taken by a patrol of Carranzistas, near Valle de los Olivos, while trying to rejoin Pancho Villa.

He was quickly tried and, on November 24th, was sentenced to die by a firing squad. On the night before his execution he wrote: *"I know that my death must benefit democracy, for the blood of martyrs fertilizers great causes . . ."*

Felipe Angeles died as he had lived: bravely, quietly, with a great air of human dignity.

In death his eyes remained half-open and glassy, his mouth was crooked, and his adam's apple looked too big. The soldier who had lived immaculately had fallen in a rumpled suit, needing a shave. His devotion to freedom and justice had both robbed and killed him.

XXX. AT TLAXCALANTONGO

BY APRIL, 1920, all that Carranza had built and schemed for was tumbling down.

Fearing Obregón's ambitions, Carranza tried to implicate him in a plot against the presidency, but the canny pea-merchant-General had fled. Now Obregón, like Villa, was turning on Carranza for a show down which had been inevitable since the start of their alliance. Others, *políticos* and *generales,* sick of the Old Badger's monomaniacal rule, were also in arms.

Near the end of his term, the news of uprisings within the Capital forced Venustiano Carranza to evacuate Mexico City. Once more he turned toward Veracruz, but his trains were blockaded and his own troops began defecting to the approaching rebels. Perhaps recalling Villa's successes, Carranza elected to take to the mountains, by horseback to Veracruz, picking up loyal garrisons along the way. On the night of May 20th, he stopped at the tiny *Pueblo* of Tlaxcalantongo. It was raining heavily, and his personal guard found him a small, conical hut in which to sleep.

About 3:30 A.M., May 21st, a yell of "*Viva* Obregón!" was heard outside. A shadowy group of men surrounded the *presidente's* hut and opened fire. Before the party was half awake Carranza had been struck in the left leg, twice through the intestines and once through the lung and liver. His agony lasted only minutes.

The door was open for Álvaro Obregón's candidacy—and it had been opened by Carranza's own bodyguards.

XXXI. "TRILLO, I'M TIRED..."

"WELL, *mi general.* What do you think?" said Miguel Trillo, riding close to Pancho.

"*Pues?* What do you imagine I think?"

"*Demonio.* What a pity. Pablo Seánez was a good general and troop commander once, wasn't he? A brave boy."

"A good boy all the way around. And a good soldier, but a constant loser in everything else. He took his dog's luck with him when he deserted, after Fierro's death. Now he's brought it back with him."

Pancho Villa leaned forward, gently patting his lathered animal. The Chihuahua desert was savage. Even Villa felt a slight dizziness, and little Miguel, his faithful secretary and military aide of many months now, looked absolutely drenched in dust and sweat.

"I shouldn't have forgiven him," said Villa. "But I kept thinking of Rodolfo. I couldn't make myself kill him when he came back. They were friends. And the way Pablo begged for a chance to make things up . . ."

Villa slapped his thigh. His burned and tired face showed frustration. "That stinking pair!" he said. "They've always rotted everything—everyone—they touched. I hope Carranza died kicking and screaming—and may Obregón soon follow the old bastard to the devil!"

"Maybe you're wrong this time," said Trillo hopefully.

"No," said Villa. "No, Trillito. I see it in his eyes. That same look Tomás had. That look I've seen in the faces of so many old friends these last few years. He reeks of treachery. It's that Goddamned reward Carranza offered for my head."

"But with Carranza dead, who would pay it?"

"Somebody would," said Villa bitterly. "Don't fool yourself,

Trillito. You could fill a large cesspool with men who'd pay to
see me dead. Betrayal was Carranza's weapon, and Obregón's
even better at it. Good enough to reach clear to Tlaxcalantongo.
Look at Zapata. How else could they have gotten him?"

Trillo, gentle and compassionate, shook his head.

"Well, it's almost over," said Villa. "We'll be in good country
for it soon. I figure 20 or 30 more kilometers farther north.
Where Pablo knows the country. Where there's good cover.
There's where he'll spring it on me."

2

He wasn't quite asleep, but in that easy state in which the
mind can float away, sailing above the pressures of the earth. All
consciousness was expanded, the senses quickened to the most
infinitesimal things. A tiny fly buzzed about his face, its steady
droning loud as an eagle's cries. The sounds of horses were
meaningless, the voices of men remote and unintelligible. Pancho
Villa lay catnapping under the short shadow of a large stone. A
lizard scurried somewhere, its movements on the sand sounded
like the rustling of stiff lace curtains by an open window. His
head lay on his nearly empty canteen, his hat was over his eyes.
He was thinking about lace curtains. Daydreaming about Lucita
and an open window. He could almost feel the sweet, dark cool-
ness of that house, and his mind even heard the insistent whirl
of a sewing machine.

The desert was empty and silent. The sounds of horses, and
the voices of his men meant nothing. They were parts of the
desert, overly familiar, like the nervous scurrying of tiny reptiles
and the shifting of the wind.

He knew that if he looked behind him, and above onto the
rocks, he would see a man standing on the highest peak, with a
rifle in his hand. It was always that way, because it had to be.
And he knew that if he looked straight ahead, into the shallow
gully where the flashfloods swept southward through the desert
after the cloudbursts, he would see his tired, skinny horses; saddle-

sore and weary as the gaunt, filthy scarecrows who rode them day and night, without end.

They had broiled a jackrabbit for lunch, and he could taste its bitter, stringy flesh between his teeth yet. A bit of breeze came up, and he was grateful for it. An ant crawled over his hand, but he ignored it.

One of his men started playing a guitar. He played softly, idly. "Christ, I'm in no mood for it," said the man. "Here, *nieto.* Sing us a little tune."

The man's nephew caught the guitar which made a *thuuung!* sound in landing. Then he began softly like a breeze rising, like a fish playing, like a memory of other times:

"*La Cucaracha, La Cucaracha—Ya no puede caminar . . .*"

"No, not that goddamn thing!" said the man. "Play something happy. Something that will be kinder to us."

"*Hombre,*" said Trillo's annoyed voice. "Why are you such a fool? Why say a stupid thing like that?"

"You're right," said the man. "I don't give a damn what you play, *nieto.* Play *La Adelita.*"

> "If Adelita should go with another,
> I would pursue her by land and by sea:
> If by sea, I would sail in a warship;
> And if by land, on a military train . . ."

"I wish to hell we had a military train," said the man sadly. "We'd show somebody."

> "*Y si Adelita se fuera con otro,*
> *Le seguiria por tierra y por mar:*
> *Si por mar en un buque de guerra;*
> *Y si por tierra en un tren militar.*"

Lying there he tried to think back to the last time, to remember who it had been. Lucita? That girl in Parral? No, the one near Jiménez, passing down from Camargo. *Ay, Chihuahua!* That sweet-smelling, little farm girl with eyes like a bitch-in-heat, and the juciest little handles a man could want to hang on to . . . He'd stopped for water there, with his band, and she'd made such eyes at him that he had to take her for a little stroll around the pastures. And then:

"*Ay, señor general.* I can't."

"And why not, *mi hijita?*"

"I can't, *señor.* I'm—I'm afraid."

He'd laughed loudly, stroking her soft, quivering, little behind while his other hand drew her to him. "You don't have to be like that with me, *lindita,* because—well, you don't know what I'm going to give you."

"I know what you want to give me," she said.

"And you've never had it before?"

"Well . . . once or twice."

"Would you like it again?"

"I told you," she said, "I'm afraid. *Ay, señor.* What are you doing now?"

"Just touching."

"*Ay, señor.*"

"Do you like it?"

"*Pues, señor,* I do. But somebody will come and see us lying here, in the grass."

"We'll tell them I'm your cousin."

"*Ay, por favor, señor.* Really, I'm afraid. We have to go back. What are you doing to my dress? *Ay,* you mustn't do that."

"I'm just feeling how soft your leg is. Do you know that your mouth is beautiful? Do you like to be kissed, *niñita?*"

"Sometimes. It depends who."

"Like this . . . and this?"

"*Ay, Dios mío.* You mustn't. Just because you're a general—"

"And this . . . and there . . . and here . . .?"

"Stop . . . I can't . . . I—"

"And here, and there . . ."

"*Ay, Dios mío. Ay, señor.* You're going to think I'm a bad girl, aren't you?"

"Never, *gatita.* Rise up a little. That's it, little cat. Do you like that, when I touch you right there?"

"*Ay, sí . . . Ay, señor,* more."

"Move your legs, little kitten. Here, help me . . ."

"*Ay, señor,* what are we doing?"

"Don't you know, *chula?*"

"Yes."

3

They had been moving steadily for hours, and were well up into the high brush country, with General Pablo Seánez at the head of the scouting group, when Pancho Villa galloped up and fell in with Seánez.

"*Bueno,* Pablito," he said. "How is it going?"

"Fine, *mi general,*" said Seánez smiling boyishly. "Everything's clear up ahead."

"You sure, Pablito?"

"Absolutely sure, *mi general.*"

"Well, now I'm just as sure that you're a Goddamned lying traitor, Pablito," said Pancho. "And that there's an ambush up ahead. You see, for the past few days I've been sending my own scouting parties up ahead of yours. Why did you do it, boy?"

"Rotten dice, and worse cards, *mi general,*" said Seánez still smiling. "Fierro always said I'd come to no good."

"Fierro was usually right," said Pancho drawing his gun. "Now, Pablito, here comes what you had for me."

"Goodbye, *mi general.*"

"Goodbye," said Villa emptying his pistol into Seánez.

4

"They say it's true," insisted Ramón Contreras, "that *don* Adolfo de la Huerta is *presidente* now, and that he's been trying, every way, to communicate with you, *mi general.* I heard it through the whole territory I scouted last week."

"You remember last month," said Villa grimly, "when that treacherous *piojo,* who calls himself Governor of Chihuahua, sent word he wanted to talk to me about peace terms?"

They all recalled only too well. General Ignacio Enríquez,

having made a thousand promises, had then pulled out, supposedly to return to his capital for confirmation of his agreements. The parting had been amicable. Yet, Villa, always distrustful—and so used to treachery now that he wouldn't even eat his food until someone else tasted it first—had felt uneasy.

That night he'd ordered his troops to light camp fires, and leaving several horses in view, he and his men had withdrawn from the camp. About midnight the attack had come. Enríquez, Military Governor of Chihuahua, had personally led his men—only to discover that he'd been shooting at nothing, that Pancho Villa had tricked him into exposing his bad faith.

Three days later, on June 2, 1920, Pancho Villa assaulted, and took Parral from Enríquez' troops: "Just to show that tricky sonofawhore that nobody makes Villa's tamales out of goatmeat!" as the infuriated *guerrillero* put it.

It was late July, nearly two months later. Two more months of hiding, of endless danger, of discomfort, of futile raids and meaningless retaliation for half forgotten betrayals. In a thousand little ways the meaning of the original Revolution had become obscure. Pancho Villa was not always sure now what his goals were, or who his enemies or friends might be.

Señor Adolfo de la Huerta was President now, filling the unfinished term of Carranza.

The new President was, indeed, sending out peace feelers, offering amnesty to Villa, offering reconciliation with the new government of Mexico.

Don Adolfo a quiet and unspectacular Sonoran, a neutral, a man whom Villa felt he might be able to trust. But there was always Obregón somewhere in the background. What of the one-armed, fat, little pea-merchant? Had he gotten to De la Huerta, as he had to all the others?

Tired, hungry, forgotten. Awakening each morning with the feeling he'd been fighting forever, alone, to no purpose. Toward no goal. After learning of the new President's efforts to locate him, Pancho Villa's mind reeled with the possibilities which this implied.

They were riding along, one evening, riding in single file over a narrow pass as they had forever and ever. And they were passing rocks Villa knew they had passed a thousand times before. And Pancho Villa suddenly pulled up and said to the little man beside him, "Trillo, I'm tired."

"Bueno, mi general. We'll stop and rest here," said Trillo.

"No, Trillito. I mean tired. Right to the middle of my heart; right into the center of my bones. I'm sick of deserts, sick of running. Tired to death of everything. How do you feel?"

"The same, *mi general.*"

"Look at the men," said Pancho. "Poor, loyal bastards. They say nothing, but look at their faces, at their eyes."

"They'll never leave you, *mi general,*" said Trillo earnestly. "Neither will I."

Villa looked at his passing men for a long moment, his eyes filled with love and compassion, then he said: "I owe you as much, *amigo.* I owe everyone as much. *Bueno,* Trillito. We have one more job. We're moving into Coahuila, and we're going to take Sabinas. Make ready for a long march."

"Sí, mi general."

"Well, don't you even want to know why?"

"Because you order it, *mi general,*" said Trillo.

"No. Because there is a telegraph station in Sabinas. And because it's territory we haven't touched—and they won't expect us."

"We're starting an offensive?" asked Trillo eagerly.

"For the last time," said Villa. "For the last time we're going to show them that Pancho Villa goes where he wants, and takes what he wants. And with that in mind—we're going to sit down and bargain."

5

In the early hours of July 25th, having crossed the cruel Mapimí desert, Villa's vanguard entered the town of Sabinas and occupied it. Within the hour, word was being telegraphed to Mexico City—directly to De la Huerta—that General Francisco Villa was in possession, and ready to discuss peace with the government.

It was a time of great excitement to all of Mexico. Within hours, three trains were leaving the Capital, under command of General Eugenio Martínez, a Federal officer whom Villa trusted. The trains carried a minimum of troops, ample stores of foods, clothes, general supplies and gold with which to pay off Villa's men.

By July 27th, Sabinas was teeming with troops, reporters, government representatives, and crowds of spectators. General Martínez arrived, and peace talks were initiated with Villa, in the presence of American go-betweens, and then Pancho spoke directly to *presidente* De la Huerta by telephone to the Capital.

"I'm satisfied," said the *guerrillero* to his own men. "The President's given me his personal assurances. And I've got to start believing in something again."

On July 28, 1920, Pancho Villa accepted the government's terms. It was not a surrender, but a retirement from the field.

It had all ended so simply. So quietly. After all the blood, after the roar of cannon, the bugles, the screams of the dying, the excitement of campaign. All so quietly, and naturally, as if he had been headed toward this ending all the time.

ENTRY: On this date, July 28, 1920, *el general de División* Francisco Villa surrendered the following troops to *general* Eugenio Martínez, representing the Federal Army, and the Government of *el señor presidente de la Republica, don* Alfonso de la Huerta. TO WIT: 1 General of Division, 1 General of Brigade, 7 Brigadiers, 131 Officers, 511 Soldiers. Total: 651 Officers and Men.

As quietly as this, 20 years of blood and fire ended. Closed with a pen, not with a bayonet. Enclosed not in marble, but in a simple notebook kept in Miguel Trillo's saddlebag. The last entry for the *División del Norte,* once 50,000 strong.

XXXII. CANUTILLO

"LOOK AT THIS, *amigos*," he said smiling happily. "Just imagine, *compañeros*. All this is ours. Canutillo. Land—thousands upon thousands of acres. Homes. Even our own adobe church. All ours. *Qué te imaginás, Miguel?* Could you imagine all this, up in those hills, where we lived like animals?"

Colonel Miguel Trillo, resplendent in his new suit and a neat, well-combed moustache, grinned back. "*Qué va?*" he said shyly. "Who could imagine it?"

Villa stood up on a stout, oak table which had been dragged outside the ranch house. His heart was pounding hard, as he faced the people below him. Fifty of his staff, his *Dorado* officers, and their families. Yes, and Luz, and his children, too. They cheered him, shouting "*Viva el general* Villa! *Viva* Villa!" until he silenced them with a smile and a wave.

"*Amigos,* the war is over. For us—we Villistas—who offered our lives and our blood and our hearts to the cause of *don* Francisco Madero—for us—there must be only peace. Only work. There must be education and the betterment of our future, and of our children's futures."

"*Viva* Pancho Villa! *Viva!*" they cried happily.

"There will be schools on this ranch. I will make schools, and you will send your *niños* there, and not into the fields. There will be workshops on this ranch, and those who want to be more than ranch hands will better themselves there. I will give you and your families, forever, your part of this land. And I will advance money to you without interest. And we will show Mexicans—and people everywhere—what life should be. We here, together in peace, who were together in war. We few, who believed in *don* Francisco Madero, and in that ideal called democracy."

He started to get down, amid applause and cheers, then he

got up again, waving for silence. "One more thing, *amigos*. We can't start this great, new world until tomorrow—because tonight we're going to have a fiesta. All right?"

"*Viva* Villa! *Viva la fiesta!*" they shouted happily.

2

So it was really, and finally, all behind him now: the hills, the sounds of horses in the night, the flashes of gunfire, the killings, the hungry, merciless, lonely years. The years of searching and waiting, and finding only disappointment. It was done.

"I never want to look at another dead face," he told Trillo, his confidant. "God help me, Trillito. I want to forget all that. I want to feel someday that it never happened."

"Could you forget it, *mi general?*"

"No," said Villa. "But I want to try."

Those 20 long years. And now peace with honor. Not a surrender, but peace with dignity. Friendship. A soldier's peace. And to cement this new friendship Francisco Villa had received full restoration of his rank; full privileges, including a bodyguard of 50 *Dorados* and his staff, and all the lands and buildings of Canutillo, a rundown, but beautiful *hacienda* confiscated from the hated *hacendados* of old by the revolution.

To Pancho Villa the restoration of his land was now the greatest challenge of his life. Living like a sultan with his Luz (and a few other wives he'd acquired during his adventures— some say four, some say more) he was the law unto himself on Canutillo. He rode, he practiced pistol shooting at paper targets, and wore either plain, white cotton, *peón's* clothing with a straw-hat, or else the smartest fashions, including shiny shoes and panama hats. He also put on a little weight.

Where Villa had once commanded 50,000 men, he now ruled only 50, but he ruled them by their love, not by his guns, and he'd never been happier in his life.

He looked after them, and their families. He administered his properties, did a little business in the surrounding cities—

mostly in Parral, where he owned a townhouse and a hotel—and dedicated himself to his new, and all-consuming interest: "scientific" farming. He imported American plows, tractors, threshing machines. He bought mules and oxen. He stocked the hills with cattle and sheep. He raised fine horses and acquired two new automobiles. One of these, a grey Dodge touring car, Model 1919, had been presented him by two Durango friends, the brothers José and Pablo Valenzuela, because they knew he loved to drive —as he loved the uses of all modern machinery.

3

When man was born, he was not born to be alone, nor born to live as the beasts who have no souls, no hope . . .

He'd awakened this morning thinking about that, and understanding suddenly why he'd never been able to articulate it. It was because he'd always thought of it in terms of anguish; in moments of despair, when he should have thought of it in his happiness. He went to his desk, took out that battered little tin box, and found the piece of notepaper on which the first line was written. January of 1913 . . . Or perhaps toward the end of 1912 . . . He'd been 36 or 37 years old then, struggling desperately to find himself. Now he was 47, a mature man with all struggles and ambitions and angers behind him. With all his bitterness buried. With those years fading back . . . back.

Perhaps that was how life was meant to be. Now he would never have to worry again, for written or not, the thought had come from his heart and from his experience and from the distillation of his pain. He would never write it. But he wouldn't have to, because he could never forget it. Perhaps by the standards of great men it wasn't really a very good or profound thought. But it belonged solely to him. To Pancho Villa. And the more he considered this, the happier he grew.

He hadn't much cash. Despite his growing enterprises, he'd mortgaged Canutillo heavily to pay for its upkeep, and to lend his people money. But no matter. In another year now the ranch would begin paying everything back, with a profit. And there wasn't another place like it in all Mexico—and most of the United States. That was important. It was important that even the *gringos* now came to visit, and to see in wonder, and to believe what they'd heard about Canutillo and Pancho Villa. Given enough time, some said, General Villa might have made a damned good President for Mexico after all! But no matter about that, either. Pancho knew he could involve himself in causes or politics and grow wealthy. But public life was the last thing on earth he could bear. No. He would work hard, right there, among his people, on his land. And those supple hands which had once caused death would now scatter only the seeds of life. For he, the eternal dreamer, the indefatigable searcher, had finally found the meaning of his life. There, tending a garden in Canutillo.

"*Mi general*," said Trillo just before noon. "We'd better take a car to Parral today. We'll have to pick up some supplies, and it'll be faster all the way around. Is it all right?"

"Of course. *Seguro que si*," said Villa who sat carving a stick-horse for one of his little boys. "Do what you want."

"Let's take the grey Dodge, since there'll be six of us," said Trillo. "I've telephoned the Hidalgo and told them to put up Ramón and the boys through the 22nd. I will stay in the town-house, if you don't mind, and we'll go over those alfafa bills."

"*Muy bien*, Trillito. I'll tell Luz we'll leave the morning of the 23rd then," said Villa adding a winking eye to the pony's wooden face.

This was the 19th of July, Pancho reflected when he was alone again. He had lived on Canutillo now exactly two weeks short of three years. It scarcely seemed possible that happiness had made the time fly by so fast. Seeing his land, his friends and family around him, he knew that nowhere on earth could there be a happier, more grateful man.

Even that evening, he couldn't stop being happy as he entered Parral. And so it went for the next three days.

THE END OF THE BEGINNING...

THE YOUNG MAN stepped out and raised his hat. None of those in the grey Dodge touring car paid much attention. Miguel Trillo, sitting beside Pancho, looked directly at Juan López who raised his hat once more, then crossed the street toward a juice-vendor. It seemed to Trillo gratifying to see such courtesy in this day and age.

The others took no notice. Pancho, behind the wheel, loved driving. He smiled constantly as he guided the sleek Dodge along the streets of Parral. Daniel Tamayo, Rosalío Rosales, and Tomás Medrano chatted in the back seat. Claro Hurtado and big Ramón Contreras rode the runningboards, since they came as bodyguards.

It was 8 o'clock, July 23, 1923. The desert sun already drenched the white Chihuahua landscape, and Trillo's precise, secretarial mind had just registered the thought that at their present speed they should arrive at Canutillo Ranch in a bit over three hours.

The dodge turned off Avenida Juárez to Calle Gabina Barrera . . .

2

There were men in Mexico who couldn't stop being afraid of the Centaur. Who couldn't bear his happiness. One of these was Melitón Losoya, a young, well-to-do rancher who had never met Villa, but who nevertheless felt that his family honor had, somehow, been besmirched by the *guerrillero*. Many believed Losoya had been unofficially encouraged by the government, precisely because of his grievance against Villa. Viewed as a political maneuver, this makes some sense. It had been widely feared that Villa would leave Canutillo, come out of retirement and openly oppose the succession of Plutarco Elías Calles to the presidency. Seized by his obsession Melitón Losoya had recruited seven men—friends and relations—who were ready to die with him, if need be, to kill Francisco Villa. They realized their chances were slim, for Villa wasn't only cunning; he was fearless, dangerous, and a deadly shot with either hand. And so were the men of his bodyguard. But Losoya, like Obregón (whom some said had put the notion into his mind), could wait. Wait until the moment was exactly right. And this was what he had done.

Villa had been in Parral for three days now and might leave by several routes. But he ordinarily drove north from his townhouse at the corner of *Avenida* Juárez and *Calle* Ignacio Zaragoza, passing the small Plaza Juárez, directly in front of the ambush house, then over the Guanajuato bridge. Neither Losoya nor his men were in a hurry. By the morning of July 23rd they had been waiting 102 days in that stunted, little adobe building for everything to fall just right.

Librado, Meliton's cousin, and second-in-command, sat behind a door in the second room of the two-room building, his eye to a knothole, watching for Juan López' signal. The rest waited anxiously for the order to attack.

At a little after 8 A.M. of this 103rd day, Librado saw the grey Dodge turn the corner onto *Avenida* Juárez. He saw their lookout, Juan López, raise his hat. That meant Villa was driving.

The plotters, Jesús Salas, Ramon Guerra, José Sáenez-Prado Barraza, José Sáenez-Prado Chavira, José López Sáenez-Prado, José Guerra, and Ruperto Vara, readied their Winchesters and pistols. Not one of them had ever seen Villa, but would follow orders blindly. "They're coming," said Librado suddenly. "*Alerta!*"

Pancho was in a fine mood that morning, joking with his bodyguards and looking forward to his return to Canutillo. He'd come into Parral only to pick up a payroll for his men, and to greet a few friends. Now this was done.

Suddenly, as the Dodge neared the adobe building, a rifle shot rang out, smashing through the windshield. Pancho clutched his chest, his smile frozen on his face. More shots splintered the glass, tearing into those inside. While Pancho struggled to right the careening auto, all eight men came out and surrounded the vehicle, firing frantically at the helpless, writhing passengers.

Miguel Trillo half stood, yelled something, and fell over the door. Medrano rolled into the street, a bullet through his head. As the Dodge bounced over the sidewalk, against a tree, Hurtado crawled down, his chest torn open by bullets. Ramón Contreras staggered away, his left arm useless, firing his Winchester with one hand. But as always, it was the Centaur who proved most dangerous.

As the car stopped, and Villa saw the assassins rushing him, his right hand crossed to his left holster and drew. Ramón Guerra, almost on him, saw Villa's murderous Colt fire. The single shot caught Guerra through the heart, killing him instantly. It was Pancho Villa's last conscious act.

One arm nearly off, his intestines pouring out, his chest torn open, a bullet through his face, the Centaur of the North moved painfully behind the wheel, then leaned back into the seat. Still fighting for life, he jerked convulsively. His eyelids fluttered, then stopped, half closed. His mouth opened with a silent *"Ahhh . . ."* His fading vision perceived the circle of shadowy, dancing figures drawing closer around him. The impact of 12 bullets in his body and four in his head were finally more than flesh and spirit could endure. Slowly his arm relaxed. The fingers uncurled, releasing that deadly gun. On the threshold of unending silence Pancho Villa was heard to sigh as he leaned against his little friend, Trillo.

Now the Centaur was dead. The legend had begun.

APPENDIX A

WHEN IT WAS FIRST SUGGESTED to me that I write a book about
Pancho Villa I was skeptical, and refused. It seemed to me that
enough had been written about *Pancho Vil-la, ban-di-do,* to keep
the public wallowing in gore forever.

Yet, as my many visits through Mexico (and particularly
through Chihuahua) threw me more and more against Villista
fact and legend, I saw I'd been only half correct. Too much had
been done on Villa, the *bandit,* but almost nothing on Villa, the
man.

Many Villa fans know that as a boy Pancho killed the man
who raped his sister. They've heard various fictions regarding
his long escapade in the mountains, his alleged adventures with
Ignacio Parra, "the most famous bandit in Mexico," and blood-
curdling absurdities (such as Parra and Villa leading a virtual
army of brigands, and raiding entire towns or trains) originated
from this association. Anxious biographers seemed adamant
about ignoring the true, if less romantic fact that Parra was a
small-time, hash *bandido,* and that this "army" frequently con-
sisted of Pancho and a couple of other hungry outlaws, grateful
for the opportunity to swipe a few mules.

I felt that by discarding such pap I might make room for
Francisco Villa, a man who rose from peonage to become history;
an illiterate and purposeless outlaw who, in just four incredible
years, forged himself, singlehandedly, into the most brilliant
Guerrilla Commander this hemisphere has ever produced. I'm
not discounting Robert Rogers, Jeb Stuart, Mosby, Chiefs Joseph,
Roman Nose or Crazy Horse. Nor am I overlooking the exploits
of Simón Bolívar or of Porfirio Diaz.

To analyze properly Villa's worth one has to consider the
beginnings of his military career. One has also to consider the
time and the place. Had Villa, like Orde Wingate, Otto Skorzeny,

or that splendid antique, General George Crook, enjoyed the backing in men and supplies of a war-fitted and sympathetic nation, his achievements would have had to be reduced by the amount of backing received. But such wasn't the case. Villa's armies rose from the earth, born out of the seed of his individual determination. Nor have we the story of an educated T. E. Lawrence, functioning among a people vastly inferior to him in the grasp of his aims, or in political manipulation. On the contrary, it was Villa who was the poorer at every turn for his sparse education.

It seemed, too, that Edgcumb Pinchón's portrait of an ape-like, greasy (albeit quite loveable) *peón,* whose perpetually "sandled" feet couldn't bear shoes, and whose answer to life was instant death, was long overdue for a well-shoed kick in the *pantalones* and through the door. Everytime I think of Wallace Beery groaning *car-r-ramba!* and massaging his feet in the *Palacio Nacional* I groan, too. Yet, Mr. Pinchón's is the only close look *gringo*dom has ever had at Villa, and it was Pinchón (abetted by Ben Hecht's movie script) who almost singlehandedly formed the fat, sweaty Villa we Americans know today. All of this made me wonder if another effort—just one more—shouldn't be made to give Villa back his dignity, and to reweave him back into the texture of humanity.

Sure, there are accurate sources, mixed in with the misconceptions. There are, for example, extensive newspaper files (particularly in that little jewel of Southwestern Research, the El Paso Public Library). But who searches through the musty archives of history? Who will take the time to compare one newspaper story against another? News stories, written hastily, frequently based on hearsay, can often play hell with history.

There are, to be sure, some fairly accurate and decent books in Spanish (along with some silly ones). But again, how many of us read Spanish? One such book, translated into English, is Martín Luis Guzmán's celebrated *The Eagle and the Serpent,* a widely-read volume from which even Mr. Pinchón cautiously quotes. But, unfortunately, by my fifth or sixth reading I was discovering that *señor* Guzmán's personal observations, once so refreshingly charming (and guardedly complimentary when it comes to Villa), were thickly laced with snobbery. The best one can hope for there are those priceless moments when Guzmán's compassion shines through, despite his "intellectual" leanings.

That Villa: man, boy, bandit or freedom fighter, was often snubbed and betrayed by those he most esteemed, is abundantly clear from Guzmán's own words. And that final scene when Guzmán, himself, plants the Judas kiss on the half-suspecting, friendship-starved *guerrillero,* is doubtlessly one of the most moving ever recorded. However, little else will be gained that we don't already know, for otherwise the *guerrillero's* image is obscured by mysterious mad snipers, right out of Sherlock Holmes, lectures on government, diatribes on individuals, and other points of personal interest to *señor* Guzmán.

So, nearly 10 years after it was first suggested, it seemed to me time to do this book on Villa. It seemed high time to bring the man out from behind that gaudy, bloody legend which had obscured him for so many years.

As to my reasons for writing the book as I did, in the style of a novel, let me state that in no other way did I feel it possible to explore this enigma: Pancho Villa. That there will be charges of falsification for the sake of dramatic impact, I've no doubt. But let me set this straight right now: the book, the facts, the scenery and the characters are essentially correct—and most particularly in cases where my version varies from the popular or accepted "fact."

In the process of studying this country, this war, this man—a study which dates back more than 15 years—I've discovered that behind the printed sources stand two better sources of research. These are the nation, itself, and the people who knew Villa personally, and often intimately. *Señora* Luz Corral Viuda de Villa and I, for example, spent hours talking about *little* memories: mostly things she'd witnessed during her life with the *guerrillero,* or stories he'd told her about his lonely life in the hills. Fortunately Villa was no braggart, but no taciturn type,

either. Like Robinson Crusoe he'd known too much solitude not
to appreciate the human relationship. Thus, from her I heard
the true story of Benton's killing (she was bringing in a tray of
lunch "for the general" just as Benton and Fierro both drew).
From her, too, I learned about Villa's life in the mountains,
about his tracking prowess, and much about his inner life.

I have seen the places where he lived, the trails he rode, the
cities he attacked, and ruled. I've sat drinking warm beers by
candlelight, in tiny, adobe bars so primitive that one wouldn't
believe them possible in this day. And there, chatting casually
with the aging veterans of the *División del Norte,* I've heard,
first hand, of Fierro's death, about Urbina's life, about Villa's
horses (from some point on, he always named his favorite mount
"Seven Leagues"), about Carranza's obsession that he was a sort
of Caesar and of the thousand-one little intimacies which I have
now pieced and correlated in this book.

Was Villa really a "mouth-breather," as has been asserted by
one American reporter? Did he, indeed, sleep in his underwear?
Was he passionate about icecream? Did he discuss astronomy, as
this book suggests? Was he bowlegged? How did he speak? Why
did he kill? Did he actually launch 22,000 men into battle with
the casual wave of a black bandana?

Much of the truth is still buried with Pancho Villa, under that
concrete slab in Parral's dry, ugly cemetery. Some of it has
become confused with fiction in the minds of those who knew
him. I've tried to sort it out, to sift the mountain of legend
through the screen of common sense where actual proof or education failed me. I've dug, panned and washed, wary of those tons
of fools' gold which have a way of creeping into "histories." And
by playing it honest with my conscience, I've regretfully dis-
carded even the choicest anectodes which did not prove out.

Similarly, I didn't start out to make Villa a saint or a devil.
Like so many great men, Villa wasn't always right, yet he was
less often wrong, or he couldn't have survived. He was impulsive.
He was a bloody savage, for the Gordian knots he cut through
were often of flesh and bone. He was also incredibly tender, and

there are more people still alive who bless him than curse him. He was a thief, a murderer, a fool, a sentimentalist and, quite incidently, a genius and a leader of unimpeachable idealism.

In the long run, I contend, Villa and Zapata were the only two major figures in the Revolution who never changed their coats for anyone or anything. They lived, and died, each loyal to his credo. And that credo was *the people*.

This *peón,* who had never owned a foot of land, also designed the only people's land distribution program which has ever worked. And this includes those of Russia and Cuba today. And while I'm about it, perhaps it might be in order to point out that Mexico's Revolution—so similar in so many respects— preceded that of Russia by several years. More important, yet, may be the fact that Mexico's revolt resulted in a guided de- mocracy, while Russia's became a dictatorship.

All of this belongs in Villa's life, inasmuch as this book, in its form, could handle it. So that is what I've tried to say. I've failed, of course. All the work, of all the well-intentioned writers who ever lived, is doomed to failure before it is begun. For if one is honest, one can see that people are made of living flesh— and not of words. Paper and ink can create only shadows, and the shadows of this man, this revolution, and this era—even the best shadows my poor mind could summon up—can never be enough.

Grant me only this: that I've failed honestly, and without cheap tricks.

APPENDIX B

CHRONOLOGY:

1878
1. Villa born in Rio Grande, Durango, legitimate son of Agustín and Micaela Arango (mother's maiden name: Arambula), on June 5. Christened Doroteo Arango.

1890
2. His father dies. Twelve year old Doroteo becomes family head. Month unknown.

1895
3. Outlawed at 17 for killing an *hacendado*.

1896–1909
4. Caught, but escapes. Kills his first *rurales*. Joins with Parra. Leaves Parra. Joins with Soto, Urbina and others. Expands his influence into Chihuahua State. Wins good-will of the poor by contributing money and goods from his raids.

1910
5. Enters the Madero Revolution through *don* Abraham González in October.
6. Joins Castulo Herrera in the field on November 17.
7. Meets Orozco at Guerrero on December 5.
8. Meets and confers with other Guerrilla Leaders at Guerrero.

1911
9. Meets Madero at Hacienda de Bustillos in March.
10. Quarrels with Madero, returns to civil life between May 13–15.
11. During remainder of this year Villa operates a butcher-shop business in Chihuahua City. He is reconciled with Madero.

On two occasions visits Madero in Mexico City. Agrees to watch Orozco's activities. Keeps close contact with Antireelectionist friends, such as González and Maytorena.

1912

12. Villa takes the field against Orozco on March 3.
13. Joins forces with Huerta in Torreón, April 17.
14. Sentenced to be shot, June 3.
15. Delivered to Mexico City Penitentiary, June 7.
16. Escapes from Santiago Tlaltelolco, December 26.

1913

17. Crosses into U.S. on January 3.
18. Invades Mexico on March 28.
19. Meets Fierro in September.
20. Assumes command of the División del Norte, September 23.

1914

21. Joins Carranza, but directs own campaign. January.
22. The "Benton Affair," in February.
23. Meets Felipe Angeles. Together they plan campaigns.
24. Continues southward drive toward Mexico City. Breaks with Carranza. May–November.
25. Villa occupies Tabuca and meets with Zapata at Xochimilco on November 27.
26. Villa and Zapata lead a 50,000-man parade through Mexico City. Villa tries out the Presidential chair, December 6–8.

1915

27. Villa meets with General Scott in January. Other meetings throughout the year.
28. Díaz dead in Paris, July 2.
29. Villa kills Urbina, September 19.
30. Fierro dies, October 13.
31. Orozco dead in gunfight with Texas Rangers, near Ojinaga, in December.

1916

32. Huerta dead in El Paso, Texas, in January.
33. Villistas raid Columbus, N.M.; Villa declared an outlaw by Carranza government.
34. Pershing crosses to pursue Villa, March 15.
35. Villa accidentaly shot in Guerrero. Hides in Cave. March.
36. Villa returns to field. With Pershing gone, resumes guerrilla warfare against Carranza-Obregón, in September.

1917

37. Villa calls Angeles to rejoin him. Angeles crosses into Mexico on December 11.
38. Guerrilla campaign continues throughout the year, without significant gains, although Villa now has Carranza-Obregón garrisons on the defensive.

1918

39. Guerrilla campaign continues. Villa gains strength.

1919

40. Zapata murdered, April 10.
41. General Angeles is captured and executed by Carranzistas, November 15.

1920

42. Obregón-Carranza break. April.
43. Carranza driven from Mexico City, May 6.
44. Carranza murdered, May 21.
45. Adolfo de la Huerta, Governor of Sonora, elected to fill Carranza's unexpired term, May 24.
46. Villa surrenders remains of his army to De la Huerta government on July 28.

1920–1923

47. Villa resides peacefully in Canutillo.

1923

48. Villa is ambushed, July 23.

APPENDIX C

VILLA'S BATTLES & CAMPAIGNS:

1910

1. San Andrés* (Taken by Villa)   November
2. Santa Isabel (Taken by Villa)   November
3. The Train (Villa Defeated)   November 25.
4. Bajio del Tecolote (Villa Defeated)   November
5. Cerro Prieto (Villa Defeated)   November

1911

6. Santa Rosalía and Camargo (Taken by Villa)   February 7.
7. Juárez (#1—Taken by Villa, Orozco, Garibaldi and others)
                                                            May 9–10.

1912

8. Parral† (Captured by Villa)   March 24.
9. Parral (1st Defense Won by Villa)   March 30.
10. Parral (2nd Defense Lost by Villa)   April 3.
11. Skirmishes and Patrols (Under Huerta)   April–June.
12. Barral (#2—Taken by Villa & Rábago)   June

1913

13. Samalayuca (Taken by Villa)   March
14. San Andrés (#2—Captured by Villa)   March
15. Santa Isabel (#2—Captured by Villa)   March
16. Train at Chavarria (Captured by Villa)   March
17. Zacatecas‡ (Taken by Pánfilio Natera)   June 7.

* Indicates by combat.
† Indicates Bloodless Occupation or Light Combat.
‡ Indicates Force not yet Incorporated as the División del Norte, but should be credited to same troops.

18. Zacatecas (Lost by Natera)   June 17.
19. Durango‡ (Taken by Urbina, Domingo, Arrieta)   June 18.
20. San Andrés (#3—Taken by Villa)   August 26.
21. Torreón (Taken by Villa)   October 2.
22. Chihuahua City (Siege by Villa)   November 2.
23. Juárez (#2—Taken by Villa)   November
24. Tierra Blanca§ (Won by Villa)   November 20–25.
25. Chihuahua City (Captured by Villa)   December 3.
26. Torreón|| (Lost by Villistas)   December 9.
27. Ojinaga (Villistas Defeated)   December

1914

28. Ojinaga (Taken by Villa)   January 11.
29. Santa Rosalia and Camargo (#2—Taken by Villa) March 17.
30. Conejos (Taken by Villa)   March 19.
31. Mapimí (Taken by Villa)   March 21.
32. Bermejillo (Taken by Villa)   March 21.
33. Torreón (#2—Taken by Villa)   April 2.
34. San Pedro de las Colimas (Captured by Villa)   April.
35. Saltillo (Taken by Villa)   May 20.
36. Zacatecas (Taken by Villa)   June 23.

1915

37. Saltillo (#2—Taken by Villa)   January 5.
38. Monterrey (Taken by Villa)   January 10.
39. Irapuato (Taken by Villa)   March
40. Celaya (#1—Villa Defeated)   April 4–5–6.
41. Celaya (#2—Villa Defeated)   April 13–14–15.
42. Guadalajara (Lost by Villistas)   April
43. León (Villa Defeated)   June
44. Encarnación (Lost by Villa)   June 20.
45. Aguascalientes (Lost by Villa)   July 10.
46. Zacatecas (Lost by Villa)   July 17.
47. San Luis Potosí (Lost by Villa)   July 22.

§ Indicates Open Battle—No City Involved.
|| Indicates Villa Not Present in Active Command.

48. León
49. Celaya
50. Querétaro ⎫ (All recaptured, then relinquished
51. San Juan del Río ⎬ by Gen. Fierro during his harass- ⎱ July
52. Tula   ment of Obregón's troops to cover
53. Pachuca ⎭ main Villista body's retreat.)

54. Agua Prieta (Villa Defeated)   November 1–2–3.
55. Altamira (Villa Defeated)   November

56. Guadalupe ⎫
57. San Ignacio │ (Surrendered by Villa's garri-
58. Villa Ahumada │ son commanders without bat- ⎱ November–
59. Juárez ⎬ tle to Carranza-Obregón on   December.
60. Chihuahua City │ hearing of Agua Prieta/Al-
61. Casas Grandes ⎭ tamira defeats.)

1916
62. Guerrilla Activities (Chihuahua/Durango)¶ January–March.
63. Columbus Raid (Led by Villista Sub-Chiefs)   March 9.
64. Guerrero (Taken by Villa)   March
65. Villa Pursued by Pershing—Light Skirmishing   March 15–
                                                      September.
66. Chihuahua City (#2—Taken, then evacuated by Villa)
                                                 September 15–16.
67. Santa Rosalia and Camargo (#3—Taken by Villa)   October
68. Jiménez (#2—Taken by Villa)   November 16.
69. Chihuahua City (#3—Taken by Villa)   November 25.
70. Torreón (#3—Taken by Villa)   December 22.
1917
71. Estación (Villa Defeated)   January 2.
72. Guerrilla Activities (Chihuahua/Durango)   January through
                                                   December.

¶ Villa's *División del Norte* has vanished. He is now, through the remaining campaigns and battles, primarily a *guerrillero*, once more, and later
again is declared an outlaw.

1918
73. Guerrilla Activities Continue   January–December.

1919
74. Guerrilla Activities Continue   January–April.
75. Parral (#3—Taken by Villa)   April 19.
76. Juárez (#3—Taken by Villa, then Evacuated)   June 15–16.
77. Guerrilla Activities Continue   June–December.

1920
78. Guerrilla Activities Continue   January–July.
79. Sabinas (Taken by Villa)   July
(With Villa's surrender of 651 men and officers of the guerrilla force, the combat record of the *División del Norte* comes to an end. If one wishes to be romantic, one may count Villa's final engagement, in the streets of Parral, as Number 80, as enumerated here. The date will be July 23, 1923.)

SOURCES CONSULTED

Braddy, Haldeen. *Cock o' the Walk: Qui-qui-ri-qui!* The Legend of Pancho Villa, Albuquerque, N.M., University of New Mexico Press, 1955

Campobello, Nellie. *Apuntes Sobre la Vida Militar de Francisco Villa*, Mexico City, 1940

Casasola, Gustavo. *Historia Grafica de Mexico*, Vols. I–IV, Mexico City: Archivo Casasola, 1954

Cervantes, Federico. Francisco Villa y la Revolucion, Mexico City: Edicíones Alonso, 1960

Clendesen, Clarence. *The United States and Pancho Villa*, Ithica, N.Y.: Cornell University Press, 1961

Dromondo, Baltasar. *Francisco Villa y la Adelita*, Mexico City, 1920

Estol, Horacio. *Realidad y Leyenda de Pancho Villa,* Mexico City, 1956

Foix, Pere. *Pancho Villa,* Mexico City, 1950

Frances, Jose-Maria. *Vida y Aventuras de Pancho Villa,* Mexico City: Olimpa, 1956

George, Alexander L. and Juliette L. *Woodrow Wilson and Colonel House,* New York: The John Day Co., 1930

González, Manuel. *Contra Villa: Relatos de la campaña de 1914–1915,* Mexico City: Botas, 1935

Guzmán, Martín Luis. *The Eagle and the Serpent,* New York: Alfred Knopf, 1930.

Harris, Larry. *Pancho Villa and the Columbus Raid,* El Paso, Texas: McMath Co., 1949

Link, Arthur S. *Wilson the Diplomatist,* Baltimore, Md.: The Johns Hopkins University Press, 1957

Moore, Ernest R. *The Legend of Pancho Villa,* New York, 1934

Obregón, Álvaro. *Partes Oficiales de las Batallas de Celaya,* Mexico City, n.d.

Pinchón, Edgcumb. *Viva Villa! A Recovery of the Real Pancho Villa, Peon, Bandit, Soldier, Patriot,* New York: Harcourt & Co., 1933

Puente, Ramón. *Pascual Orozco y la Revuelta de Chihuahua,* Los Angeles, 1931

———. *Vida de Francisco Villa,* Mexico City, 1920

Robleto, Hernán. *La Mascota de Pancho Villa,* Mexico City, 1920

Roscoe, Jesse. *The Treasure Album of Pancho Villa,* El Paso, Texas: Toyahvale Press, 1962

Schuster, E. A. *Pancho Villa's Shadow,* New York: Exposition Press, 1947

Stevens, Louis. *Here Comes Pancho Villa: The Anecdotal History of a Genial Killer,* New York: Frederick A. Stokes Co., 1930

Tompkins, Frank. *Chasing Villa,* Harrisburg, Pa.: Military Service Publishing Co., 1934

Torres, Elias L., *La Cabeze de Villa, Mexico City,* 1938

———. *Veinte Vibrante Episodos de la Vida de Villa,* Mexico City, n.d.

Wagner, Henry R. *Bullion to Books,* Los Angeles, Calif.: The Zamorano Club, 1942

Wise, Jennings C. *Woodrow Wilson, Disciple of Revolution,* New York: The Paisley Press, Inc., 1938

Zayas Enriquez, Rafael de. *The Case of Mexico and the Policy of President Wilson,* New York: A. and C. Boni, 1914

NEWSPAPERS:

The El Paso Herald-Post, El Paso, Texas
The El Paso Times, El Paso, Texas
The Los Angeles Times, Los Angeles, California
The Los Angeles Examiner, Los Angeles, California